A FIRST COURSE
IN MECHANICS

BY

W. G. BORCHARDT, M.A., B.Sc.

FORMERLY ASSISTANT MASTER ON THE MILITARY AND ENGINEERING
SIDE AT CHELTENHAM COLLEGE
AND SCHOLAR OF ST. JOHN'S COLLEGE, CAMBRIDGE

SEVENTH IMPRESSION

THIRD EDITION

RIVINGTONS
34 *KING STREET, COVENT GARDEN*
LONDON
1950

Printed in Great Britain
by T. and A. CONSTABLE LTD., Hopetoun Street
Printers to the University of Edinburgh

PREFACE

THIS course has been compiled for those who prefer to have the subjects of Statics and Dynamics in the same book ; the earlier chapters will be sufficient for the School Leaving Certificate, while in the later ones will be found all that is necessary for the Higher Certificate Papers and the Higher Mathematics for Woolwich.

The order has been chosen as the result of the author's teaching experience, now extending for over thirty years, and the more elementary parts of Statics have been placed first. It is true that the beginner can easily master the ideas of velocity and acceleration, but as soon as gravity is introduced and the connection between force and acceleration, difficulties occur.

The subject of Resolution has been placed after Moments and the Triangle of Forces, as these seem to present very few difficulties in comparison. A large number of simple examples have been given on this branch, as the idea of Resolution is so important in all the subsequent work, both in Statics and Dynamics.

After the Graphical Solution of Three-Force Problems, chapters are given on Velocity, Acceleration, Gravity, and Force. The author does not hesitate to use formulae in the section on Velocity and Acceleration, as he considers that time is wasted, and much confusion of thought produced, by attempting to solve every problem in Kinematics by first principles. In dealing with Force, the gravimetric unit only is introduced, and this is continued to the end of Chapter XV, after which the absolute unit is used in connection with Mass and Momentum, thus following out the general recommendation of the Report on the ' Teaching of Mechanics ' prepared by the Mathematical Association.

Elementary Friction, Work, Horse-Power, and Machines, are followed by Resultant and Relative Velocities ; this latter branch is fruitful of errors on the part of the student, and as a result of trying many ways of attacking the subject, the author recommends that problems on the determination of Relative Velocity should be solved by first principles and the Parallelogram of Velocities, and those of finding the Real Velocity by the Triangle of Velocities.

Projectiles, Work, and Energy are then introduced. Too much stress cannot be laid on this last subject, and on the fact that the gain or loss of Kinetic Energy equals the algebraic sum of the work done by or against *all* the external forces, including gravity.

With the chapters on Mass and Momentum, the foot-poundal and erg appear for the first time, and sections are given on the collision of elastic bodies.

The theory of Centre of Gravity is followed by that of Couples and General Equilibrium ; here it is urged that (i) in all problems on equilibrium, the student should *from the first* see that one side of his original equation, either when resolving or in taking moments, is zero, (ii) in all questions dealing with a resultant, one side of the equation should contain the resultant only ; this not only prevents many mistakes in algebraic sign, but emphasises most important principles which are continually being used both in Statics and Dynamics. In the chapter on C.G., all the problems, whether they concern the C.G. of a compound body composed of the sum or the difference of simpler bodies, are solved by a uniform method, viz. that the moment of the total weight equals the algebraic sum of the moments of the smaller weights, and no special formula is given.

After Bow's Notation and Circular Motion, there are chapters on Simple Harmonic Motion, Simple and Compound Pendulums, and the Rotation of Rigid Bodies.

The course contains 433 diagrams, and there are a very large number of examples, many being quite straightforward and simple, so that the principles may the more easily be attained ; in order that the calculations may be as short as possible, ' g,' except in the last few chapters, has been taken as 32 ft.-sec. units. There are, at the same time, a supply of more difficult problems, and in some cases such sets of examples are specially marked.

Easy experiments are suggested to illustrate the general principles; for want of adequate time, these are perhaps best performed by the teacher, with the help of one or more pupils.

For the purposes of Revision, some 67 Test Papers have been provided, together with 100 Miscellaneous Examples at the end of the course.

Many of the problems are original ; others are taken from the Examination Papers set by various public boards, and thanks are due for permission to insert such questions from the Oxford and Cambridge Schools Examination Board, the Oxford Local Examinations, the Cambridge Local Examinations Syndicate, the College of Preceptors, the University Press, Cambridge, the Joint Matriculation Board, and H.M. Stationery Office.

The author also wishes to express his gratitude to his colleague Mr. C. E. Wright for many valuable suggestions and for help in verifying the Answers.

CHELTENHAM.

CONTENTS

CHAPTER I

CHAPTER II

CHAPTER III

CHAPTER IV

CHAPTER V

Contents

CHAPTER VI

CHAPTER VII

CHAPTER VIII

CHAPTER IX

CHAPTER X

CHAPTER XI

Contents

CHAPTER XII

CHAPTER XIII

CHAPTER XIV

CHAPTER XV

A FIRST COURSE IN MECHANICS

CHAPTER I

1. Force. When we lift an object from the ground, kick a football or stop a cricket ball, we are conscious of exerting a muscular effort or force ; we also exert a force if we hold a lump of lead stationary in the hand and prevent it from falling to the ground, while if we increase the force, by increasing our muscular effort, we can raise the lead into a higher position.

Newton (1642-1727), in his First Law, defined force as '*Anything which changes or tends to change a body's state of rest or uniform motion in a straight line.*'

Thus the agent which stops a moving body, gives speed to a body which was at rest, or causes a body to move in a curved path, exerts a force.

2. Newton discovered that the planets revolve in ellipses round the sun as focus, and that they are deflected into these curved paths by the attractive force of the sun, this force varying inversely as the square of the distance of the planet from the sun. He also recognised that this force is of the same nature as *gravity* or the attraction of the earth on a body, this attraction causing a body to fall to the ground, and moreover, he conceived the idea of *Universal Gravitation*—that every particle in space attracts every other particle.

The **weight** of a body is the *force* with which the earth attracts it, this force acting vertically downwards towards the centre of the earth.

Since the earth is not a perfect sphere, but is slightly flattened at the poles, the weight of a body is rather *more* at the Poles than at the Equator, while at the top of a mountain it is rather *less* than in the valley below.

3. The *unit of force* used in **Statics** (where we are concerned with the action of forces on a body at rest) is the attraction of the earth on a certain piece of platinum kept in the Exchequer Office in London ; this force is called the weight of one pound, or more shortly, **1 lb. wt.**

If copies of this Imperial Pound are hung from the extremity of a fairly strong spiral coil of wire, we find, on measurement, that they all produce the same extension in the length of the spring, and that one copy placed in one scale-pan of a common balance counterpoises another copy placed in the other scale-pan.

If we take ten separate brass weights, each marked one-tenth of a pound, and place them at the extremity of the spring, then they produce collectively the same extension as one pound.

4. Exp. 1. Hang a spiral spring from a fixed support and suspend a scale-pan from the end, a needle point being attached to the bottom of the spring, and the whole placed in front of a metre rule.

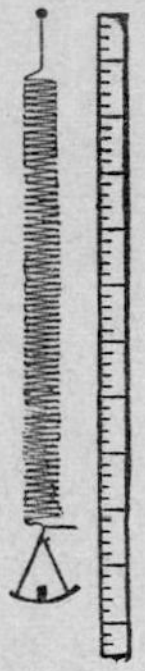

Note the graduation opposite the needle point and then add a weight of $\frac{1}{10}$ lb. to the scale-pan and observe the reading of the pointer.

Add another $\frac{1}{10}$ lb., observe the reading, and continue the process, adding $\frac{1}{10}$ lb. each time.

We find that the *extensions* for each additional weight of $\frac{1}{10}$ lb. are *equal*, so that the extension for a weight of 1 lb. in the scale-pan is ten times that for $\frac{1}{10}$ lb., and

the extensions are proportional to the weights added;

this result is known as Hooke's Law.

It is thus an easy matter to graduate a *spring-balance* and use it for estimating weights, or for measuring any force which may be applied to the hook at the bottom.

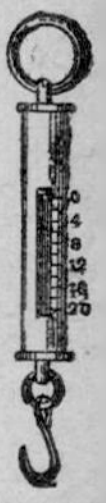

FIG. 1.

FIG. 2.

In some cases the compression, instead of the extension, of a spring is measured.

5. Action and Reaction. All forces occur in pairs, and are of the nature of a **stress** or mutual action between two bodies; if an agent exerts a force, this force meets with a resistance. In the case of a man standing on the ground, the earth attracts him downwards with a force which is his weight, but he does not sink into the ground because the ground is pressing him upwards with an equal force. If a rope is being pulled in opposite directions and remains stationary, then the forces exerted at its two extremities are equal and opposite. If a nail is being pressed into a piece of wood, and the pressure continued when no further motion takes place, it is because the pressure is equal and opposite to the resistance of the wood.

These facts are contained in Newton's Third Law : *To every action there is an equal and opposite reaction.*

We can illustrate this result by hooking two spring-balances together at **A** and pulling them outwards; it will be observed that the readings of the two balances are equal, and that the balances are in the same straight line.

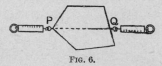

FIG. 3.

When we stretch a piece of elastic by pulling each extremity with, say, a force of 2 lb. wt., then the stress is said to be a **tension** of 2 lb. wt., and the beginner must guard against calling it a tension of 4 lb. wt.

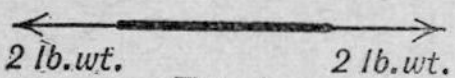

2 *lb.wt.*   2 *lb.wt.*
FIG. 4.

The stress is a pressure or **thrust** if the forces act towards one another, as in the case of an iron girder between two walls of a building; if the walls tend to fall inwards, they exert a pressure inwards at the extremities of the girder, while the girder itself exerts outward thrusts on the walls.

FIG. 5.

6. In order to obtain a clear idea of the nature of a force acting on a body, it is necessary to know the particular *point* to which it is applied, the *direction* of the force, and its *magnitude*. These can all be represented by a line of given length drawn from a particular point in a given direction. It will be convenient to represent the direction by inserting an arrow on the line drawn.

Bodies are said to be **smooth** when, if placed in contact, and we try to slide one over the other, the reaction of the one on the other is at right angles to their common surface of contact.

If the reaction is not at right angles to the common surface, then on trying to slide one over the other, resistance is set up, and this resisting force along the surface is called the force of **friction**.

7. Equilibrium. If a body does not move when several forces act on it, these forces are said to be in *equilibrium*. The simplest case is when a body is acted on by *two equal forces acting in opposite directions in the same straight line;* in Fig. 3, we see that the point **A** is pulled in opposite directions by two equal forces. Again, if a flat piece of wood, resting on a table, is pulled by two spring-balances attached to **P** and **Q**, it moves until these spring-balances are in the same straight line, and when it comes to rest we find that the readings of the balances are the same.

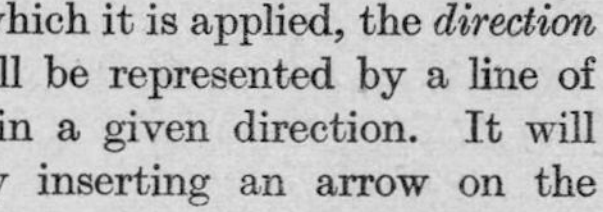

FIG. 6.

4 Pulleys

8. Resultant. If several forces act on a body, then the single force which produces the same effect is called the *resultant* of the forces.

9. Exp. 2. Pass a string over a smoothly-running pulley **A** which is attached to a fixed support; at one extremity of the string, tie a weight

2 lb.

FIG. 7.

of about 2 lb. and at the other attach a light spring-balance with its extremity **B** fixed. It will be found that the reading of the spring-balance is approximately 2 lb., and the lighter the balance and the smoother the bearings of the pulley, the more nearly will the reading approach 2 lb. In whatever direction we hold the spring-balance, the reading will be the same.

We can thus obtain a tension of 2 lb. wt. on a string fastened at one end, by passing it in a given direction over a pulley and suspending a weight of 2 lb. from the free end.

For instance, if a nail is fastened into a wall, a spring-balance **B** attached to the nail, and a string from the balance passed horizontally over a fixed pulley **A** to a weight of 2 lb., then the reading of the spring-balance will be 2 lb.

2 lb. wt.

FIG. 8.

It is instructive to notice the forces on the nail, spring-balance, pulley and 2 lb. weight.

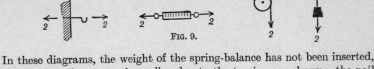

FIG. 9.

In these diagrams, the weight of the spring-balance has not been inserted, and only those forces on the pulley due to the tension are shown; the nail is kept at rest by the force exerted by the spring-balance in one direction and the resistance of the wall in the opposite direction.

Exp. 3. If two strings are fastened to a spring-balance and pass in the same direction over two fixed pulleys with weights **P** lb. and **Q** lb. at their

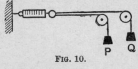
P   Q

FIG. 10.

extremities, then these weights produce tensions of **P** lb. wt. and **Q** lb. wt. in their respective strings, and consequently the total force on the spring-balance is (**P**+**Q**) lb. wt.; this can be verified by observing that the reading in the spring-balance is (**P**+**Q**) lb. wt.

Exp. 4. Suspend a pulley of P lb. wt. by two vertical strings to two spring-balances, and from the pulley hang a weight of Q lb., and verify that the reading of each spring-balance is ½(P+Q) lb. wt.

Thus the sum of the two parallel tensions upwards on the combined body, consisting of the pulley and weight, equals the total weight downwards.

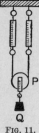

FIG. 11.

10. Centre of Gravity. If a flat piece of cardboard is suspended from a point **A** by a piece of string, then when it comes to rest, the forces acting on it will be the tension **R** in the string vertically upwards, and the weights of the various particles of the cardboard vertically downwards. For equilibrium, the resultant weight must act in the same straight line as **R**, and consequently the direction of this weight can be pencilled on the cardboard.

If the body is then hung up from various other points, pencil lines can be drawn on the cardboard in each case. It will be found that all these pencil lines pass through the same point on the cardboard.

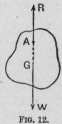

FIG. 12.

The centre of gravity (C.G.) of a body, is the point, fixed relatively to the body, through which the total weight always passes, no matter in what position the body is placed.

In the case of a uniform rod, *i.e.* one of the same material and thickness throughout, the C.G. is at the middle point.

EXERCISE I

1. If two men pull a rope in opposite directions, each with a force of 50 lb. wt., what is the tension in the rope ?

2. If a 2 lb. wt. is hung by a string from a nail in the ceiling, explain the nature and magnitude of the forces acting on the weight of 2 lb., the string, and the nail.

3. If a 3 lb. weight stretches a spring 1½ inches, by how much would a 4 lb. wt. stretch it ?

4. If a 4 lb. wt. stretches a spring 1½ inches, what weight is necessary to stretch it 2 inches ?

5. A weight of 5 lb. is held by a string. What force is it necessary to exert (i) to keep it stationary, (ii) to raise it at a constant speed ?

6. If two rectangular blocks of wood, each of weight 1 lb., rest one on the top of the other, on a horizontal table, draw diagrams representing all the forces acting on each block.

7. Two spring-balances are suspended, one below the other, from a fixed hook ; from the lower of the spring-balances is hung a weight of 3 lb. What are the readings of the spring-balances if (i) their weights are neglected, (ii) each weighs $\frac{1}{4}$ lb. ?

8. A rope passes over a pulley ; to one end of the rope is attached a basket in which a man sits holding the other end of the rope. If the basket weighs 10 lb. and the man 156 lb., what pull must he exert to keep himself suspended above ground ?

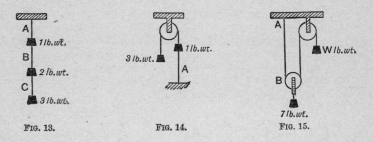

FIG. 13.   FIG. 14.   FIG. 15.

9. If weights of 1 lb., 2 lb., 3 lb. are suspended as shown in Fig. 13, what are the tensions in the three strings A, B, C ?

10. In the arrangement shown in Fig. 14, find the tension in the string A which is fixed at its lower extremity. What is the total downward force on the pulley caused by the tension in the string passing round it ?

11. In Fig. 15, find the tension in AB and the value of W, neglecting weight of pulley.

12. If in Fig. 15, $W=2$, and W is fastened to a table below it by a vertical string, what is the tension in this string if the weight of the pulley is neglected ?

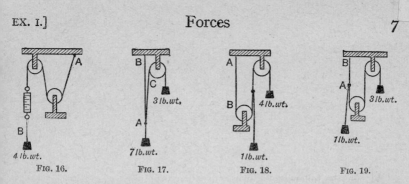

FIG. 16.   FIG. 17.   FIG. 18.   FIG. 19.

13. In Fig. 16, the spring-balance weighs $\frac{1}{4}$ lb., and from its lower extremity a weight of 4 lb. is suspended by a string B. Find the tension in B and in the string at A.

14. In Fig. 17, consider the two strings BA, CA, which are knotted at A, to be vertical. What is the tension in AB ?

15. In Fig. 18, considering all the strings to be vertical, find the tension in AB.

16. In Fig. 19, if all the strings are considered to be vertical, find the tension in AB.

17. A man weighing 140 lb. stands on two rectangular blocks of wood which are placed on the ground ; if the upper block weighs 8 lb. and the lower 10 lb., find the magnitude of the reaction between the two blocks, and also between the lower block and the ground.

CHAPTER II

MOMENTS

11. In the following experiments, a uniform wooden rod, with holes at regular intervals, has been used. A brass pin placed through a hole enables

Fig. 20.

the rod to be fastened to any convenient point of a framework, and weights can be suspended from it either by hooks or loops of string passing over the rod. Alternative methods are to balance the rod on a knife-edge or to suspend it from a loop of string.

In drawing diagrams it is frequently more convenient to show the rod resting on a knife-edge.

12. Exp. 5. Balance a rod at the middle point **O** and place a weight of **P** lb. at **A**; now add a weight of **Q** lb. on the other side of the knife-edge and move it to a point **B** so that the rod or *lever* once more comes to rest in a horizontal position.

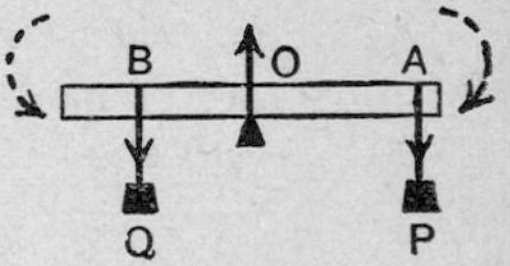

Find the values of **P** × **OA** and **Q** × **OB** and verify that

$$Q . OB - P . OA = 0.$$

[This result was first enunciated by *Archimedes*, 287–212 B.C.]

Fig. 21.

The two weights are trying to turn the lever in opposite directions round the knife-edge or **fulcrum**, and this tendency to turn depends partly on the magnitude of the weight and partly on the length of the **lever-arm OA** or **OB**.

If **P** is kept fixed at its position **A**, then if **Q** is increased, it will be found

that **OB** must be shortened, or if **Q** is diminished then **OB** must be increased.

The tendency of a force **F** to turn a body round a given point **O** is measured by the product of the force and the perpendicular drawn from the point on its line of action, this product **F** × **OA** being called the **Moment of the Force** about the given point.

Fig. 22.

If the force is measured in lb. wt. and the perpendicular in feet, then the moment is measured in lb. ft. units.

It will be convenient to call the moments of forces which tend to turn a body in a *clockwise* direction *negative*, and those tending to turn it in a *counter-clockwise* direction *positive*, this being the same convention as that used for rotation in Trigonometry.

It will be noticed in Fig. 21 that the reaction of the hinge has been inserted at **O**, so that we may have the complete set of forces on the lever in the diagram. It is obvious that this reaction has no turning effect about **O** ; we could not, for instance, raise the lid of a desk by applying a force at any point on the line of the hinges.

We have thus verified the fact that

the algebraic sum of the moments about the fulcrum of all the forces acting on the lever is zero.

13. Exp. 6. Balance a rod at its middle point; hang a weight of **W** lb. from some point on the right of **O**, and bring the rod into a horizontal position by hanging two weights **P** lb. and **Q** lb. to the left of **O**.

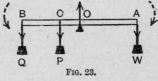

Fig. 23.

The moment of **W** about **O** is clockwise and numerically equal to **W . OA**,

,,   **P**   ,,   counter-clockwise   ,,   ,,   **P . OC**,

,,   **Q**   ,,   ,,   ,,   ,,   **Q . OB**.

Verify that

$$\mathbf{Q . OB} + \mathbf{P . OC} - \mathbf{W . OA} = 0,$$

i.e. *the algebraic sum of the moments of all the forces about the fulcrum is zero.*

Exp. 7. In this experiment hinge the rod at a point **O** to the left of the middle point. Since the weight of the rod will produce a turning effect round **O**, its value *w* must be taken into consideration, while the turning effect of the reaction at **O** is zero. Place another weight **W** at **B** and keep the rod horizontal by exerting an upward force **T** by means of a spring-balance attached at its upper end to a fixed point.

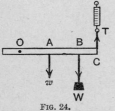

Fig. 24.

Verify that

$$\mathbf{T . OC} - w \mathbf{. OA} - \mathbf{W . OB} = 0.$$

The results of these experiments justify us in concluding that, if a body capable of turning about a fixed point is in equilibrium, and is acted on by *parallel forces* (vertical in these experiments), then

> the algebraic sum of the moments of all the forces about the fixed point is zero.

14. Ex. 1. *A light straight rod* AB, 7 *decimetres long, balances about a point* C *when loaded with weights* 3, 4, 5, 6 *hectograms at* A, E, D, B *respectively. If* AE=1 *dm.,* AC=3 *dm.,* CB=4 *dm., find the position of* D.

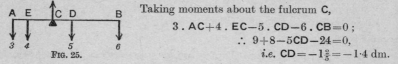

Fig. 25.

Taking moments about the fulcrum C,

$$3 \cdot AC + 4 \cdot EC - 5 \cdot CD - 6 \cdot CB = 0 \; ;$$
$$\therefore \; 9 + 8 - 5CD - 24 = 0,$$
$$\text{i.e. } CD = -1\tfrac{2}{5} = -1 \cdot 4 \text{ dm.}$$

The negative sign indicates that D has been placed in the wrong position, and that it should be 1·4 dm. to the left of C.

Ex. 2. *A pair of scissors, whose handles are 3 inches long, can just cut a piece of wire placed between the blades at a distance of* ½ *inch from the hinge, when a force of* 20 *lb. wt. is applied to the handles. Find the force which must be exerted to cut the same wire, placed at the same distance from the fulcrum if the handles of the scissors are* 5 *inches long.*

If BE and BC are the handles,

$$AB = DB = \tfrac{1}{2} \text{ in.,} \quad BE = BC = 3 \text{ in.}$$

Let P lb. wt. be the force exerted at E and C, and W lb. wt. the resistance overcome.

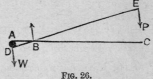

Fig. 26.

In Fig. 26, the forces on the lever DBE only are shown, and they may be assumed to be at right angles to the lever.

Taking moments about B for the equilibrium of DBE,

$$W \cdot DB - P \cdot EB = 0,$$
$$\therefore \; W \times \tfrac{1}{2} = 20 \times 3 = 60 \quad . \quad . \quad . \quad \text{(i)}$$

If now the length of EB is 5 inches, and the new force exerted at E is Q lb. wt.,

$$W \cdot DB - Q \cdot EB = 0,$$
$$\therefore \; W \times \tfrac{1}{2} = 5Q. \quad . \quad . \quad . \quad \text{(ii)}$$

From (i) and (ii), $5Q = 60,$ $\therefore \; Q = 12$ lb. wt.

EXERCISE II

1. *ABCD* is a rectangle in which *AB*=5 ft. and *BC*=8 ft., *BC* is produced to *E*, where *CE*=4 ft. Forces of 2, 3, 4, 5 lb. wt. act as shown in Fig. 27. Find the moment of each force about (i) the point *A*, (ii) the point *C*, (iii) the point *E*.

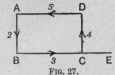

FIG. 27.

2. Find the moment about *O* of a force of 5 kilograms weight acting at *A* along a line *AB*, when *OA*=5 metres, and angle *OAB* equals (i) 10°, (ii) 55°.

3. A vertically downward push of 40 lb. wt. acts on a 6-inch crank of a bicycle, when the crank is 50° below the horizontal. What is the magnitude of the moment about the axle ? If the push is produced at right angles to the crank in the same position, what must be the magnitude of the force to produce the same moment as before ?

4. A uniform rod, 2 ft. 4 in. long and weighing 3·5 lb., is suspended 4 in. from one end. What weight, suspended 2 in. from this end, would be required to keep the rod horizontal ?

5. A uniform bar is balanced about its middle point. If a weight of 6 lb. is fastened at a distance of 14 inches from the middle point, where must a weight of 7 lb. be placed to keep the rod horizontal ?

6. A pole has one end fastened into a wall and projects out a distance of 10 ft. The pole would break if a weight of 60 lb. was hung from the end. How far along the pole may a man of 12 stone venture if the pole does not break ?

7. A gate 6 ft. wide from hinge to latch requires a horizontal force of 5·2 lb. wt. applied at the latch to open it. What force must be applied (*a*) in the middle, (*b*) 1½ ft. from the hinge, to open the gate ?

8. A light rod is 18 in. long, and weights of 1 lb. and 10 lb. are hung at the middle point and end respectively. At what point must the rod be supported in order that it may rest horizontally ?

9. A 'see-saw' is formed of a uniform plank 10 ft. long weighing 84 lb. and rests on a fulcrum 4½ ft. from one end. A boy weighing 112 lb. sits on this end and is balanced by another boy who sits at the other end. Find the weight of the second boy.

10. A uniform straight rod 15 ft. long balances about a point 4⅜ ft. from one end when a weight of 12 lb. is hung at that end, and one of 2 lb. at the other end. Find the weight of the rod.

11. A uniform bar weighs 3 lb. per ft., and has a 45 lb. weight attached at one end. If it balances about a point 2 ft. from that end, how long is the bar ?

12. A uniform bar *AB* is 5 ft. long and weighs 30 lb. It balances about a point *C* in it, when weights of 20 lb. and 25 lb. are suspended from the ends *A* and *B* respectively. Find the distance of *C* from *A*.

13. In a nutcracker a force of 8 lb. wt. is applied at a distance of 5½ in. from the hinge. If the nut is ⅝ in. from the hinge, what is the force that crushes it ?

14. A rock is to be raised by means of a horizontal steel lever 40 in. long. The rock exerts a vertical force of 200 lb. wt. on one end of the lever.

What is the greatest distance from this end that the fulcrum can be placed so that a force of just over 50 lb. wt. applied at the other end may raise the rock ? Neglect the weight of the lever.

Fig. 28.

15. A walking-stick balances about a point 24 in. from the thin end. When a weight of 4 oz. is hung from this end, the fulcrum has to be shifted 8 in. to restore equilibrium. Find the weight of the stick.

16. Weights of 2, 4, 5, 8 lb. respectively are placed along a weightless rod at distances 3, 5, 7, 10 ft. from one end. Find the distance, from that end, of the point about which the rod will balance.

17. A uniform rod, of length 6 decimetres and weight 8 dekagrams, rests on a table with 15 cm. of its length projecting over the edge. What is the greatest distance from the table at which a weight of 24 dekagrams may be attached to the rod without upsetting it ?

18. A uniform straight rod 48 inches long projects over the edge of a horizontal table to the extent of 7¾ in. ; if the greatest weight that can be suspended from its free end be 16¼ lb., what is the weight of the rod ?

19. A nut is placed one inch from the hinge of a pair of nutcrackers, and a pressure of 5 lb. wt. is applied at a distance of 5½ in. from the hinge ; if the pressure just suffices to crack the nut, what resistance is offered by the latter ?

20. In a pair of pincers the jaws meet at $1\frac{1}{2}$ in. from the pin of the joint. The handles are grasped with a force of 35 lb. wt. on each handle at a distance of 8 in. from the pin. Find the force of compression on an object held between the jaws.

FIG. 29.

21. The back wheel of a bicycle has a diameter of 28 in. ; it is raised off the ground and caused to rotate by pulling at the top of the rim with a horizontal force of 10 lb. wt. What is the moment of this force about the axle ? If the wheel over which the chain runs has a diameter of 3 in., what tension must be exerted by the chain to prevent the wheel rotating ?

22. A straight rod ACB, whose weight is negligible, is supported at C. A weight of X lb. at A is balanced by one of P lb. at B, while X lb. at B is balanced by Q lb. at A. Find the ratio $AC : CB$, and the value of X, in terms of P and Q.

23. A lever safety-valve ABC turns about a fulcrum A ; the resultant pressure of steam on the valve acts vertically up at B, and the valve is held down by a weight at C. If C is 20 in. from B, and B is 3 in. from A, calculate the weight which must be applied so that the valve may just blow when the upward thrust on the valve is 700 lb. wt.

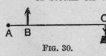

FIG. 30.

24. Parallel forces of 3, 5, 8 lb. wt. act in one direction, and $\frac{1}{2}$ lb. wt. in the opposite direction, at right angles to a lever at points A, B, C, D respectively. If $AB=1$ ft., $BC=3$ ft., $CD=8$ ft., and the weight of the lever is negligible, find at what point the lever will balance.

25. A straight rod PQ is 8 ft. long and is not uniform. It can be balanced at a point 2 ft. from the end P with a weight of 6 lb. suspended at P ; it can also be balanced at a point 2 ft. from the end Q with a weight of 12 lb. suspended at Q. Find the weight of the rod, and the distance of its centre of gravity from P.

15. Exp. 8. Suspend a piece of cardboard by means of a spring-balance from a fixed point and hang a weight of **W** lb. by means of string from a drawing-pin placed at **A**. Then place two more drawing-pins in the same vertical line at **B** and **C** and take the reading of the spring-balance.

If the weight **W** is suspended from **B** and **C** in turn, it will be found that the readings of the spring-balance are the same in all three cases.

FIG. 31.

We thus conclude that a force acting at any point of a rigid body may be considered to have its point of application at any other point in its line of action, provided that point is rigidly connected with the body.

This result is known as the **Principle of the Transmissibility of Force.**

16. We shall now consider some experiments in which the forces acting on a body are not all vertical.

Exp. 9. Place a pin through the middle point of a rod **AB** and attach strings to **A** and **B**; let these strings pass over pulleys and have weights

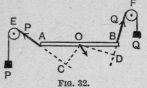

FIG. 32.

of **P** lb. and **Q** lb. at their other extremities.

Since these forces are acting, generally speaking, upwards on the rod, it is reasonable to suppose that the action of the pin on the rod will be downwards, though for reasons which will be given subsequently, it will not necessarily be vertical.

To find the moments of **P** and **Q**, which act on the rod along **AE** and **BF** respectively, about **O**, we must produce the directions of **P** and **Q** backwards, and draw perpendiculars **OC** and **OD**. Practically, these are obtained by means of a set-square and metre ruler.

The moment of **P** about **O** is **P . OC** and is clockwise,

      ,,   **Q**   ,,   **Q . OD**   ,,   counter-clockwise.

Verify that   **Q . OD − P . OC = 0.**

[Note that the perpendiculars on the forces are **OC** and **OD**, and not **OA, OB.**]

Exp. 10. Hinge a rod at **A**, hang a weight **P** lb. at its extremity **B**, and incline it to the vertical by attaching a string at **B**, the other extremity of the string being fastened to a weight **Q** lb.; this string passes over a fixed pulley and the weight **Q** is adjusted so that the string is horizontal and exerts a horizontal force on the rod. The weight of the rod w lb. exerts a turning effect, and must consequently be considered.

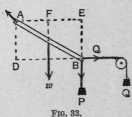

FIG. 33.

To find the moments of the various forces about **A**, perpendiculars **AF, AE, AD** are drawn on to the directions of the forces, the values being obtained practically by means of a set-square and ruler.

Verify that   **Q . AD − w . AF − P . AE = 0.**

These experiments show that even if the forces are *not parallel*,

the algebraic sum of the moments of all the forces about the fulcrum is zero.

17. Ex. 1. *A bent lever* **AOB** *is capable of turning about a fixed point* **O**, *and is acted on by forces of* 100 *and* P *lb. wt. at* **A** *and* **B**, *along lines making angles of* 140° *and* 130° *with* **OA** *and* **OB**. *If* **OA** = 12 *in. and* **OB** = 14 *in.*, *find the value of* P *if the lever is at rest.*

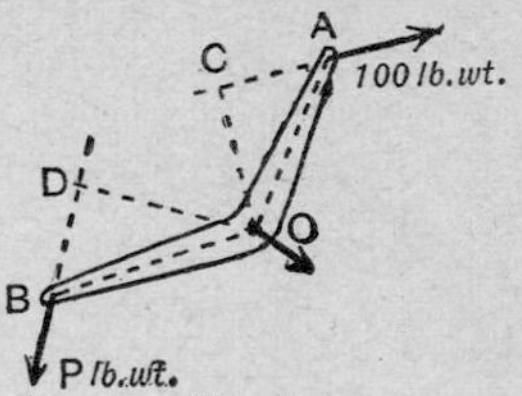

Draw perps. **OC, OD** on to the directions of the forces produced backwards.

Taking moments about the fulcrum **O**,

$$P \cdot OD - 100 \cdot OC = 0.$$

Now
$$OD = OB \sin 50° = 14 \sin 50°,$$
$$OC = OA \sin 40° = 12 \sin 40°,$$
$$\therefore P \cdot 14 \sin 50° - 100 \cdot 12 \sin 40° = 0,$$
$$\therefore P = \frac{1200 \sin 40°}{14 \sin 50°} = \frac{600}{7} \tan 40° = 71 \cdot 9 \text{ lb. wt.}$$

Fig. 34.

Ex. 2. *A rectangular column, 16 ft. high and 4 ft. square in section, is not fixed to the ground but merely rests on it. What force acting perpendicular to a face at its centre would overturn it, if the weight of the column is* 35,000 *lb.?*

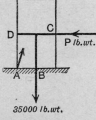

35000 *lb.wt.*

Fig. 35.

Consider a vertical section passing through the centre of gravity of the solid.

When the column is about to turn, it will do so about the edge passing through **A**, so that the reaction of the ground passes through this edge, which may be considered as a fulcrum.

Taking moments about the edge through **A**,

$$P \cdot AD - 35000 \, AB = 0 ;$$
$$\therefore P \cdot 8 - 35000 \cdot 2 = 0,$$
$$i.e \; P = 8750 \text{ lb. wt.}$$

EXERCISE III

1. A straight rod *AB*, whose weight may be neglected, can turn about a point *O*. If *AO* = 12 in., *OB* = 7 in., what horizontal force acting at *A* would be required to balance a weight of 12 lb. hanging from *B*, if the rod makes an angle of 35° with the horizontal ?

2. A uniform rod can turn freely about one of its ends and is pulled aside from the vertical by a horizontal force acting at the other end of the rod and equal to one-third of its weight. Find the inclination of the rod to the vertical when it is at rest.

3. A weight of 34 lb. is hung 3 ft. from the fulcrum of a horizontal lever 4 ft. long pivoted at one end. At the other end of the lever a force balancing the weight is applied at an angle of 30° with the lever. Find the magnitude of the force.

4. *ABC* is a strip of metal bent so that the angle *ABC* is a right angle. It is pivoted at *B* and a force of 10 lb. wt. is applied at *A* parallel to *BC*. Find the magnitude of the force applied at *C* at an angle of 30° with *BC*, which produces equilibrium. *AB*=6 in., *BC*=8 in., and the weight of the metal strip may be neglected.

5. A telegraph post is 20 ft. high and carries a wire attached horizontally at the top, the tension in the wire being 400 lb. wt. The post is provided with a stay which is attached to the post 7 ft. from the top and makes an angle of 60° with the horizontal. Find the tension in the stay so that there may be no tendency for the post to turn round the point where it enters the ground.

6. *DE* is a flagstaff of weight 150 lb. and its centre of gravity is at *G*. If it will turn about *E* and is to be raised by a rope *DA* making an angle of 40° with the ground, what will be the tension in the rope when the flagstaff is just clear of the ground?

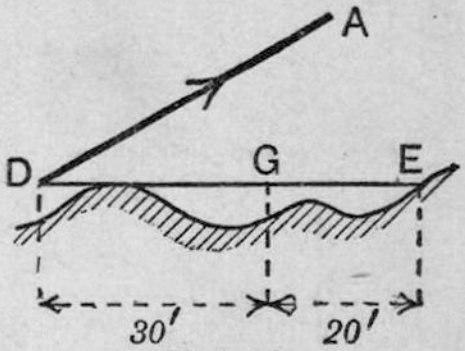

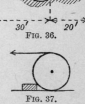

FIG. 36.

7. A wheel 30 in. in diameter and weighing 75 lb. is being rolled up a step 3 in. high. What horizontal force must be exerted at the highest point of the wheel before the wheel can begin to move?

FIG. 37.

8. A wall is 1 ft. thick and 10 ft. high, and is built of stone weighing 150 lb. per cu. ft. The wind pressure may be taken as acting at the centre of the exposed face. What is the greatest wind pressure, in lb. wt. per sq. ft., that the wall can sustain by virtue of its weight, without being overturned?

9. A uniform pole AB, weighing 5 lb., is hinged at A, and is held at an angle of 60° to the vertical by a string joining the end B to a point C vertically above A, ABC being an equilateral triangle. Find the magnitude of the tension of the string.

10. A string ABC, to which a weight of W grams is attached at one end, is fastened to a nail at A and passes over a pulley at C; if a second weight of 50 grams hangs from B, find the value of W, given that $A\hat{B}C = 110°$, $C\hat{B}D = 100°$. [Take moments about A.]

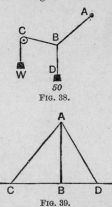

FIG. 38.

11. A vertical post AB is kept in position by two wires AC and AD fixed to the ground at C and D. If $B\hat{A}C = 40°$, $B\hat{A}D = 30°$, and the tension in AC is 35 lb. wt., find the tension in AD.

FIG. 39.

12. A stiff light rod ABC, bent so that ABC is a right angle and pivoted to a fixed point at A, has a weight of 12 lb. attached to it at C, and is maintained with AB vertical and BC horizontal by a horizontal string fastened to C. If the tension of the string is 8 lb. wt. and BC is 4 inches, find the length of AB.

13. AOB is a bent lever with the fulcrum at O. A force of 1000 lb. wt. acts at A, its direction making an angle of 35° with AO on the side remote from B; a force of P lb. wt. acts at B, making an angle of 130° with BO on the side remote from A. If $AO = 11$ inches, $BO = 20$ inches, find the value of P.

14. A uniform solid circular cylinder, 10 inches in diameter, 5 feet long, and weighing 300 lb., stands vertically on a rough plane. (i) Find the magnitude of a horizontal push applied symmetrically at the top which will just tilt the cylinder. (ii) Find the magnitude of the least force which will tilt it.

15. A square plate $ABCD$ rests on a smooth horizontal table and is free to turn about a fixed vertical axis through the corner A. A force of 5 lb. wt. acts at the corner B along the side BC, and a force of 4 lb. wt. at the corner D along the side DC. At what point of the side AB should a horizontal force of 2 lb. wt. act parallel to CB so as to keep the plate at rest?

16. A uniform ladder, 30 feet long and weighing 60 lb., lies on the ground at right angles to the wall of a house, and the foot of the ladder touches the house. Find the least force that must be used to raise the top of the ladder from the ground (*a*) by a man on the ground, (*b*) by a man at a window 40 ft. above, hauling at a rope fastened to the top of the ladder.

17. A fisherman's rod 8 ft. long, firmly fixed at one end, and at an angle of 45° with the horizontal, is pulled with a force of 2 lb. wt. at right angles to the rod and at a distance of 1 ft. from the end. The line runs to a fish from the top of the rod at an angle of 30° with the horizontal. Find the tension the fish exerts on the line.

18. The lengths of the arms of a bent lever with its centre of gravity at the fulcrum, are in the ratio 3 : 1, and are inclined at an angle of 120°. A weight *W* hangs from the end of the shorter arm. If it is pivoted at the bend, find the least force which, applied at the end of the longer arm, will balance the weight when the longer arm is inclined at an angle of 30° to the horizontal.

18. Exp. 11. Fasten weights P lb. and Q lb. to the extremities of a uniform rod AC, whose weight *w* lb. acts at the middle point D.

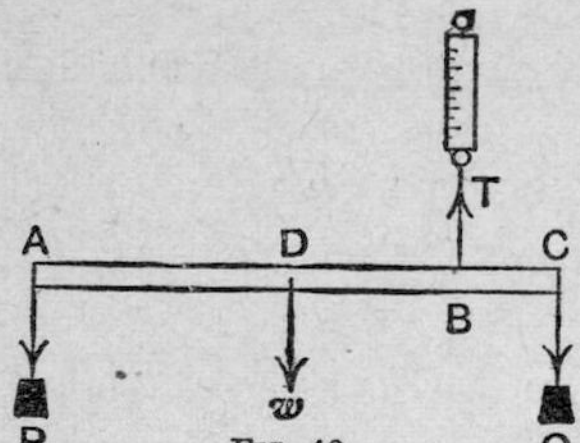

Suspend by a spring-balance and adjust its position so that the rod is horizontal; let the reading of the spring-balance be T lb. wt.

It will be noticed that we have no fixed fulcrum in this experiment.

Verify the fact that if we take moments about A, D, B, C respectively,

$$T \cdot AB - w \cdot AD - Q \cdot AC = 0,$$
$$P \cdot AD + T \cdot DB - Q \cdot DC = 0,$$
$$P \cdot AB + w \cdot DB - Q \cdot CB = 0,$$
$$P \cdot AC + w \cdot DC - T \cdot BC = 0.$$

It should also be observed that
$$T - P - w - Q = 0.$$

Fig. 40.

Exp. 12. Make four holes in a piece of cardboard at E, F, G, H, and suspend it in a vertical plane by strings attached to these points, three passing over pulleys and one hanging vertically, weights being fastened to the other extremities of the strings.

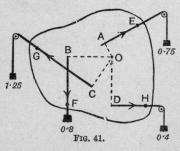

Fig. 41.

Mark any point **O** in the plane of the cardboard and pencil on it the directions of the strings; detach the cardboard and draw perpendiculars **OA, OB, OC, OD** on to the lines of action of the tensions.

In an experiment performed,
algebraic sum of moments about **O**

$$= -(0.75 \times OA) + (0.4 \times OD) + (0.8 \times OB) - (1.25 \times OC)$$
$$= -(0.75 \times 1.74) + (0.4 \times 5.1) + (0.8 \times 4.8) - (1.25 \times 3.5)$$
$$= -1.31 + 2.04 + 3.84 - 4.38$$
$$= 0.19;$$

i.e. the result is approximately zero.

This is an example of a more general result, that if a number of coplanar forces act on a body in equilibrium,

the algebraic sum of the moments of all the forces about any point in their plane is zero.

Also it has been noted that if the forces are parallel, the *algebraic sum of the forces is zero.*

19. Ex. 1. *The weight of a motor car, whose wheel base (distance between front and rear axles) is 8 ft., is 2000 lb., and acts 4 ft. 6 in. in front of the rear axle. If the weight of the passengers is 600 lb., acting 1 ft. 8 in. in front of the rear axle, what is the load on each axle?*

Let **A** and **D** be the front and rear axles respectively; if **P** lb. wt. and **Q** lb. wt. are the pressures on the axles downwards, then the corresponding reactions on the rest of the car will be upwards.

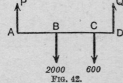

FIG. 42.

$$CD = 1\tfrac{2}{3} \text{ ft.,} \quad BD = 4\tfrac{1}{2} \text{ ft.,} \quad AD = 8 \text{ ft.}$$

Taking moments about **D**,

$$600 \cdot CD + 2000 \cdot BD - P \cdot AD = 0;$$
$$\therefore \ (600 \times \tfrac{5}{3}) + (2000 \times \tfrac{9}{2}) - (P \times 8) = 0,$$
$$8P = 1000 + 9000, \qquad \qquad \therefore \ P = 1250 \text{ lb. wt.}$$

Also, $\qquad P + Q - 2600 = 0, \qquad \qquad \therefore \ Q = 1350 \text{ lb. wt.}$

Ex. 2. *A uniform plank, 14 ft. long, rests on two trestles 8 ft. apart; 4 ft. overhang at one end and a weight of 150 lb. on this end just makes the plank tilt. Find the load on the other end which will just cause tilting.*

Let the weight of the rod, **W** lb. act at **C**, the middle point of **AE**.

$$AB = 4 \text{ ft.,} \quad BC = 3 \text{ ft.,} \quad CD = 5 \text{ ft.,} \quad DE = 2 \text{ ft.}$$

(i) When the rod is about to tilt round **B**, the reaction at **D** is zero.

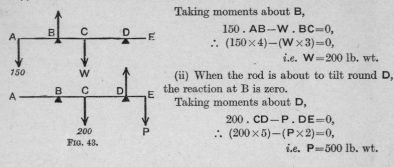

Taking moments about **B**,

$$150 \cdot AB - W \cdot BC = 0,$$
$$\therefore (150 \times 4) - (W \times 3) = 0,$$
$$\textit{i.e. } W = 200 \text{ lb. wt.}$$

(ii) When the rod is about to tilt round **D**, the reaction at **B** is zero.

Taking moments about **D**,

$$200 \cdot CD - P \cdot DE = 0,$$
$$\therefore (200 \times 5) - (P \times 2) = 0,$$
$$\textit{i.e. } P = 500 \text{ lb. wt.}$$

Fig. 43.

EXERCISE IV

1. A weightless beam, carrying a weight of 5 tons at 3 ft. from the left-hand support, rests freely with its ends upon two supports 20 ft. apart. Calculate the pressure on each of the supports.

2. Two men carry a weight of 56 lb. slung on a light rod 15 ft. long, each holding one end of the pole. If the weight is 6 ft. from one end, what is the pressure on each man's shoulder ?

3. A straight uniform rod AB of length 7 ft., weighing 24 lb., rests on two supports F, G, such that $AF = 1$ ft., $GB = 2$ ft. Find the pressures on the supports.

4. Two men carry a weight of 280 lb. suspended from a light pole 7 ft. long, the ends of which rest on the shoulders of the men. Find at what point the weight must be suspended so that one man has only a weight of 125 lb. to support.

5. A and B (Fig. 44) are two pegs in a wall, 8 inches apart; a rod, of negligible weight, rests in a horizontal position, passing under A and over B. At a point C, 14 in. beyond B, a weight of 12 lb. is attached to the rod. What are the pressures on the rod at A and B ?

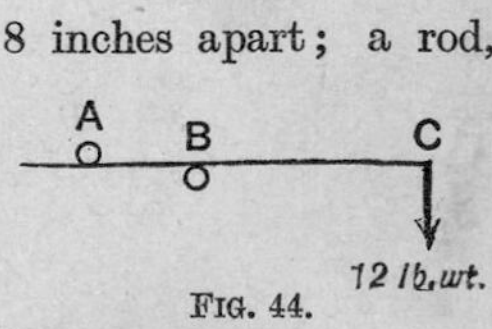

Fig. 44.

6. A uniform rod, 20 inches long, and weighing 8 oz., is attached at each end to a spring-balance. Determine the position at which a 2 oz. weight must be placed so that the indication of the nearer balance may be $5\frac{1}{2}$ oz.

7. A load of 200 lb. is placed on a uniform heavy plank, 10 ft. long, which is supported at its ends. Find the position of the load if the pressures on the supports are 140 and 100 lb. wt.

8. A uniform bar AB, of length 6 ft. and weighing 12 lb., rests in a horizontal position on supports at A and B. A body whose weight is 18 lb. is suspended from the bar at C. Find the length of BC if the pressure at B is double the pressure at A.

9. $ABCD$ is a light rod, 21 in. long, resting on pegs at B and C, which are 10 in. apart in a horizontal line. Weights of 3 lb. and 4 lb. are hung from A and D respectively. What must the distance AB be in order that the pressures on the two pegs may be equal ?

10. A uniform beam 12 ft. long, weighing 200 lb., is supported at its ends. Find the pressures on the supports when a weight of 40 lb. is suspended 2 ft. from one end and 120 lb. 4 ft. from the other end of the beam.

11. A tricycle weighs 70 lb. and the rider weighs 172 lb. The horizontal distance between the axles of the front wheel and back wheels is 3 ft., and the centre of gravity of the machine and rider are respectively 1 ft. and 2 ft. distant horizontally from the front wheel axle. Find the pressure of each of the wheels on the ground.

12. A uniform rod AB rests in a horizontal position on a peg C and under a peg D, the distances AC, CD, DB being all equal. The rod weighs 2 lb., and a weight of 5 lb. is attached at A. Find the pressure on each peg.

13. Two weights P and 10 lb., at A and B respectively, balance on a uniform lever AB, 24 inches long and of weight W, the fulcrum being 6 inches from B. Weights of P and 1 lb., at A and B respectively, also balance the same lever, the fulcrum being now 6 in. from A. Find the weight of the lever and the force on the fulcrum in each case.

14. A uniform beam, 12 ft. long and weighing 50 lb., rests on two trestles at equal distances from its ends. Find the maximum value of this distance so that a man weighing 11 stone may stand anywhere on the beam without tilting it.

15. A uniform plank AB, 8 ft. long and weighing 20 lb., rests on supports at C and D, distant respectively 1 ft. from A and 2 ft. from B. Find the reaction at D.

A weight of 10 lb. is added at such a point E that the reactions at C and D become equal. Find the position of E.

16. A car weighing 6 tons stands on a girder bridge of 40 ft. span. Find the change in the reactions on the supports of the bridge when the car moves through a distance of 5 ft.

17. A light straight bar is supported at two points A and B 16 inches apart. A weight of 10 lb. is hung from the bar midway between A and B, and a weight of 8 lb. is hung from a point C of the bar between A and B. If the thrust on the support B is twice the thrust on the support A, find the distance between B and C.

18. A uniform plank AB, 20 ft. long and weighing 30 lb., is nailed in a horizontal position across two upright posts 12 ft. apart, one post being at the end A. A weight of 100 lb. is suspended from the end B. Determine the magnitude and direction of the forces on the posts.

19. $ABCDE$ is a uniform bar 8 ft. long and weighing 10 lb. $AB=4$ ft., $BC=CD=DE$. The bar rests in a horizontal position on smooth pegs at C and D, being kept in equilibrium by a weight hanging from E. What are the greatest and least values of the weight needed to keep the bar at rest ?

20. AE represents the side view of a table top, supported on trestles at B, D. Its weight, which is 100 lb., may be assumed to act at its centre. If a weight of 150 lb. is hung at E and

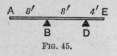

FIG. 45.

equilibrium maintained by a weight W at A, find the limits between which the value of W must lie. If $W=120$ lb., what are the pressures on the trestles ?

21. A wheelbarrow's handles are 5 ft. and the legs 3 ft. from the hub of the wheel. A force of 40 lb. wt. applied vertically at the hub of the wheel will just raise it off the ground, and a force of 30 lb. wt. applied vertically at the handles will just raise the legs off the ground. Find the weight of the barrow and the distance of its centre of gravity from the hub.

22. A plain bench consists of a uniform plank 8 ft. long and 20 lb. in weight, resting on wooden supports each 5 lb. in weight fixed to the plank at points 1 ft. 6 in. from each end. One person, weighing 150 lb., sits in the middle of the bench, and another, weighing 200 lb., over a point 6 in. from one end. Find

FIG. 46.

the pressure on the ground at each support. Will the bench upset if the first person gets up ?

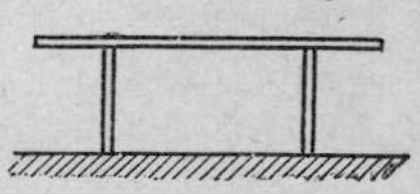

23. A trap-door AB, 6 ft. long and weight 20 lb., can turn round a hinge
at A. If its weight acts at its middle point
and a weight of 35 lb. is placed at D, where
$DB = 1$ ft., find the force which must be applied
along BE at an angle of 30° to
the horizontal, if the trap-door
is just about to rise.

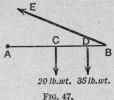

20 lb.wt.   35 lb.wt.

FIG. 47.

24. A stand weighing 6 lb. has a square
base of edge 8 inches, a vertical
rod being fixed to the middle
point of the base. A pulley is fixed at the top of the
rod and a string passes over it; the string is fixed at
one end and carries a weight of 4 lb. at the other end.
If the horizontal part of the string is parallel to an edge
of the base, find the greatest length the vertical rod
can have, if the stand does not turn over one edge.

FIG. 48.

20. The Common Balance.

This is used for the comparison of weights
and is made with arms of equal length. The fulcrum of the beam, which
is usually placed above the middle point of the beam, is, in balances intended
for accurate weighing, made of a triangular prism of hard steel with one
edge downwards resting on a plate of hard steel or agate. The extremities
of the beam are fitted with hard steel prisms with an edge upwards, from
which are suspended the scale-pans.

The beam is also fitted with a long pointer at right angles to the beam
and attached to the middle point, so that when the beam is horizontal,
the pointer is vertical.

Examples in what are called false balances follow; in some the arms
are unequal in length, and in others the C.G. of the machine is not at the
fulcrum.

Ex. 1. *A body appears to weigh 24 lb. when placed
in one scale-pan and 25 lb. when placed in the other,
the arms of the balance being unequal in length and the
centre of gravity of the machine being at the fulcrum.
Find the real weight of the body.*

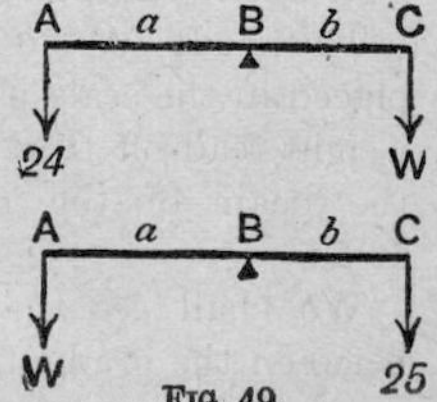

Let **AC** be the beam, **B** the fulcrum;

$$AB = a, \quad BC = b.$$

FIG. 49.

If the real weight of the body is W lb., taking moments about the fulcrum in each case,

$$24 . a - W . b = 0,$$
$$W . a - 25 . b = 0.$$

From these two equations,

$$\frac{W}{24} = \frac{a}{b} = \frac{25}{W},$$

$$\therefore W^2 = 600, \qquad\qquad i.e. \ W = 24{\cdot}5 \text{ lb.}$$

Ex. 2. *The beam of a balance is unjustly loaded (i.e. the centre of gravity of the machine is not at the fulcrum), but the arms are equal in length ; what is the true weight of a body which appears to weigh 5 lb. and 5½ lb. when placed in the two scale-pans successively ?*

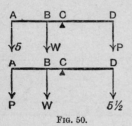

FIG. 50.

Let AD be the beam, C the fulcrum, B the centre of gravity of the machine. Let the machine weigh W lb. and the body P lb.

$$\text{Let } AC = CD = a, \ BC = b.$$

Taking moments about C in each case,

$$5 . a + W . b - P . a = 0,$$
$$P . a + W . b - \tfrac{11}{2} . a = 0.$$

Subtracting,

$$(5 - P)a - (P - \tfrac{11}{2}) \, a = 0,$$

$$\therefore \ 5 - P = P - \tfrac{11}{2}, \qquad i.e. \ P = 5\tfrac{1}{4} \text{ lb.}$$

21. The Common Steelyard. AB is a straight rod with centre of gravity at G, movable about a fulcrum at C, from which, by means of a hook, the instrument can be suspended.

The body W to be weighed is placed in the scale-pan at A, and its weight read off from the position on the beam of the movable weight at D.

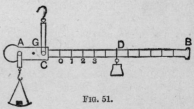

FIG. 51.

We shall see that the distances between the graduations representing lb. are equal for equal increases of the weight W.

Ex. 3. *The beam of a steelyard is 30 inches long, and with the rider removed and no weight suspended, balances about the fulcrum, which is 1·5 inches from one end. The scale-pan is 1·3 inches from the fulcrum and the weight of the rider is $\frac{1}{4}$ lb. Calculate the positions in which the rider will balance weights of 1, 2, and 3 lb. What is the greatest weight that can be weighed ?*

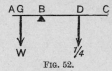

FIG. 52.

Let **AC** be the beam and **G** the point of attachment of the body to be weighed, **D** the position of the rider when the body weighs **W** lb.

$$\mathbf{GB}=1\cdot3 \text{ inches,} \quad \mathbf{BC}=28\cdot5 \text{ inches,} \quad \mathbf{BD}=x \text{ inches.}$$

(i) Taking moments about **B**,

$$\mathbf{W}\,.\,\mathbf{GB}-\tfrac{1}{4}\,\mathbf{DB}=0,$$

i.e. $(\mathbf{W}\times1\cdot3)-\tfrac{1}{4}x=0, \qquad \therefore \ x=5\cdot2\mathbf{W}.$

If
$$\mathbf{W}=1 \text{ lb.,} \qquad x=5\cdot2 \text{ in.,}$$
$$\mathbf{W}=2 \text{ lb.,} \qquad x=10\cdot4 \text{ in.,}$$
$$\mathbf{W}=3 \text{ lb.,} \qquad x=15\cdot6 \text{ in.}$$

We thus see that for each additional 1 lb. in the scale-pan, the rider must be moved 5·2 inches.

(ii) When the greatest possible weight is at **G**, the rider will be at **C**. Taking moments about **B**,

$$\mathbf{W}\,.\,\mathbf{GB}-\tfrac{1}{4}\,.\,\mathbf{CB}=0,$$

i.e. $(\mathbf{W}\times1\cdot3)-(\tfrac{1}{4}\times28\cdot5)=0, \qquad \therefore \ \mathbf{W}=5\cdot48 \text{ lb.}$

22. Wheel and Axle.
This machine is useful in lifting weights by means of a rope wound up on a cylinder or axle, which rotates about an axis resting in fixed supports, while the effort is applied to a rope resting in a groove round a *wheel*, which has its plane at right angles to the axis of the cylinder; the ropes round the wheel and axle, which are fixed rigidly together, are coiled in opposite directions, so that as the effort **P** descends, the load **W** is raised.

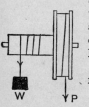

FIG. 53

Since the machine acts like a lever **BCA** (Fig. 54), the fulcrum of which is **C**, we have, taking moments about **C**,

$$\mathbf{W}\,.\,b-\mathbf{P}\,.\,a=0,$$

$$\therefore \ \mathbf{P}=\frac{b}{a}\,\mathbf{W}.$$

The *Windlass* (or Winch) and *Capstan* are modified forms of this machine. In the Windlass the axle is horizontal and the effort applied at the extremity of a handle; this form being used in raising a bucket from a well. In the Capstan the axle is vertical and the effort applied at the end of one or more long poles rotating in a horizontal plane; this machine is used at the seaside for hauling boats up the beach.

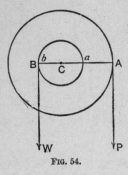

FIG. 54.

Ex. 4. *Four men work a capstan, each exerting a force of 25 lb. weight at a distance of 4½ ft. from the axis. The rope is wound on a drum 1 ft. in diameter. Neglecting friction, find the pull on the rope which balances the pressure on the handles.*

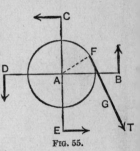

FIG. 55.

Let the efforts be applied at B, C, D, E, at right angles to the arms AB, AC, AD, AE respectively, and let the tension of the rope be T lb. wt.

Taking moments about A,

$$(4 \times 25 \times 4\tfrac{1}{2}) - (T \times \tfrac{1}{2}) = 0,$$
$$\therefore \ T = 900 \text{ lb. wt.}$$

EXERCISE V

1. If the two arms of a balance are unequal and the centre of gravity at the fulcrum, the apparent weight of a body in one of the scale-pans is 8 lb., and when placed in the other scale-pan 12½ lb. Find the true weight.

2. The arms of a balance, whose weight may be neglected, are of unequal length. If a body appears to weigh 6 lb. when placed in one pan and 5 lb. when placed in the other, what is its true weight?

3. The arms of a balance are of unequal length, and the centre of gravity of the balance is not at the fulcrum. A weight of 8 lb. appears to weigh 7 lb. when placed in one scale-pan and $9\frac{1}{15}$ lb. when placed in the other. Find the ratio of the lengths of the arms.

4. The bar of a common steelyard is 2 ft. long, weighs 3 lb., and is suspended at a point distant 2 inches from one end, and its centre of gravity is distant 3 inches from the same end. Find the greatest weight that can be weighed with this steelyard, the movable weight being 5 lb.

5. A steelyard is 5 ft. long, its centre of gravity is 10 inches and its fulcrum 6 inches from the point of attachment of the scale-pan. The machine weighing 5 lb. and the movable weight 2 lb., find the distance of the graduation marking 12 lb. from the free end of the beam.

6. The beam of a steelyard is 30 inches long, and the body to be weighed is attached to the end A; the fulcrum is distant 4 in. and the C.G. $5\frac{3}{4}$ in. from A. The weight of the beam is 1 lb. and the greatest weight that can be weighed 24 lb. Find the movable weight.

7. A steelyard is 12 in. long, and with the scale-pan weighs 1 lb., the C.G. of the two being 2 in. from the end to which the scale-pan is attached. Find the position of the fulcrum when the movable weight is 1 lb., and the greatest weight that can be ascertained by means of the steelyard is 12 lb.

8. A uniform rod is 3 ft. long and weighs 3 lb. It is used as a steelyard with the fulcrum 3 in. from the end to which the body to be weighed is attached, and the sliding weight is $\frac{1}{2}$ lb. Find the greatest and least weights which can be weighed by the machine, and also the distance between successive $\frac{1}{4}$ lb. graduations.

9. In a Danish steelyard, the C.G. of the instrument is at G, and the body is weighed by moving the hook A until the rod is horizontal, and noting the graduation at A. If the instrument weighs 6 lb., and $AB=4$ inches when the body weighed is 18 lb., determine the weight in the scale-pan when $AB=6$ inches.

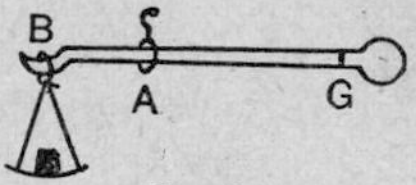

FIG. 56.

10. In a Danish steelyard, the instrument weighs 8 lb. and $BG=20$ inches. Take the weight in the scale-pan as 8 lb., 16 lb., 24 lb. successively, and prove that BA equals $\frac{1}{2}BG$, $\frac{1}{3}BG$, $\frac{1}{4}BG$ in turn.

11. The drum of a windlass is 4 in. in diameter, and the effort is applied to the handle 20 in. from the axis. Find the force necessary to sustain a weight of 100 lb.

12. A wheel and axle is used to raise water from a well. The radius of the axle is 6 in., and that of the wheel, to the circumference of which the handle is fixed, is 2 ft. What force must be exerted on the handle if the bucket full of water weighs 45 lb. ?

13. A windlass is used to hoist a stone weighing $\frac{1}{2}$ ton. If the rope coils on to a drum 3 in. in radius, and if there is a handle at each end, 18 in. from the axis, find what force each of the two winders must exert to raise the stone.

14. A capstan is used for raising the anchor of a ship, two men pushing at the ends of bars, at right angles to the bars, at points 6 ft. from the central axis. If the diameter of the axle, on which the chain is coiled, is 1 ft. 6 in., and the men exert forces of 55 lb. wt., what is the pull in the chain ?

15. Four sailors, each exerting a force of 112 lb. wt., lift an anchor by means of a capstan. The drum of the capstan has a radius of 1 ft. 2 in. and its spokes are 8 ft. long (measured from the axis). What is the weight of the anchor ?

16. Two wheels, whose radii are 3 and 4 ft. respectively, are attached to the same axle ; a force of 120 lb. weight acts at the smaller wheel, and a force of 96 lb. weight at the larger, both on the same side of the axle. Find the weight sustained by them, the radius of the axle being 8 inches.

17. The beam of a balance is 35 in. long, and the point of support, about which the scale-pans balance when empty, is $\frac{5}{16}$ of an inch from the vertical through the centre of the beam. A quantity of tea less than 1 lb. when placed in one scale-pan appears to weigh 1 lb. What is its true weight ?

18. In a wheel and axle of radii R, r, two weights, each w lb., are fastened to points on the circumference of the wheel at an angular distance from each other of 120°. Find the position of the wheel when the greatest possible weight is supported on the axle, and find what is this greatest weight.

19. A tradesman's balance has arms whose lengths are 11 and 12 inches, and it rests horizontally when the scales are empty. If he sells to each of two customers 1 lb. of tea at 2s. 9d. a lb., putting his weights into different scale-pans for the two transactions, how much does he gain or lose ?

CHAPTER III

TRIANGLE OF FORCES

23. As we have already seen, a force is fully determined if we know its line of action, magnitude, and the direction in which it acts ; it follows that it can be represented by a *straight line of definite length drawn in a given direction.*

Thus if a force is represented by **AB**, we mean that it acts from **A** to **B** and is represented in magnitude by the length of **AB** ; if a force is represented by **PQ**, we mean that it acts from **P** to **Q** and is represented in magnitude by the length of **PQ**. The use of an arrow is an obvious method of indicating the direction of a force in a diagram.

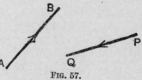

FIG. 57.

24. We already know, from our experiments on the lever, that it is possible for a body to be in equilibrium under the action of three *parallel forces*, but

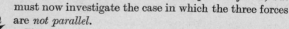

FIG. 58.

must now investigate the case in which the three forces are *not parallel*.

If a piece of cardboard is suspended by two strings attached to **A** and **B**, and weights **P** and **Q** are fastened to the other ends of the strings which pass over pulleys, while a weight **W** hangs from **C**, we know that the algebraic sum of the moments of the three forces about any point in their plane is zero.

If the lines of action of **P** and **Q** are produced to meet at **O**, then the algebraic sum of the moments of **P, Q, W** about **O** must be zero ; now since the directions of **P** and **Q** pass through **O**, it follows that their moments are separately zero, so that the moment of **W** about **O** must be zero, *i.e.* the line of action of **W** must pass through **O**.

From these results we see that if **three forces in one plane act on a body in equilibrium, they must either be parallel or pass through the same point.**

25. Triangle of Forces.

Exp. 13. Attach a weight **R** to a piece of cardboard, and then suspend the cardboard in a vertical plane by two strings fastened at **B** and **C**

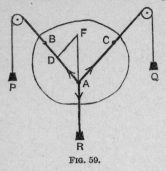

and passing over pulleys, the other ends of the strings being loaded with weights **P** and **Q**. (Fig. 59.)

The cardboard is kept at rest by the three forces **P**, **Q**, **R**, and we know that the lines of action of these three forces meet in a point.

Pencil on the cardboard the lines of action of the forces; produce the direction of **R** backwards to meet the other forces at **A**, and mark off along **AB** a distance proportional to **P**; from **D** draw **DF** parallel to **AC** to meet the line of action of **R** at **F**.

On measurement, it will be found that **DF**

FIG. 59.

and **FA** represent **Q** and **R** on the same scale that **AD** represents **P**. If this triangle is drawn separately, as in Fig. 60, and the directions of the forces marked by arrows, we see that

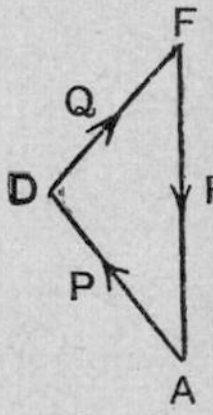

If three forces acting at a point are in equilibrium, they can be represented in magnitude and direction by the sides of a triangle taken in order.

By '*taken in order*' we mean that all the arrows follow one another the same way round the triangle.

It should be noticed that the triangle can be drawn anywhere in the plane of the forces, so that the sides of the triangle do not necessarily give any of the actual lines of action of the forces, but they are always parallel to the forces.

FIG. 60.

The *converse* of this result is also true, and if three forces acting at a point can be represented in magnitude and direction, but not in position, by the sides of a triangle taken in order, then the forces are in equilbirium.

Exp. 14. In a model of a **jib-crane,** a wooden rod **AB** is fastened at the lower extremity to a compression balance at **A**, a weight **W** hung at **B**, and the rod held in position by a string **BC** containing a spring-balance.

The point **B** is kept in equilibrium by 3 forces; the weight **W** vertically downwards, the tension of the string **BC** and the force along **AB**.

BC is called the *tie* and **AB** the *strut* or *jib*.

The tension in **BC** can be read from the spring-balance and the force of compression in **AB** from the dynamometer, and the results verified by constructing a Triangle of Forces.

DE is drawn vertically on *any scale* to represent the weight **W**.

From **E** draw **EF** parallel to **AB**; from **D** draw **DF** parallel to **CB**.

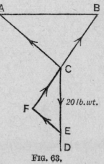

FIG. 61.

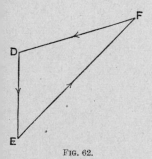

FIG. 62.

Then, on the *same scale*,

the length of **EF** represents the force in the strut **AB**,

the length of **DF** represents the tension in the tie **BC**.

NOTE that since the forces are in equilibrium, their directions must all be the same way round in the triangle **DEF**, and knowing that the force in the direction **DE** is downwards, the directions of the other two forces are as shown. These forces are those acting on **B**; it consequently follows that the reaction of **B** on the tie is in the direction **DF**, and the reaction of **B** on the strut in the direction **FE**.

26. Ex. 1. *A weight of 20 lb. is supported by two strings of length 10 and 12 inches respectively, the ends of which are attached to two points in a horizontal line at a distance 15 inches apart. Find the tensions of the strings.*

Draw **AB** on a *scale of 1 cm. to 2 in.*; with **A** and **B** as centres draw arcs of radii 6 cm. and 5 cm. respectively, cutting at **C**; through **C** draw **CD** at right angles to **AB** to represent a vertical direction.

The knot **C** is kept at rest by tensions along **CA** and **CB** and the weight of 20 lb. along **CE**.

20 lb. wt.

FIG. 63.

From **CD** cut off **CE**=5 cm. to represent 20 lb. wt. on a *scale of 1 cm. to 4 lb. wt.*

Produce **BC** and from **E** draw **EF** parallel to **CA**.

The triangle **CEF** has its sides parallel to the three forces and is therefore a Triangle of Forces for the equilibrium of the knot **C**, and inserting the arrows in the directions of the forces, we see that they follow one another round the triangle.

On measurement,   **EF**=3 cm.,   ∴ tension in **CA**=12 lb. wt.,
                   FC=3·8 cm., ∴ tension in **CB**=15·2 lb. wt.

NOTE that the triangle can be drawn on the other side of **CD**, or anywhere else on the paper, but it is more convenient and compact to use some of the lines already drawn ; it is then only necessary to draw one parallel.

Also, two scales have been used ; one for the *lengths* of the strings, and another for the *forces*.

Ex. 2. AB *and* AC *are two equal light rods which are hinged at* A, *from which hangs a weight of* 10 *lb. Find the thrusts produced in the rods* AB *and* AC. *Angle* BAC=60°.

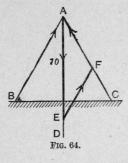

FIG. 64.

Along **AD** cut off **AE** to represent 10 lb. wt. on a scale of 1 cm. to 2 lb. wt.

From **E** draw **EF** parallel to **BA**.

The triangle **AEF** has its sides parallel to the three forces acting on the hinge **A**.

If we did not know the directions in which the forces along the rods acted on the hinge, the triangle of forces **AEF** would determine these directions, since the arrows must follow one another round the triangle and we know that the weight of 10 lb. acts downwards along **AE**.

On measurement,

     EF=2·9 cm., ∴ force along **BA**=5·8 lb. wt.,
     FA=2·9 cm., ∴ force along **CA**=5·8 lb. wt.

EXERCISE VI

(To be solved graphically)

Two weights *P* and *Q* hang over pulleys and are kept in equilibrium by a third weight *R*, as shown in Fig. 65.

Triangle of Forces

Find the values of P and Q, if

1. $R=5$ lb. wt., $\qquad A\hat{O}C=120°$, $\qquad B\hat{O}C=130°$.
2. $R=8$ kg. wt., $\qquad A\hat{O}C=108°$, $\qquad B\hat{O}C=125°$.
3. $R=10$ gm. wt., $\qquad A\hat{O}C=135°$, $\qquad A\hat{O}B=77°$.

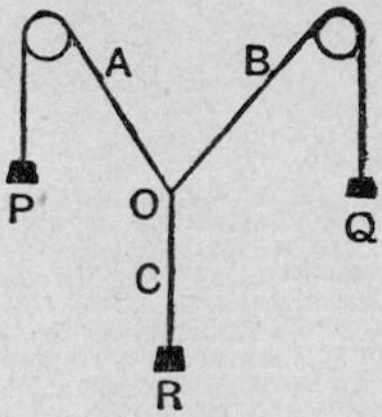

Find the value of R, if

4. $P=10$ lb. wt., $\qquad Q=15$ lb. wt., $\qquad A\hat{O}B=30°$.
5. $P=14$ lb. wt., $\qquad Q=20$ lb. wt., $\qquad A\hat{O}B=100°$.
6. $P=250$ gm. wt., $\qquad Q=130$ gm. wt., $\qquad A\hat{O}B=80°$.

Find the angles AOC, BOC, if

7. $P=10$ lb. wt., $\qquad Q=14$ lb. wt., $\qquad R=12$ lb. wt.
8. $P=15$ lb. wt., $\qquad Q=12$ lb. wt., $\qquad R=17\cdot5$ lb. wt.
9. $P=20$ gm. wt., $\qquad Q=15\cdot8$ gm. wt., $\qquad R=16\cdot5$ gm. wt.

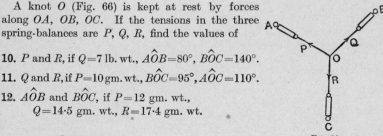

Fig. 65.

A knot O (Fig. 66) is kept at rest by forces along OA, OB, OC. If the tensions in the three spring-balances are P, Q, R, find the values of

10. P and R, if $Q=7$ lb. wt., $A\hat{O}B=80°$, $B\hat{O}C=140°$.
11. Q and R, if $P=10$ gm. wt., $B\hat{O}C=95°$, $A\hat{O}C=110°$.
12. $A\hat{O}B$ and $B\hat{O}C$, if $P=12$ gm. wt., $Q=14\cdot5$ gm. wt., $R=17\cdot4$ gm. wt.

Fig. 66.

13. A weight of 20 lb. hangs from a ring which is free to slip along a wire fixed at both ends. In the position of equilibrium, the parts of the wire on each side of the ring are inclined at 20° to the horizontal. Find the tension in the wire.

Fig. 67

14. A light cord, of length 12 ft., has its ends fastened to two pegs A and B situated 10 ft. apart in a horizontal line, and it carries a load of 30 lb. by means of a second cord knotted to it at a point 5 ft. 6 in. from the end A. Determine the tensions of the two portions of the first cord.

15. A weight of 20 kilograms is slung on a cord 20 inches long, the two ends of which are fastened to two points in the same horizontal line 15 inches apart. Find the tension in the cord.

16. If a boat is pulled by forces of 40 lb. wt. towards the east and 30 lb. wt. towards the north-east, what other force must act on it to keep it at rest ? Give the magnitude and direction.

17. A ball weighing 25 lb., suspended from a fixed point by a light string 2 ft. long, is kept at a distance of 6 in. from the vertical through the point of suspension by a man exerting a thrust, which is horizontal. What is the magnitude of the thrust ? (Fig. 68.)

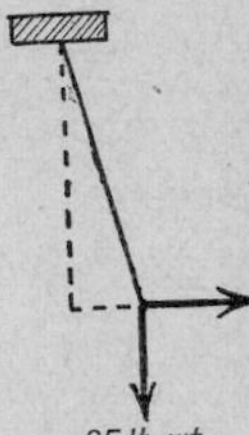

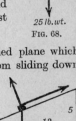

18. A railway truck is free to move along a line of smooth rails, and is pulled by forces of 250 and 300 lb. wt. acting at a point on the same side of the truck, at angles 25° and 150° to the rails. Find the perpendicular pressure against the rails.

25 lb.wt.

Fig. 68.

19. A body weighing 104 lb. is placed on a smooth inclined plane which rises 5 vertical to 12 horizontal, and is prevented from sliding down by a rope whose upper end is fixed to a point higher up the plane. Find the tension of the rope and the pressure of the body on the plane. (Fig. 69.)

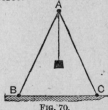

104 lb.wt.

Fig. 69.

20. A small ring of weight 5 oz. can slide on a smooth rod AB. A fine string is tied to the ring and to the end B of the rod. The rod is held at an angle of 30° to the horizontal, the end B being uppermost. Find the tension in the string.

21. A body weighing 12 lb. is kept at rest on a smooth incline of 35° by a horizontal force. Find the magnitude of the force.

22. AB, AC are two equal rods which are hinged at A, from which hangs a weight of 25 lb. Find the thrusts produced in the rods. Angle $BAC = 50°$. (Fig. 70.)

Fig. 70.

23. *AB* is a string 20 in. long; its upper end *A* is fastened to a fixed point, and *B* is attached to a weight of 8 lb. Find the force required to hold *B* at a distance of 10 in. from the vertical through *A*, when the force is applied (i) horizontally, (ii) at right angles to *AB*.

24. A weight of 200 lb. is to be hauled up a smooth slope inclined at 30° to the horizontal, the direction of the pull being inclined at 30° to the line of greatest slope. Find the force required to do this, and find the pressure between the weight and the slope.

In a crane, *AB* is the strut and *CB* the tie. Find the tension in the tie and the thrust in *AB* if

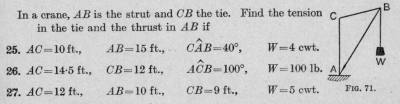

25. *AC* = 10 ft.,   *AB* = 15 ft.,   *CÂB* = 40°,   *W* = 4 cwt.

26. *AC* = 14·5 ft.,   *CB* = 12 ft.,   *AĈB* = 100°,   *W* = 100 lb.

27. *AC* = 12 ft.,   *AB* = 10 ft.,   *CB* = 9 ft.,   *W* = 5 cwt.

FIG. 71.

28. A vertical pole 30 ft. high is used to support an aerial, which is a horizontal wire attached to the top of the pole. A rope is fastened to the top of the pole and to a point in the ground 15 ft. from the base of the pole, on the side opposite to the aerial. The resultant force on the pole is vertical and the pull on the aerial is 50 lb. wt. Find the tension in the rope.

29. Two weights are resting on smooth planes and connected by a string passing over a smooth pulley. Find the value of *W*. (Draw a triangle of forces for each weight, and note that the tension of the string is the same on both weights.)

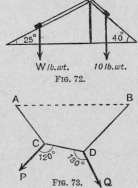

W lb.wt.   *10 lb.wt.*

FIG. 72.

30. The points *A* and *B* are fixed; *AC*, *CD*, *DB* are three strings. *AB*, *AC*, *BD* are 6 ft., 2 ft., 3 ft. respectively. The forces *P* and *Q* are applied at *C* and *D*. If the tension in *AC* is 2 lb. wt., find the values of *P* and *Q*, given that *BÂC* = *AB̂D* = 45°.

FIG. 73.

CHAPTER IV

RESULTANTS

27. By an experiment similar to Exp. 11, but taking the weights **P** and **Q** sufficiently heavy to be able to neglect the weight of the rod, we find that

$$T-P-Q=0,$$
$$P.AB-Q.BC=0,$$
$$P.AC-T.BC=0.$$

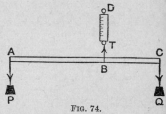

Fig. 74.

The force **T** may be regarded as the *equilibrant* of **P** and **Q**, and equals **P**+**Q**.

If two or more forces act on a body, then the single force which produces the same effect is called the **resultant** of these forces.

Thus in the above experiment **T** must balance the resultant of **P** and **Q** and consequently **T** must be equal and opposite to this resultant. In fact, *the resultant of any number of forces is always equal and opposite to their equilibrant*

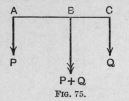

Fig. 75.

We now see that

(i) the magnitude of the resultant of two *like* *parallel* forces equals their *sum*,

(ii) it acts in the same sense as the two forces,

(iii) its line of action cuts the lever in a point such that the algebraic sum of the moments of the two forces about that point is zero.

From the same experiment, **Q** may be regarded as the equilibrant of **P** and **T**, and consequently **Q** reversed will be the resultant of **P** and **T**, where **Q**=**T**−**P**.

In this case, where **T** > **P**,

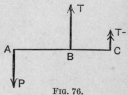

Fig. 76.

(i) the magnitude of the resultant of two *unlike* *parallel* forces equals their *difference*,

(ii) it acts in the same sense as the *greater*,

(iii) its line of action cuts the lever produced, on the side of the greater, in a point such that the algebraic sum of the moments of the two forces about that point is zero.

It is convenient to represent the resultant by a *double arrow*; in this way, it is easily distinguished from the constituent forces.

If the two unlike parallel forces are equal, the system reduces to what is called a *Couple*, the theory of which is considered in Chapter XIX; a couple always tends to produce rotation in the body on which it acts.

28. A more general result is that contained in a Theorem first enunciated by *Varignon* in 1687 :

The moment of the resultant of two parallel forces about any point in their plane is equal to the algebraic sum of the moments of the forces about the same point.

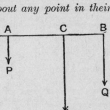

FIG. 77.

Let the two forces be **P** and **Q**, the resultant **R**, and the given point **O**.

In the case of like forces, $R = P + Q$.

From **O** draw a line perpendicular to the directions of the forces, cutting these lines in **A**, **B**, **C**.

The moment of the resultant about **O**

$$= R \cdot CO = (P+Q)CO$$
$$= P(CA + AO) + Q(BO - BC)$$
$$= P \cdot AO + Q \cdot BO, \quad \text{since } P \cdot AC - Q \cdot BC = 0,$$
$$= \text{algebraic sum of moments of } P \text{ and } Q \text{ about } O.$$

Other cases where **O** is between **A** and **B**, and where the forces are unlike can be proved in a similar manner.

This result can easily be extended to the case of the resultant of *any number* of parallel forces, for

> the algebraic sum of the moments of the *first two* forces
> > = the moment of their resultant ;

> the algebraic sum of the moments of the *first three* forces
> > = the algebraic sum of the moments of the *first two*, and the moment of the *third* force
> > = the algebraic sum of the moment of the *resultant of the first two*, and the moment of the *third* force
> > = the moment of the resultant of the *first three forces*, and so on ;

the magnitude of the resultant being the algebraic sum of the magnitude of the forces.

NOTE that in solving any problem by the method of moments, one side of the initial equation

    (i) should be zero, if there is equilibrium,

    (ii) should contain the moment of the resultant only, if the resultant is involved.

29. Ex. 1. *Two like parallel forces* 10 *lb. wt. and* 15 *lb. wt. act at the extremities of a lever* **AB**, 8 *feet long. Find the magnitude and position of their resultant.*

Let **AC**=x ft., and **CB**=$(8-x)$ ft.

If **R** is the resultant,

$$R=10+15=25 \text{ lb. wt.}$$

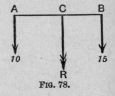

Taking moments about **C**,

$$10 \cdot \mathbf{AC} - 15 \cdot \mathbf{CB} = 0,$$
$$\therefore \ 10x - 15(8-x) = 0,$$
$$\therefore \ 25x = 120, \quad i.e. \ x = 4\tfrac{4}{5} \text{ ft.}$$

FIG. 78.

Ex. 2. *Two unlike parallel forces of magnitude* 6 *lb. wt. and* 10 *lb. wt. respectively act at a distance of* 8 *ft. from one another. Find the magnitude and position of their resultant.*

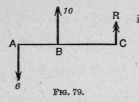

The resultant **R**=10−6=4 lb. wt., and acts at **C** in **AB** produced, in the same sense as the greater.

Let **BC**=x ft.

Taking moments about C,

$$6 \cdot \mathbf{AC} - 10 \cdot \mathbf{BC} = 0,$$
$$\therefore \ 6(8+x) - 10x = 0,$$
$$\therefore \ 4x = 48, \quad i.e. \ x = 12 \text{ ft.}$$

FIG. 79.

Ex. 3. *Parallel forces* 5 *lb. wt. and* 7 *lb. wt. act in one direction and* 8 *lb. wt. and* 10 *lb. wt. in the opposite direction at points* **A, C, B, D** *in a straight line. If* **AB**=4 *ft.,* **BC**=3 *ft.,* **CD**=6 *ft., find the magnitude and line of action of the resultant.*

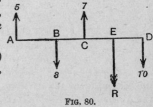

Let the resultant **R** act at **E** (where **DE**=x) in the direction of the 8 lb. wt. and 10 lb. wt., since $(8+10)$ is greater than $(5+7)$.

$$R=(10+8)-(5+7)=6 \text{ lb. wt.}$$

FIG. 80.

Since the moment of **R** about any point equals the algebraic sum of the moments of the original forces about the same point, we have,

taking moments about D,

$$-5 \cdot AD + 8 \cdot BD - 7CD = R \cdot ED,$$
$$\therefore \ -5 \cdot 13 + 8 \cdot 9 - 7 \cdot 6 = 6x,$$
$$\therefore \ x = -5\tfrac{5}{6} \text{ ft.}$$

The negative sign indicates that **R** has been placed in the wrong position in the diagram and that **E** should be to the right of **D** and not to the left, and **DE** $= 5\tfrac{5}{6}$ ft. (Fig. 81.)

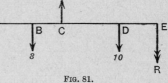

FIG. 81.

EXERCISE VII

Two parallel forces act at points A and B, and the resultant meets AB or AB produced in C. Find the magnitude of the resultant and the length of AC, when

1. $P = 12$ lb. wt., $Q = 20$ lb. wt., $AB = 12$ ft., (like forces).
2. $P = 50$ lb. wt., $Q = 72$ lb. wt., $AB = 14$ ft.,   ,,
3. $P = 15$ lb. wt., $Q = 20$ lb. wt., $AB = 15$ ft., (unlike forces).
4. $P = 7$ lb. wt., $Q = 9$ lb. wt., $AB = 9$ in.,   ,,

5. A and B are two points 8 ft. apart; like parallel forces of 7 lb. wt. and 9 lb. wt. act at A and B respectively; find the point O in the line AB, through which their resultant passes. If the forces had been unlike, what would have been the value of BO?

6. Parallel forces of 2, 4, 8 lb. wt. in one direction and 9 lb. wt. in the opposite direction, act at points A, B, D, C on a straight line, where $AB = 1$ ft., $BC = 2$ ft., $CD = 3$ ft. If the resultant acts at E, find the magnitude of the resultant and the length AE.

7. Parallel forces of 3, 5, 7, 9 lb. wt. act at A, B, C, D in a straight line where $AB = 2$ ft., $BC = 1$ ft., $CD = 3$ ft. If the forces act alternately up and down and the resultant meets AD (or AD produced) at E, find the magnitude of the resultant and the length AE.

8. B is the middle point of a straight line AC. Like parallel forces of 4 lb. wt. and 2 lb. wt. act at A and C respectively, and an unlike parallel force of 4 lb. wt. acts at B. Find the magnitude and line of action of the resultant force.

9. Find the magnitude and position of the resultant of parallel forces of
1, 2, 3, 4, 5, 6 lb. wt. acting in vertical lines at distances 1 foot apart
in the same vertical plane, the forces of 1, 3, 5 lb. wt. acting upwards,
and the forces 2, 4, 6 lb. wt. acting downwards. Give the distance
of the resultant from the force of 1 lb. wt.

10. *ABCD* is a straight line, and $AB = 24$ in., $BC = 36$ in., $CD = 36$ in. Forces
of 1 lb. wt. and 5 lb. wt. act vertically upwards at *A* and *C*, and forces
3 lb. wt. and 9 lb. wt. act vertically downwards at *B* and *D*. Find
the magnitude and line of action of the resultant.

30. Resultant of two Inclined Forces.

In the experiment performed to illustrate the principle
of the Triangle of Forces, with three forces acting at a
point in equilibrium, we found that if **AD** and **DF** are
drawn parallel and proportional to two of the forces **P** and
Q, then the *equilibrant* is represented by **FA**, the *arrows
following one another round the triangle.*

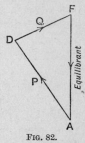

FIG. 82.

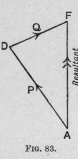

The *resultant* of **P** and **Q**, being equal
and opposite to their equilibrant, will be
represented by **AF**. Note therefore that
the double arrow giving the direction of the *resultant* points
in the opposite sense round the triangle to those which give
the directions of **P** and **Q**. This line **AF** does not give the
actual line of action, since the resultant of **P** and **Q** must
obviously act through **D**.

In a variation of Exp. 13, a
complete parallelogram **ADFE** may
be constructed, so that if **AD** represents **P** and **AE** represents **Q**, then

FIG. 83.

AF represents their resultant. For we have already
seen that **FA** represents the equilibrant **G**, and the
resultant of **P** and **Q** is equal and opposite to their
equilibrant.

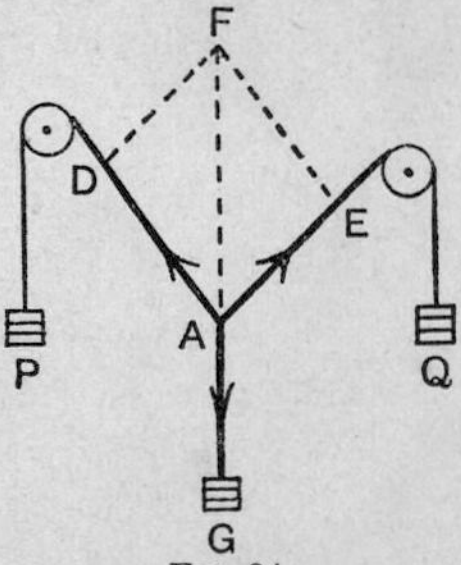

This result is known as the **Parallelogram of
Forces,** and may be stated as follows :—

FIG. 84.

*If two forces, acting at a point, be represented in magnitude and direction
by the two adjacent sides of a parallelogram drawn from the point, their resultant
is represented, on the same scale, both in magnitude and direction, by the diagonal
of the parallelogram drawn from the point.*

Stevinus (1548-1620) arrived at this result without putting it into a definite statement.

Ex. *If two forces of 5 and 8 lb. wt., making an angle of 50° with one another, act on a particle, find the magnitude of the resultant and the angle it makes with the greater force.*

Draw **OA** of length 8 cm. to represent the force of 8 lb. wt. on a scale of 1 cm. to 1 lb. wt. ; also draw **OB** of length 5 cm. to represent the force of 5 lb. wt., making the angle **AOB**=50°.

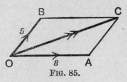

FIG. 85.

Complete the parallelogram **OACB** and measure the diagonal **OC**; this line **OC** represents the resultant on a scale of 1 cm. to 1 lb. wt.

By measurement,   **OC**=11·9 cm., ∴ resultant=11·9 lb. wt.

also angle **COA**=19°.

Another method is to draw a triangle instead of a parallelogram.

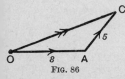

FIG. 86

OA and **AC** are drawn parallel and proportional to the forces of 8 lb. wt. and 5 lb. wt., the angle **OAC** being (180°−50°), *i.e.* 130°.

Then **OC** represents the resultant in magnitude and direction, but not in actual line of action.

NOTE that the arrow giving the direction of the resultant has the same starting point as the arrows giving the directions of the original forces.

Also observe that in Fig. 85 all the arrows are pointing *away* from the point **O**, though in some problems they might all point *towards* **O**.

EXERCISE VIII

(*To be solved graphically*)

Find the magnitude of the resultant of two forces *P* and *Q* acting on a particle at an angle *a*, and the angle its direction makes with the smaller of the forces—

1. $P=12$ lb. wt., $Q=18$ lb. wt., $a=35°$.
2. $P=120$ lb. wt., $Q=200$ lb. wt., $a=45°$.
3. $P=5$ gm. wt., $Q=5$ gm. wt., $a=50°$.
4. $P=10$ gm. wt., $Q=15$ gm. wt., $a=100°$.
5. $P=8$ lb. wt., $Q=12$ lb. wt., $a=130°$.
6. $P=9$ lb. wt., $Q=9$ lb. wt., $a=125°$.

7. Resolve a force of 25 lb. wt. into two others making angles of 25° and 45° with it.

8. Resolve a force of 33 lb. wt. into two others making with it angles of 35° and 60°.

9. Resolve a force of 50 lb. wt. into two others making angles of 45° and 78° with it.

10. Find the angle between two forces 3 lb. wt. and 7 lb. wt., if the magnitude of the resultant is   (i) 7 lb. wt.,   (ii) 6 lb. wt.,   (iii) 8 lb. wt.

11. If the resultant of two forces of 11 lb. wt. and 12 lb. wt. is 15 lb. wt., find the angles the resultant makes with the forces.

12. The resultant of two forces is 14 kg. wt. ; one of the forces is 6 kg. wt. and makes an angle of 32° with the resultant. Find the magnitude of the other force.

13. The resultant of two forces is 14 lb. wt. and one of the forces is 10 lb. wt. and makes an angle of 40° with it. Find the magnitude of the other force.

14. A rope passes round a smooth pillar, the two straight portions being inclined at an angle of 80° to one another. If the pillar can support a thrust of 560 lb. wt., what is the greatest pull which can be exerted on each end of the rope ?

15. A boat is towed along a canal, parallel to its banks, by two horizontal ropes, one to each bank. One rope makes 60° and the other 30° with the line of the canal. The pull on the former is 100 lb. wt. ; what is the pull on the latter ?

16. ABC is a triangular lamina, the sides BC, CA, AB being of lengths 5 in., 9 in., 10 in. respectively. A force of 5 lb. wt. acts at A parallel to BC, and a force of 10 lb. wt. acts at C parallel to BA. Show that their resultant passes through B, and find its magnitude.

17. A string ABC is fixed at one end to a point A and, after passing over a pulley at B, supports a weight of 18 lb. at its other extremity C. Find the resultant force on the pulley at B, due to the tension in the strings, if $A\hat{B}C = 84°$. (Fig. 87.)

FIG. 87.   18 lb

31. Resultant of any number of forces acting at a point.

Let the forces **P, Q, R, S** act at a point **O**.

From any point **A**, draw **AB, BC, CD, DE** parallel and proportional to the forces **P, Q, R, S**; then these lines represent the forces in magnitude and direction.

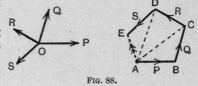

The resultant of the forces along **AB** and **BC** is represented by **AC** in magnitude and direction.

The resultant of the forces along **AC** and **CD** is represented by **AD** in magnitude and direction.

FIG. 88.

The resultant of the forces along **AD** and **DE** is represented by **AE** in magnitude and direction,

> *i.e.* the resultant of **P, Q, R, S** is represented by the line **AE**,
>
> *i.e.* by the line required to close the polygon **ABCDE**.

NOTE that the arrow representing the resultant has the same starting point as the arrows representing the directions of the original forces.

The shape of the polygon will depend on which force is taken first and which next; but in all cases the resultant will be the same.

If it should have happened that the point **E** coincided with **A**, then the resultant would have been zero, and the forces would have been in equilibrium. This leads us to the statement known as the **Polygon of Forces.**

If any number of forces acting at a point can be represented in magnitude and direction, but not in position, by the sides of a polygon taken in order, then the forces are in equilibrium.

32. The *converse* of the Polygon of Forces is easily seen to be true, and if any number of forces acting at a point are in equilibrium then a closed polygon can be drawn, the sides of which represent the forces in magnitude and direction; for if lines are drawn, end to end, parallel and proportional to the forces, and an unclosed polygon is produced, then the forces will have a resultant represented by the line which it is necessary to draw to close the polygon, and therefore there will not be equilibrium.

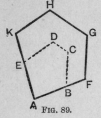

It is important to notice that if *any* polygon is constructed with its sides parallel to the forces, the lengths of the sides *do not necessarily* represent the *magnitudes* of the forces, as they did with a triangle. If the polygons shown in Fig. 89 have their sides parallel to the forces, the sides of these polygons cannot both represent the forces, since the polygons though equiangular are not similar ; and as $\dfrac{AB}{AF}$ is not equal to $\dfrac{BC}{FG}$, it follows that if

AF, FG . . . represent the forces in magnitude, **AB, BC** . . . would not do so.

Fig. 89.

33. Ex. *Find the resultant of a force of 25 lb. wt. and two others of 15 lb. wt. and 20 lb. wt. respectively, making angles of 45° and 125° with it.*

On a scale of 1 inch to 10 lb. (reduced in the Fig.), draw **AB** of length 2·5 in. and parallel to the force of 25 lb. wt. ; from **B** draw **BC** of length 1·5 in. parallel to the force of 15 lb. wt. ; from **C** draw **CD** of length 2 in. parallel to the force of 20 lb. wt., all the arrows being continuous.

AD represents the resultant in magnitude and direction.

By measurement,

$$AD = 3\cdot6 \text{ in.,}$$
$$\therefore \text{ resultant} = 36 \text{ lb. wt. ;}$$
$$\widehat{BAD} = 48°.$$

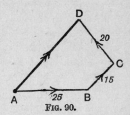

Fig. 90.

EXERCISE IX

(To be solved graphically.)

1. The following forces act at a point : 5 lb. wt. 15° W. of N., 10 lb. wt. 20° E. of N., 15 lb. wt. 10° E. of S. Find the magnitude of the resultant.

2. A man walks successively distances of 15, 20, 10 miles in directions E., 30° E. of N. and 15° W. of N. respectively. Find the distance and direction of his final position from the starting point.

3. Forces of 15, 20, 25 lb. wt. act on a particle O at angles 15°, 33°, 58° respectively to a line OA. Find the magnitude of their resultant and the angle its direction makes with OA.

4. If three forces of 18, 27, 36 kg. wt. act on a particle at O in directions N. 15° W., N. 30° E., N. 25° E. respectively, find the magnitude and direction of the resultant.

5. Forces of 2, 4, 6, 7 lb. wt. act respectively at a point in directions E., N.E., N., S.E. Determine the magnitude of their resultant and the angle its direction makes with the north.

6. Four forces of magnitudes 15, 21, 19, 34 lb. wt. act at a point in directions E., N., S.W., and S.E. respectively. Find the magnitude and direction of their resultant.

7. $PQRS$ is a square. A force of 3 lb. wt. acts from Q to P, a force of 8 lb. wt. from Q to R, and a force of 3 lb. wt. from R to S. Find the magnitude of their resultant and the angle it makes with QR.

8. A telegraph pole has 3 wires radiating from it in one horizontal plane ; one wire runs due S., another S.E., and the third runs 30° E. of N. The tensions in these wires are 80, 40 and 100 lb. wt. respectively. Find the direction and tension of a fourth wire placed so that the four tensions form a system in equilibrium.

9. A force of 12 lb. wt. acting in a direction 40° E. of N. is replaced by three components, two of which are (i) 8 lb. wt. acting 60° E. of N. and (ii) 6 lb. wt. acting 50° E. of S. Find the magnitude and direction of the third component.

10. Five forces in a horizontal plane acting at a point are in equilibrium. One is a force of 5 lb. wt. acting E., one a force of 10 lb. wt. acting 20° E. of N., and one a force of 8 lb. wt. acting 15° W. of N. The remaining two forces act S. and S.W. respectively. Find their magnitudes.

11. The strings make angles of 45° with the vertical. Find the values of P and W. (Fig. 91.)

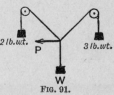

FIG. 91.

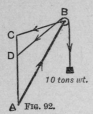

FIG. 92.

12. In a crane (Fig. 92) *AB* is the strut, *BC* the tie, and a weight of 10 tons is attached by means of a rope over a smooth pulley at *B* to a point *D* in the vertical post *AC*. If *CB*, *DB*, *AB* make angles of 75°, 55°, 30° with the vertical, find the tension in the tie and the thrust in *AB*.

13. Four bars of steel, *AB*, *AC*, *AD*, *AE*, all in a vertical plane, meet at a point and support a load of 2 tons. *AB* is a horizontal tie-bar carrying a tension of 4·3 tons wt., *CA* thrusts downwards at 60° to the tie-bar with a force of 0·85 ton wt., while *AD* and *AE* make angles 135° and 200° with the tie-bar. Find the stresses in these two bars and state whether they are in tension or compression. (Fig. 93.)

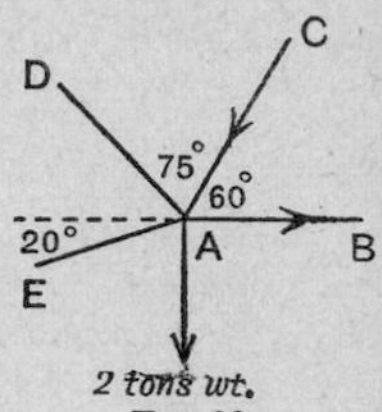

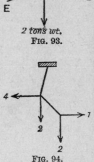

2 tons wt.
FIG. 93.

14. Two weights (Fig. 94), each of 2 lb., are attached to different points of a string which hangs from a fixed support. The upper weight is acted on by a horizontal force of 4 lb. wt. and the lower weight by a horizontal force of 1 lb. wt. Find the tension of each portion of the string when in equilibrium, and the angle which each portion makes with the vertical.

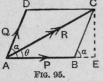

FIG. 94.

34. Calculation of Resultant of two Inclined Forces.

Let the two forces, **P** and **Q**, be represented by the lines **AB**, **AD**, then completing the parallelogram **ABCD**, the resultant **R** is represented by the diagonal **AC**. From the extremity **C** of the diagonal, draw **CE** perpendicular to **AB** produced.

$$R^2 = AC^2 = AE^2 + EC^2$$
$$= (AB + BE)^2 + EC^2$$
$$= (P + Q \cos a)^2 + (Q \sin a)^2$$
$$= P^2 + Q^2(\cos^2 a + \sin^2 a) + 2PQ \cos a$$
$$= P^2 + Q^2 + 2PQ \cos a.$$

FIG. 95.

NOTE that if the angle a is obtuse, then $\cos a$ is negative.

If the resultant makes an angle θ with **P**, then

$$\tan \theta = \frac{\mathbf{EC}}{\mathbf{AE}} = \frac{\mathbf{Q} \sin \alpha}{\mathbf{P} + \mathbf{Q} \cos \alpha}.$$

An alternative method is to find $\sin \theta$ from the fact that

$$\sin \theta = \frac{\mathbf{CE}}{\mathbf{AC}} = \frac{\mathbf{Q} \sin \alpha}{\mathbf{R}}.$$

N.B.—If the two forces are at right angles, the parallelogram becomes a rectangle, and

$$\mathbf{R}^2 = \mathbf{P}^2 + \mathbf{Q}^2,$$
$$\tan \theta = \frac{\mathbf{Q}}{\mathbf{P}}.$$

Ex. 1. *Find the resultant of two forces of 14 and 17 lb. wt. acting at a point at an angle of 55°.*

Draw **CE** perp. to **AB** produced.

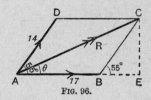

FIG. 96.

$$
\begin{aligned}
\mathbf{R}^2 = \mathbf{AC}^2 &= \mathbf{AE}^2 + \mathbf{EC}^2 \\
&= (\mathbf{AB} + \mathbf{BE})^2 + \mathbf{EC}^2 \\
&= (17 + 14 \cos 55°)^2 + (14 \sin 55°)^2 \\
&= 17^2 + 14^2 + 2 \cdot 17 \cdot 14 \cos 55° \\
&= 289 + 196 + 273 \cdot 0 = 758 \cdot 0 \,;
\end{aligned}
$$

$$\therefore \ \mathrm{R} = 27 \cdot 5 \text{ lb. wt.}$$

If θ is the angle the resultant makes with **AB**,

$$\tan \theta = \frac{\mathbf{CE}}{\mathbf{AE}} = \frac{14 \sin 55°}{17 + 14 \cos 55°} = \frac{14 \sin 55°}{25 \cdot 03},$$

$$\therefore \ \theta = 25° \text{ (to the nearest degree).}$$

Ex. 2. *Forces of* 14 *and* 17 *lb. wt. act at a point at an angle of* 115°. *Find their resultant.*

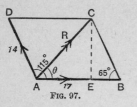

FIG. 97.

Draw **CE** perp. to **AB**.

$$R^2 = AC^2 = AE^2 + EC^2$$
$$= (AB - EB)^2 + EC^2$$
$$= (17 - 14\cos 65°)^2 + (14\sin 65°)^2$$
$$= 17^2 + 14^2 - 2 \cdot 17 \cdot 14 \cos 65°$$
$$= 289 + 196 - 201 \cdot 1 = 283 \cdot 9 ;$$
$$\therefore \ R = 16 \cdot 9 \text{ lb. wt.}$$

If θ is the angle the resultant makes with **AB**,

$$\tan \theta = \frac{\mathsf{CE}}{\mathsf{AE}} = \frac{14 \sin 65°}{17 - 14 \cos 65°} = \frac{14 \sin 65°}{11 \cdot 08},$$

$$\therefore \ \theta = 49° \text{ (to the nearest degree).}$$

N.B.—In each of these examples, **R** may be obtained from the formula

$$R^2 = P^2 + Q^2 + 2PQ \cos \alpha.$$

In Ex. 2, $\qquad R^2 = 17^2 + 14^2 + 2 \cdot 17 \cdot 14 \cos 115°$
$$= 17^2 + 14^2 - 2 \cdot 17 \cdot 14 \cos 65°.$$

EXERCISE X

Two forces P and Q act at an angle α ; find the magnitude of their resultant, and the angle (to the nearest degree) it makes with the smaller force if

1. $P = 15$ lb. wt., $Q = 25$ lb. wt., $\alpha = 55°$.
2. $P = 25$ lb. wt., $Q = 45$ lb. wt., $\alpha = 70°$.
3. $P = 18$ gm. wt., $Q = 35$ gm. wt., $\alpha = 140°$.
4. $P = 50$ lb. wt., $Q = 65$ lb. wt., $\alpha = 125°$.

5. If two men pull a box by means of ropes inclined at 65°, and pull with forces of 140 lb. wt. and 155 lb. wt. respectively, what is the magnitude of the resultant pull ?

6. Two strings, inclined to each other at 80°, are fastened to a nail in the wall, and the tensions in the strings are 5 lb. wt. and 6 lb. wt. respectively. Find the resultant pull on the nail.

7. Two forces, each of 5 lb. wt., acting at a point, are in equilibrium with a force of 8 lb. wt. What is the magnitude of the angle between the lines of action of the two equal forces ?

8. A 10 lb. wt. is suspended by two strings which pass over smooth pulleys, and have attached to the free ends weights of 9 lb. and 8 lb. respectively. What is the angle between the two strings ?

9. A weight of 50 lb. is suspended by two similar wires, equally inclined to the vertical. If the breaking tension of the wires is 34 lb. wt., find the greatest angle of inclination of the two wires.

10. Two forces are inclined at an angle of 50° and their resultant is 15 lb. wt. If one of the forces is 10 lb. wt., find the magnitude of the other.

11. The resultant of two forces which act at an angle of 65° is 21 gm. wt. If one of the forces is 15 gm. wt., find the magnitude of the other.

12. Two forces acting at a point are inclined at an angle of 52° ; one of the forces is 12 lb. wt. and the resultant is 15 lb. wt. Find the magnitude of the other force.

13. The resultant of two forces is 100 lb. wt. One of the forces is 90 lb. wt. and makes an angle of 31° with the resultant. Find the magnitude of the other.

14. A string, 31 inches long, passes through a small ring of 4 ounces weight, and has its extremities fixed at two points 25 inches apart, and in the same horizontal line. Find the tension of the string in the position of equilibrium, in ounces weight, correct to 2 places of decimals.

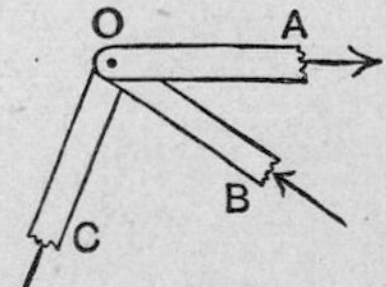

15. Three rods OA, OB, OC are hinged at a point O. If a force of 6 tons wt. acts along BO and 4·5 tons wt. along OA, what is the force along OC ? Angle AOC = 100°. (Fig. 98.)

FIG. 98.

16. B, C are two smooth rings fixed in space at a distance 25 inches apart, B being 9 in. and C 16 in. above the ground. A string ABCD passes through the rings and supports equal weights 10 lb. at its extremities A, D. Find the resultant pressure of the strings upon the rings. (Fig. 99.)

10 lb. wt.

10 lb.wt.

FIG. 99.

CHAPTER V

RESOLUTION

35. The resolved parts of a force.

From the converse of the Parallelogram of Forces, it follows that any force represented by **OC** can be decomposed into two others acting along the lines Ox and Oy, by constructing a parallelogram with **OC** for diagonal and the sides along Ox and Oy.

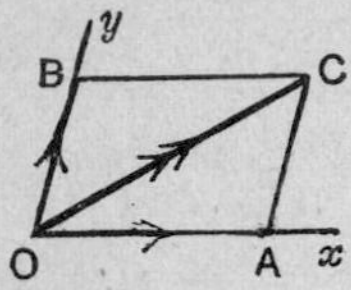

FIG. 100.

If a force is decomposed into two others along two particular directions at *right angles*, then these two forces are called the **Resolved Parts** of the original force in those directions.

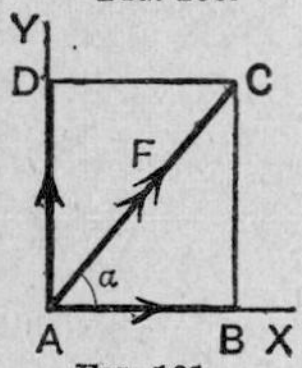

Let **AC** represent a force **F**, making an angle α with **AX**, then

the resolved part of F along $AX = AB = F \cos \alpha$,

$\quad$,, $\quad$,, $\quad$,, $\qquad AY = AD = BC = F \sin \alpha$.

FIG. 101.

Thus, *the resolved part of a force along a line which makes an angle α with its direction is* $F \cos \alpha$, *and along the line perpendicular to this direction* $F \sin \alpha$.

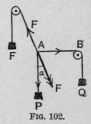

Exp. 15. This result may be verified by the apparatus shown in Fig. 102 in which the knot at **A** is kept at rest by three strings in which the tensions are **P, Q, F**; the forces **P** and **Q** act vertically and horizontally on the knot, while if **F** is reversed it will be the resultant of **P** and **Q**.

Show that

$$P = F \cos \alpha, \quad Q = F \sin \alpha.$$

FIG. 102.

36.
A horse is frequently made to pull a van along a railway line by means of a rope inclined to the rails; the tension in the rope may be considered resolved into two parts, one in the direction of the

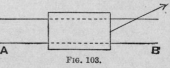

FIG. 103.

50

rails, and the other at right angles to the rails; the former moves the van along the rails and the latter balances the reaction of the rails.

Similarly a barge can be towed parallel to a canal bank provided the rudder is turned at the proper angle. The pull in the rope can be resolved into two parts, one parallel to the bank and the other at right angles to it; the former balances the resistance of the water to the forward motion of the barge, while the latter balances the side pressure of the water on the barge.

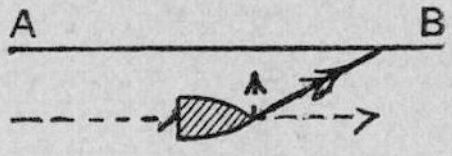

FIG. 104.

37. In the solution of many statical problems, it will be found convenient to replace the forces by their resolved parts in two particular. directions. Since a force in one direction has no effect in a direction at right angles to itself, it follows that if a body is in *equilibrium* under the action of forces *meeting in a point*, and all the forces are resolved in two directions, *the algebraic sum of the resolved parts of the forces in these directions must be separately zero;* this ensures that the body does not move in either direction and therefore does not move at all.

38. Ex. 1.

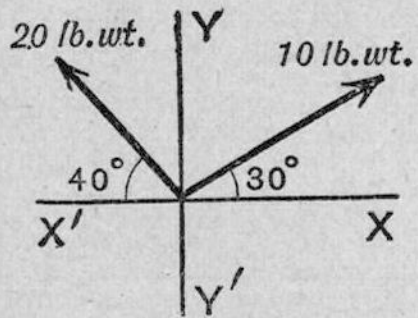

(i) The resolved part of the force of 10 lb. wt.

along **OX** = $10 \cos 30° = 8\cdot66$ lb. wt.,
or ,, **OX**′ = $-10 \cos 30° = -8\cdot66$ lb. wt.,
,, **OY** = $10 \sin 30° = 5$ lb. wt.,
or ,, **OY**′ = $-10 \sin 30° = -5$ lb. wt.

20 lb.wt.   10 lb.wt.

40°   30°

FIG. 105.

(ii) The resolved part of the force of 20 lb. wt.

along **OX**′ = $20 \cos 40° = 15\cdot3$ lb. wt.,
or ,, **OX** = $-20 \cos 40° = -15\cdot3$ lb. wt.,
,, **OY** = $20 \sin 40° = 12\cdot9$ lb. wt.,
or ,, **OY**′ = $-20 \sin 40° = -12\cdot9$ lb. wt.

Ex. 2. *A force* **F** *lb. wt. makes an angle of 40° with the vertical and its horizontal resolved part is 10 lb. wt. Find the magnitude of the force.*

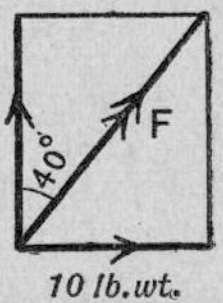

The vertical resolved part of **F** is **F** cos 40°,
horizontal ,, ,, **F** sin 40°;

∴ **F** sin 40° = 10,
i.e. **F** = 10 cosec 40° = 15·6 lb. wt.

10 lb.wt.
FIG. 106.

Ex. 3. *Find what force acting up a smooth inclined plane of angle 35° will support a weight of 10 lb. resting on the plane.*

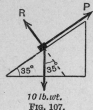

Since **P** and **R** act at right angles, it is convenient to resolve all the forces in these two directions.

The vertical force of 10 lb. wt. makes an angle of 35° with **R** reversed, and can therefore be resolved into

10 cos 35° along this direction
and   10 sin 35° down the plane.

10 lb.wt.
FIG. 107.

This rearrangement of the forces, which are now in two directions at right angles, is shown in Fig. 108;

FIG. 108.

for equilibrium, the algebraic sum of the forces in the two directions must be separately zero,

$$\therefore \ \mathbf{P} - 10 \sin 35° = 0, \qquad i.e. \ \mathbf{P} = 5·74 \text{ lb. wt.}$$

Ex. 4. *A body weighing 8 lb. rests on a smooth inclined plane of angle 25° under the action of a horizontal force. Find the magnitude of the force and the reaction of the plane.*

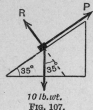

8 lb.wt.
FIG. 109.

In this example, the forces **F** and 8 lb. wt. are at right angles, and consequently it is most convenient to resolve all the forces horizontally and vertically.

NOTE that **R** makes an angle 25° with the vertical.

Resolving vertically,

$$\mathbf{R} \cos 25° - 8 = 0,$$
$$\therefore \ \mathbf{R} = 8 \sec 25° = 8·83 \text{ lb. wt.}$$

Resolving horizontally,

$$\mathbf{F} - \mathbf{R} \sin 25° = 0,$$
$$\therefore \ \mathbf{F} = 8 \sec 25° \sin 25° = 8 \tan 25° = 3·73 \text{ lb. wt.}$$

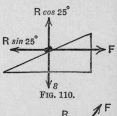

FIG. 110.

Ex. 5. *A body weighing 10 lb. rests on a smooth inclined plane of angle 20°. Find the force which will maintain equilibrium when it acts at an angle of 54° with the horizontal. Also find the reaction of the plane.*

In this example, none of the forces are at right angles to one another.

By resolving along the plane and at right angles

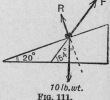

10 lb.wt.
FIG. 111.

to it, it will be found that one of the equations contains only *one* unknown, whereas if we resolve horizontally and vertically each equation contains *two* unknowns.

NOTE that F makes an angle of 34° with the plane, and 10 lb. wt. makes an angle of 20° with R reversed.

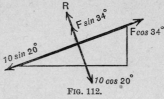

FIG. 112.

Resolving along the plane,

$$F \cos 34° - 10 \sin 20° = 0.$$
$$\therefore \ F = 10 \sin 20° \sec 34° = 4·13 \text{ lb. wt.}$$

Resolving at right angles to the plane,

$$R + F \sin 34° - 10 \cos 20° = 0,$$
$$\therefore \ R = 10 \cos 20° - F \sin 34°$$
$$= 10 \cos 20° - 10 \sin 20° \sec 34° \sin 34°$$
$$= 10 \cos 20° - 10 \sin 20° \tan 34°$$
$$= 9·397 - 2·308 = 7·09 \text{ lb. wt.}$$

EXERCISE XI

A force of P lb. wt. acts at an angle α with OX, and OY is perpendicular to OX. Find its resolved parts along

1. OX and OY, if $P = 10$, $\alpha = 40°$.
2. OX and OY, ,, $P = 15$, $\alpha = 60°$.
3. OX and OY', ,, $P = 20$, $\alpha = 55°$.
4. OX' and OY', ,, $P = 25$, $\alpha = 35°$.
5. OX' and OY, ,, $P = 20$, $\alpha = 45°$.
6. OX and OY, ,, $P = 10$, $\alpha = 100°$.
7. OX' and OY, ,, $P = 15$, $\alpha = 125°$.
8. OX and OY', ,, $P = 20$, $\alpha = 140°$.
9. OX' and OY', ,, $P = 20$, $\alpha = 200°$.
10. OX and OY, ,, $P = 10$, $\alpha = 240°$.
11. OX and OY', ,, $P = 15$, $\alpha = 300°$.
12. OX' and OY', ,, $P = 25$, $\alpha = 320°$.

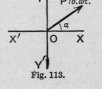

Fig. 113.

13. If in Fig. 113 a force of 12 lb. wt. acts along OX, what are its resolved parts along OX', OY, OY' respectively ?

14. Forces of 2, 3, 4, 5 lb. wt. act along *OA, OB, OC, OD* respectively (Fig. 114). Find the resolved part of

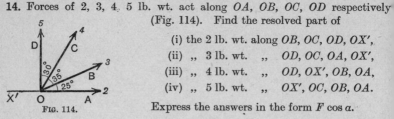
FIG. 114.

(i) the 2 lb. wt. along *OB, OC, OD, OX′*,

(ii) ,, 3 lb. wt. ,, *OD, OC, OA, OX′*,

(iii) ,, 4 lb. wt. ,, *OD, OX′, OB, OA*,

(iv) ,, 5 lb. wt. ,, *OX′, OC, OB, OA*.

Express the answers in the form $F \cos \alpha$.

15. A force makes an angle of 50° with the vertical; its horizontal resolved part is 50 lb. wt. Find the magnitude of the force.

16. A force of 25 lb. wt. makes an angle α with the vertical; if the horizontal resolved part is 21 lb. wt., find the value of α to the nearest degree.

17. A barge is being towed by a horse on the river bank, the pull of the rope being 800 lb. wt., and the rope making an angle 15° with the direction of motion of the barge. Find the force (i) tending to move the barge parallel to the bank, (ii) tending to pull it into the bank.

18. A barge, weighing with its cargo 24 tons, is being towed along a canal by a horse. The point of attachment of the rope to the barge is 17 ft. from the canal bank, and the point of attachment to the horse is 4 ft. on the land side of the canal bank. If the length of the tow rope is 75 ft., and if the pull exerted by the horse is 168 lb. wt., determine the resistance, in lb. wt./ton, to the forward motion of the barge.

EXERCISE XII

1. Find what force acting up a smooth inclined plane of angle 25° will support a weight of 25 lb. resting on the plane.

2. A body weighing 5 lb. rests on a smooth inclined plane of angle 40° under the action of a horizontal force. Find the magnitude of this force and the reaction of the plane on the body.

3. A force of 20 lb. wt. acting directly up a smooth plane inclined to the horizontal at an angle of 40° maintains a body in equilibrium on the plane. Calculate the weight of the body and the pressure which it exerts on the plane.

4. A weight of 100 lb. is kept in equilibrium on a smooth plane, inclined at 20° to the horizontal, by a force of P lb. wt. acting up the plane. Find P.

5. A man finds that by exerting a force of 100 lb. wt. he can just pull a cask weighing 12 stone up a smooth inclined plank. Find the inclination of the plank to the horizontal.

6. A force of 8 lb. wt. acting along an inclined plane supports a heavy body resting on the plane and pressing against it with a force of 15 lb. wt. Find the weight of the body.

7. Find the magnitude of the force, inclined at an angle of 50° to the horizontal, which will support a weight of 2 lb. resting on a smooth inclined plane of angle 20°.

8. A weight of 10 lb. is supported on a smooth plane, which is inclined to the horizontal at an angle of 30°, by a string which makes an angle of 30° with the plane. Find the tension in the string and the pressure on the plane.

9. A truck, having frictionless wheels, is being hauled up a plane inclined at 30° to the horizontal by means of a rope inclined at 45° to the horizontal. If the truck weighs 1 cwt., find the tension in the rope.

10. A body weighing 12 lb. rests on a smooth inclined plane of angle 35°. Find the force which will maintain equilibrium when (i) it acts horizontally, (ii) it acts at an angle of 55° to the horizontal.

11. If a body suspended by a thread weighs 1 lb., find the horizontal force necessary to push it 30° away from the vertical. (Fig. 115.)

FIG. 115.

12. A bullet weighing 4 oz., suspended from a fixed point by a string 25 inches long, is kept in equilibrium by a horizontal force, at a distance of 15 inches from the vertical line through the point of suspension. Find the tension in the string.

13. A window-sash requires a vertical thrust of 40 lb. wt. to push it up. It is opened by pushing with a pole held at 30° with the vertical. Find the minimum thrust required.

14. A cat weighing 4 lb. climbs up the roof of a shed at an angle of 30° to the horizontal. Find the force *down* the roof (*up* on the cat) overcome by the cat's claws, and the force exerted by its paws at right angles to the roof.

15. A weight of 160 lb. is supported on a smooth slope, which rises 1 foot for each 8 feet along the slope, by means of a rope which makes an angle of 34° with the slope. Find the tension of the rope.

16. A loaded truck weighing 8 cwt. is hauled up an inclined plane by a rope parallel to the plane. As the truck moves 12 feet up the incline, it rises 5 feet vertically. What is the least force on the rope that will move the truck, if the resistances to motion other than gravity amount to 1½ cwt.?

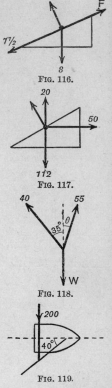

FIG. 116.

FIG. 117.

17. A body whose weight is 1 cwt. rests on a smooth inclined plane. It is maintained in position by two forces, one of 20 lb. wt. vertically upwards and one of 50 lb. wt. acting horizontally. Find the angle of inclination of the plane.

18. Two men are lifting a block by ropes. The one exerts a force of 40 lb. wt., his rope making an angle of 35° with the vertical, and the other exerts a force of 55 lb. wt. Determine the weight of the block and the direction of the second rope. (Resolve horizontally and vertically.)

FIG. 118.

19. A boat sailing due east has a sail set at 40° to its line of motion. A wind coming from the north impinges on the sail with a force of 200 lb. wt. Calculate (i) the force exerted perpendicular to the sail, (ii) the resolved part of this force in the direction the boat is sailing.

FIG. 119.

20. A body of weight W rests on a smooth plane inclined at an angle of 35° to the horizontal, and is kept in position by a string inclined at an angle θ to the plane. Find the magnitude of θ, when the tension in the string is $\frac{2}{3}W$.

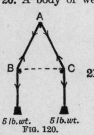

5 lb.wt.   5 lb.wt.
FIG. 120.

21. Two equal weights of 5 lb. are attached to the extremities of a string which passes over three smooth pegs A, B, C in the form of an isosceles triangle with the base BC horizontal. If the angle BAC is 50°, find the pressure on each peg. (Fig. 120.)

22. A body A of weight 10 lb. is supported against a smooth plane of angle $50°$. Find the pressure of the body on the plane and the pull in the string which is parallel to the slope. A second body B, on a second plane of angle $40°$, is connected to A by a string passing over a smooth pulley on the ridge. For equilibrium, what must be the weight of B ?

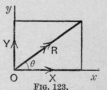

FIG. 121.

39. Calculation of the Resultant of any number of coplanar forces acting at a point.

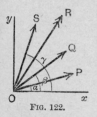

FIG. 122.

Let the forces P, Q, S . . . acting at O make angles a, β, γ . . . with a line Ox, and let Oy be perpendicular to Ox.

Each of the given forces may be resolved into its components along Ox and Oy, and if X and Y are the algebraic sum of these components,

$$X = P \cos a + Q \cos \beta + S \cos \gamma + \quad . \quad . \quad . \quad \text{(i)}$$
$$Y = P \sin a + Q \sin \beta + S \sin \gamma + \quad . \quad . \quad . \quad \text{(ii)}$$

Thus all the given forces are equivalent to X and Y along Ox and Oy; if R is their resultant,

$$R^2 = X^2 + Y^2, \qquad \tan \theta = \frac{Y}{X}.$$

Equations (i) and (ii) contain the general principle that if several coplanar forces meet in a point, then

the algebraic sum of the resolved parts of the forces in any direction equals the resolved part of the resultant in the same direction.

N.B.—We are at liberty to choose Ox in any direction, and it is frequently convenient to take it along the direction of one of the forces; in calculating the resolved parts of the forces, it is simplest to find the acute angles the directions of the forces make with Ox and Oy or these lines reversed; if the resolved parts along Ox are considered positive, then those in the opposite direction are negative; if the resolved parts along Oy are considered positive, then those along Oy reversed are negative.

Ex 1. *Forces of 6, 7, 8, 3 lb. wt. act at a point* **O** *in directions shown in the diagram. Find their resultant.*

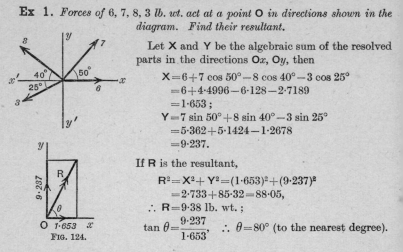

Let **X** and **Y** be the algebraic sum of the resolved parts in the directions Ox, Oy, then

$$X = 6 + 7 \cos 50° - 8 \cos 40° - 3 \cos 25°$$
$$= 6 + 4 \cdot 4996 - 6 \cdot 128 - 2 \cdot 7189$$
$$= 1 \cdot 653 ;$$
$$Y = 7 \sin 50° + 8 \sin 40° - 3 \sin 25°$$
$$= 5 \cdot 362 + 5 \cdot 1424 - 1 \cdot 2678$$
$$= 9 \cdot 237.$$

If **R** is the resultant,

$$R^2 = X^2 + Y^2 = (1 \cdot 653)^2 + (9 \cdot 237)^2$$
$$= 2 \cdot 733 + 85 \cdot 32 = 88 \cdot 05,$$
$$\therefore R = 9 \cdot 38 \text{ lb. wt. ;}$$
$$\tan \theta = \frac{9 \cdot 237}{1 \cdot 653}, \quad \therefore \theta = 80° \text{ (to the nearest degree).}$$

FIG. 124.

N.B.—If on calculation **X** or **Y** are found to be negative, then these forces would act along Ox' or Oy'.

EXERCISE XIII

1. Forces of 3, 4 and 6 lb. wt. make angles of 90°, 60° and 30° respectively with a force of 2 lb. wt. (the angles being measured in the same direction). Find the magnitude of the resultant, and the angle (to the nearest degree) it makes with the 2 lb. wt. force.

2. Forces equal to 5, 7, 3, 9 lb. wt. act on a particle, the angle between the first and second being 60°, between the second and third 30°, between the third and fourth 120°. Find the magnitude of the resultant of these four forces.

3. Find the resultant of the following forces acting at a point, viz. 5 lb. wt. due N., 10 lb. wt. 30° S. of W., 15 lb. wt. 60° N. of E., 12½ lb. wt. S.E. Find also the angle its direction makes with the East.

4. A telegraph pole has three wires radiating from it in one horizontal plane. One wire runs due S., another S.E., and the third runs 25° E. of N. The tensions in these wires are 80, 45 and 100 lb. wt. respectively. Find the direction and tension of a fourth wire placed so that the four tensions are in equilibrium.

5. Four forces 5, 10, 8, 7 lb. wt. act at a point in directions N., W., 70° W. of S., 40° E. of S. Find the magnitude and direction of their resultant.

6. Forces 4, 2, 8, 12 lb. wt. act on a particle in directions N. 40° E., E., S. 70° E., S. Find the magnitude and direction of their resultant.

7. Four forces act in directions N. 20° E., N. 35° W., S. 40° W., S. 45° E., and their magnitudes are 5, 10, 15, 12 lb. wt. respectively. Find their resultant in magnitude and direction.

8. Forces of magnitude 2, 5, 9, 10 lb. wt. respectively act at a point in directions N. 55° E., N. 25° E., N. 65° W., S. Find the magnitude and direction of their resultant.

9. Five forces in a horizontal plane, acting at a point, are in equilibrium. One is a force of 5 lb. wt. acting E., one a force of 10 lb. wt. acting 20° E. of N., and one a force of 8 lb. wt. acting 15° W. of N. The remaining two forces act S. and S.W. respectively. Find their magnitudes.

40. Lami's Theorem.

If two forces P and Q, acting at A, be represented by AB and AD, then their resultant R is represented by AC; consequently if R is reversed, this new force along AE, together with P and Q, are a system of three forces in equilibrium.

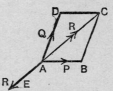

FIG. 125.

$$P : Q : R = AB : BC : AC$$
$$= \sin\ ACB : \sin BAC : \sin ABC$$
$$= \sin\ DAC : \sin BAC : \sin ABC$$
$$= \sin\ DAE : \sin BAE : \sin BAD;$$

i.e. $\dfrac{P}{\sin \widehat{QR}} = \dfrac{Q}{\sin \widehat{PR}} = \dfrac{R}{\sin \widehat{PQ}}.$

This result may be stated as follows :—

If three forces acting at a point maintain equilibrium, each is proportional to the sine of the angle between the other two.

This theorem may be used for such problems as those in connection with the equilibrium of a body on an inclined plane, which have already been solved by resolution.

Ex. *A weight of* 10 *tons hangs vertically at the point* **A.** *What will be the forces acting along the two bars* **AB, AC** *; and assuming that the surface at which the points* **B** *and* **C** *rest is smooth, what must be the tension in the bar* **BC** *in order to prevent the two bars* **AB** *and* **AC** *slipping sideways ?*

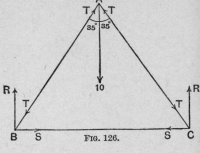

FIG. 126.

Since the figure is symmetrical about the vertical through **A,** it follows that the stresses in the rods **AB** and **AC** are equal, as also the reactions of the ground at **B** and **C,** these reactions being at right angles to **BC,** since the ground is smooth.

Considering the equilibrium of **A,**

$$\frac{T}{\sin 35°} = \frac{10}{\sin 70°},$$

$$\therefore \ T = 10 \sin 35° \operatorname{cosec} 70° = 6·10 \text{ tons wt.}$$

From the equilibrium of **B,**

$$\frac{T}{\sin 90°} = \frac{S}{\sin 35°},$$

$$\therefore \ S = T \sin 35° = 3·50 \text{ tons wt.}$$

NOTE that it has been assumed that the weights of the rods are negligible. If the weights are considerable, there would be a downward force on the joint **A** as well, so that the total forces exerted by the rods on **A** would not be along the rods.

EXERCISE XIV

1. A weight of 15 lb. is hung up by two strings inclined at angles of 25° and 55° to the vertical. Find the tensions in the strings.

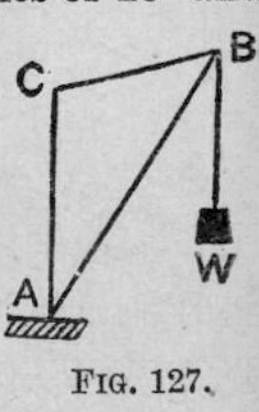

2. In a jib-crane, the tie *CB* points upwards at an angle 65° to the vertical, and the strut *AB* at an angle 40°; if a weight of 10 cwt. is hung from *B*, find the forces acting at *B* along *BC* and *AB*. (Fig. 127.)

FIG. 127.

3. A body of weight 25 grams rests on a smooth plane inclined at 50° to the horizontal, and is supported by a force acting parallel to the plane. Find the magnitude of the force and the reaction of the plane.

4. If a weight of 75 lb. is slung on a cord so that each portion makes an angle of 40° with the vertical, find the tension of the cord.

5. Two cords, one of which is horizontal and the other inclined at an angle of 30° with the vertical, support a weight of 20 kilograms. Find the tension in each cord.

6. A body weighing 12 lb. rests on a smooth inclined plane (angle 35°) under the action of a horizontal force. Find the magnitude of this force and the reaction of the plane.

7. Three bars *OA*, *OB*, *OC*, in equilibrium, are jointed together at *O*, the angle *AOB* being 65° and *BOC* being 40°. The bar *OC* is in tension and the force in it is 3·5 tons wt. Find the forces in the bars *OA* and *OB* and determine whether the bars are in tension or compression.

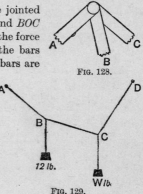

Fig. 128.

8. A string *ABCD* is fastened to two points *A* and *D* and carries weights of 12 lb. and *W* lb. which hang knotted from *B* and *C*. If *AB*, *BC*, *CD* make angles of 40°, 20°, 50° with the horizontal, calculate the tensions in the strings, and the weight *W*.

Fig. 129.

9. A string *ABCDE*, attached to fixed points at *A* and *E*, hangs in a vertical plane, and carries weights at *B*, *C*, *D*. The angles made by the segments of the string with the horizontal are *AB* 60°, *BC* 30°, *CD* 30°, and *DE* 45°. If the weight at *C* is 10 lb., find the values of the other weights and the tensions in the different portions of the string.

10. A string *ABCDE* has weights of 4 lb., *P* lb., *Q* lb., knotted at *B*, *C*, *D* respectively, the extremities *A* and *E* being fastened to fixed points in the same horizontal line. Find *P* and *Q* and the tensions in *AB*, *BC*, *CD*, *DE*, if the angles *EAB*, *ABC*, *BCD*, *CDE* equal 35°, 165°, 150°, 160° respectively.

CHAPTER VI

GRAPHICAL SOLUTION OF THREE-FORCE PROBLEMS

41. In the solution of these problems, we must remember that if three forces acting on a body are in equilibrium, then the *forces* (if not parallel) *all pass through the same point.*

In the case of a uniform rod, the C.G. is at the middle point ; for a sphere at the centre ; for a cylinder at the middle point of the axis ; for a rectangular lamina at the intersection of the diagonals.

Ex. *A uniform rod* **AB**, *4 feet long, is hinged to a vertical wall at* **A** *and supported in a horizontal position by a string* **CD** *attached to the rod at* **C** *and the wall at* **D**, *a point 4 feet above* **A**. *If the weight of the rod is 10 lb., and* **AC** *is 3 feet, find the tension in the string and the magnitude and line of action of the reaction of the hinge.*

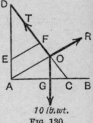

10 lb.wt.
FIG. 130.

The weight of the rod acts vertically through the middle point **G**, and since this vertical and **CD** the line of action of the tension **T** meet at **O**, it follows that the third force **R**, the reaction at **A**, must also pass through **O**, and therefore act along **AO**.

We now have the directions of all the forces and can therefore draw a Triangle of Forces.

Measure **DE**=5 cm. (reduced in Fig. 130) to represent 10 lb., and draw **EF** parallel to **AO** to meet **DO** in **F**, then **DEF** is the triangle required.

By measurement, $\quad$ **DF**=4·2 cm., $\quad\quad$ ∴ **T**=8·4 lb. wt.,
$\quad\quad\quad\quad\quad\quad\quad\quad$ **EF**=3·0 cm., $\quad\quad$ ∴ **R**=6·0 lb. wt.

NOTE that the △**ADO** has its sides parallel and therefore proportional to the forces, so that the problem could be solved by finding **DA, AO, OD**.

EXERCISE XV

(To be solved graphically.)

1. A uniform rod *AB* weighing 10 lb. is smoothly pivoted at *A*, and is supported at an angle of 60° to the vertical by a horizontal string attached at *B*. Find the tension in the string and the reaction at *A*.

2. A uniform rod, 3 ft. long, weighing 5 lb., is hinged to a fixed point at one end, and is supported at an inclination of 30° to the horizontal by a string attached to the other end, whose inclination to the horizontal is also 30°. Find the tension of the string.

3. A uniform rod, 3 feet in length, is supported at both ends by a light string of length 4 feet passing over a smooth peg, and rests horizontally. The weight of the rod is 5 lb. Find the tension of the string.

4. A horizontal rod AB is 3 feet long, its C.G. is 1 foot from A, and its weight is 20 lb. It is supported by a string at A and another at B. If the string at B makes an angle of 45° with the horizontal, find the direction of the string at A and the tension in each string.

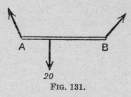

Fig. 131.

5. A uniform rod 13 ft. long and weighing 10 lb. is suspended from a point by two strings of lengths 5 ft. and 12 ft. respectively attached to its ends. Find the tension in each string.

6. A and B are two points 8 ft. apart in the same horizontal line. A uniform beam of length 6 ft. and weight 10 lb. has one end at A, about which it can turn freely, and the other end is attached to B by a light string 3 ft. long. Determine the tension in the string and the reaction at A.

7. A rod AB, which is 10 ft. long, rests partly inside a smooth fixed hemispherical bowl of radius 5 ft. at an angle of 25° to the horizontal. Find the distance of the C.G. of the rod from A.

[The reaction at C is at right angles to AB.]

Fig. 132.

8. A uniform rod AB of weight 10 lb. is hinged at A and pulled out to an angle of 40° with the vertical by a horizontal force at B. Find the magnitude of the force and the reaction at A.

9. A light rod AB, length 3·2 ft., can turn in a vertical plane about a hinge at A, and supports a weight of 10 lb. at D, its middle point, and it is supported in a horizontal position by a light rod CB, C being 2·4 ft. vertically under A. Find the thrust in the rod CB.

10. A trap-door 6 ft. long is of uniform thickness and weighs 500 lb.; it is held open, inclined at 30° to the horizontal, by means of a chain attached to a point 5 ft. vertically above the centre of the axis about which it turns, and also to the middle point of the opposite side. Find the tension in the chain and the force at each hinge.

11. The uniform lid of a desk weighs 3 lb. It is kept open at 45° to the horizontal by means of a stay attached to the edge of the lid furthest from the hinges, the stay making an angle of 60° with the horizontal and an angle of 75° with the lid. Find the magnitude of the reaction of the stay.

12. A uniform bar AB, 1 yard long, weighing 2 lb., hangs from a nail C by two strings CA, CB, respectively 1 ft. 6 in. and 2 ft. 6 in. long. Find the angle the bar makes with the horizontal and the tensions of the strings.

13. A uniform gate weighs 125 lb., and its C.G. is 3 ft. 6 in. from the line joining the hinges, which are 4 ft. apart. The weight of the gate being entirely supported by the lower hinge (*i.e.* the action at the upper hinge is horizontal), find the magnitudes of the reactions at the hinges.

14. A rod AB rests over a smooth horizontal rail at C and with its lower end up against a smooth wall. If the rail is 8 in. from the wall and the rod makes an angle of 60° with the vertical, find the distance of the C.G. of the rod from A.

FIG. 133.

15. Three nails A, B and C, are driven into a board which rests on a smooth table. A and C are 3 in. apart and B is in the same straight line with A and C. Strings attached to A and C, and on the same side of AC, are pulled with forces of 6 and 8 lb. wt. in directions which make angles of 60° with each other and with AC. The board is kept from moving by a string attached to B. Find the distance AB and the pull of the string at B.

16. A sphere of radius 3 in. is attached to a point A in a vertical smooth wall by a string AB of length 4 inches. If the weight of the sphere is 5 lb., find the tension of the string. (Fig. 134.)

FIG. 134.

17. A uniform rod of weight 4 lb. is at rest, in a horizontal position, with one end in contact with a smooth inclined plane of inclination 30° and the other end supported by a string. Find the angle the string makes with the vertical, the tension of the string and the pressure on the plane.

18. A kite is flying with its plane at an angle of 65° with the vertical. Its weight (4 lb.) acts at G, and the effective wind pressure, which is at right angles to the kite, acts at A, while the string is fastened to B. If $GA=5$ in. and $AB=2$ in., what is the tension in the string ?

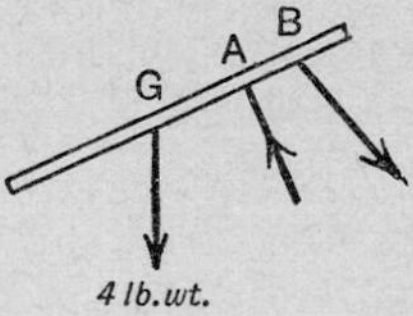

4 lb. wt.

FIG. 135.

REVISION PAPERS

Moments and Triangle of Forces

PAPER 1

1. A uniform ladder 16 ft. long is carried by two boys. If the younger boy holds it at one end, how far from the other end must the elder boy hold it in order that he may bear two-thirds of the weight ?

2. A light horizontal shelf 4 ft. long is supported by a bracket at each end. On the shelf are placed three jars weighing 1 lb., 2 lb. and 3 lb., their respective distances from one end being 1 ft., 2 ft. and 3 ft. Find the thrust on each bracket.

3. A rectangular column, 20 ft. high and 4 ft. square in section, is not fixed to the ground but merely rests upon it. What force acting perpendicular to a face at its centre would overturn it, the material weighing 150 lb. per cu. ft. ?

4. A force of 100 lb. wt. acts at one end of a straight lever, but at an angle of 60° to it. What force acting at the other end of the lever, at an angle of 45° to it, will keep the lever at rest, if the distance of the fulcrum from the point of application of the first force equals half that from the second ?

5. The arms of a balance are unequal in length, but the beam remains horizontal when the scale-pans are unloaded. A body appears to weigh 10 lb. when placed in one pan and 10½ lb. when placed in the other. Find its true weight.

PAPER 2

1. Two boys carry a bucket of water weighing 30 lb. by means of a uniform horizontal pole of weight 10 lb. and length 6 ft. If the boys support the pole at its extreme ends and the bucket is suspended 1 ft. from the centre of the pole, find the total weight supported by each boy.

2. A uniform plank 18 ft. long, weighing 98 lb., rests on a platform with 4 ft. of its length projecting. A boy whose weight is 140 lb. walks along the projecting part of the plank. How near the end can he stand without the plank tipping up ?

3. A nine-foot lever AB has its fulcrum 2 ft. from B. What weight can be lifted at B by applying three forces each of 75 lb. wt. simultaneously to the lever at A, C, D where $AC = CD = 2$ ft. ?

4. A common steelyard weighs 10 lb. ; the weight is suspended from a point 4 in. from the fulcrum, and the C.G. of the steelyard is 3 in. on the other side of the fulcrum. The movable weight is 12 lb. Where should the graduation corresponding to 1 cwt. be situated ?

5. ABC is a bent lever which can turn round the pivot B. $AB = 3$ ft., $BC = 5$ ft., $B\hat{A}D = 40°$, $B\hat{C}E = 35°$. If the force along CE is 5 lb. wt., calculate the force along AD if the lever is at rest.

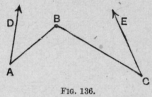

Fig. 136.

PAPER 3

1. A uniform rod AB, whose length is 10 ft., and whose weight is 6 lb., can turn freely about a smooth fixed hinge at A, and is supported in a horizontal position by a prop at a point 7 ft. from A. Find the pressure on the prop and the action at the hinge when a weight of 11 lb. is suspended from B.

2. If the crank turning a windlass is 15 in. long, measured from the centre of the axle, find the diameter of the axle if a man exerting a force of 50 lb. wt. at the end of the crank raises a load of 220 lb.

3. Find the pull on the chain of a bicycle, if the chain-wheel has a diameter of $9\frac{1}{2}$ in., and the pressure on the pedal is 70 lb. wt. at right angles to a crank of length 7 in.

4. A light rod AB, 2 ft. long, rests in a horizontal position, supported by two nails, 4 in. apart, driven into a wall. One nail is at the end A, and the rod passes underneath it ; the other nail is at C, and the rod passes above it. Either nail will support a load of 60 lb., but no more. What is the least downward force applied to the rod at B that will cause one of the nails to give way ? Which nail will give way ?

5. In a steelyard, the distance of the fulcrum from the point of suspension of the weight is 2 inches, and the movable weight 4 oz. The movable weight must be placed 7 inches from the fulcrum to weigh 12 lb. ; where must it be placed to weigh 15 lb. ?

PAPER 4

1. AB is a uniform bar 8 ft. long weighing 150 lb., and is supported in a horizontal position on two vertical props at A and B. How near an end may a load of 200 lb. be placed, if the pressure on a prop may not exceed 250 lb. wt. ?

2. AB is a straight lever whose weight is unknown. It is found that when a 5 lb. weight is hung from B, the lever can be balanced on a knife-edge distant 2 inches from B, while, if a 2 lb. weight is hung from B, the knife-edge must be 3 inches from B to allow a balance. Calculate the weight of the lever.

3. A, B, C are points in a straight line, and $AB=BC=3$ ft. Like parallel forces of 10 lb. wt. and 20 lb. wt. act at A and C, and an unlike parallel force of 15 lb. wt. acts at B. What force will be required to balance these, and at what point in AC must it act ?

4. A weight of 30 grams is suspended by a string. Find graphically the horizontal force that must be applied to the weight to displace it until the string makes an angle of 30° with the vertical.

5. A pair of nutcrackers is $4\frac{1}{2}$ inches long, and a nut is placed $\frac{5}{8}$ inch from the hinge. What pressure applied at the ends will crack the nut, if a weight of $20\frac{1}{4}$ lb., when simply placed on the top of the nut, will crack it ?

PAPER 5

1. A and B are two points in a horizontal line, 12 in. apart. A 4 lb. weight is suspended from A by a string AC, 6 in. long. Another string attached to the weight at C passes over a smooth peg at B and is pulled so that AC makes an angle 30° with the vertical. By taking moments about A, find the tension of the string CB.

2. A stiff wire weighing 10 grams is bent through a right angle at its middle point and placed on a smooth nail. If a weight of 30 grams is attached to one end of the wire, what is the angle α which the weighted arm makes with the horizontal ? (Fig. 137.)

FIG. 137.

3. A uniform bar, 8 ft. long and weighing 16 lb., rests horizontally on supports at its ends. The bar carries loads of 4 and 6 lb., distant 3 ft. and 4 ft. from one end. Find the pressure on each support.

4. Forces of 8, 10, 14 lb. wt. acting at a point are in equilibrium. Find graphically the angles between their lines of action.

5. In a steelyard whose weight is 20 lb. the point of suspension of the body to be weighed is 4 inches from the fulcrum, while the C.G. of the beam is 1 inch from the fulcrum measured in the opposite direction. If the sliding weight is 7 lb., find the distance from the fulcrum of the graduations marked respectively 14, 28, 56, 112 lb.

PAPER 6

1. A uniform straight rod AB of weight 10 lb. is pivoted at one end A. The rod is kept horizontal by means of a string attached to the end B and to a point C vertically above A. If $AB=AC$, find the tension of the string.

2. AB is a straight horizontal beam 30 ft. long. It carries loads of 10 tons at A, 8 tons at B, and 12 tons at C, which is 20 ft. from A. It is supported by two props, one placed 8 ft. from A and the other at such a point that the load is equally divided between the props. Find the distance of the second prop from A.

3. A uniform plank, which is 10 ft. long and weighs 50 lb., sticks out over a canal, projecting 7 ft. over the water, and is held down at the other end by the weight of two boys, so that another boy may walk out along the plank. The combined weight of the two boys who hold down the plank is 200 lb., and this weight may be considered to act 6 in. from the end; the weight of the boy walking along the plank is 80 lb. How far can he walk without upsetting the plank?

4. Strings AC and BC are attached to fixed points A and B; and a string CD, attached to them at C, carries a weight of 10 lb. at D. If the angles ACD and BCD are respectively 120° and 135°, find graphically the tensions of the strings AC and BC.

5. A force of 10 lb. wt. acts tangentially at the circumference of a pulley 2 ft. in diameter. If friction is neglected, what force must be applied to a rope coiled round the shaft, to which the pulley is fixed, to prevent the pulley from turning? The diameter of the shaft is 3 inches.

Including Resultant, Resolution, Lami, Three-Force Problems

PAPER 7

1. A cubical box, weighing 100 lb., rests on the ground. Find the least force that must be applied at right angles to one of the top edges and at an angle of 30° to the horizontal, so as just to tilt the box about the opposite bottom edge.

2. P and Q are two like parallel forces acting respectively at points A and B of a body. If C is the point in the straight line AB through which the resultant passes, find AC and BC, given that $P = 11$ oz. wt., $Q = 4$ oz. wt., $AB = 14$ inches.

3. Weights of 10 and 12 lb. are in equilibrium when suspended from the extremities of a weightless lever. When 4 lb. are added to the latter, the fulcrum must be moved through 10 in. to preserve equilibrium. What is the length of the lever ?

4. Four forces act outwardly at a joint of a frame. One force of 6 tons wt. is horizontal; two others, of 3 tons wt. and 11 tons wt. respectively, make angles of 60° and 171° (measured in the same direction) with the horizontal force. If there is equilibrium, find graphically the magnitude of the remaining force.

5. A wheel has five equally spaced radial spokes, all in tension. If the tensions of three consecutive spokes are 1500, 2500, 2000 lb. wt. respectively, find graphically the tensions in the other two.

PAPER 8

1. Two weights P and Q balance on a weightless lever, the fulcrum being $1\frac{1}{4}$ inches from the middle point of the lever. If each weight is increased by 1 lb., the fulcrum must be moved $\frac{1}{4}$ inch in order to preserve equilibrium. Find the pressure on the fulcrum in each case.

2. Two unlike parallel forces act at points A and B, 12 inches apart. Their resultant is a force of 15 lb. wt. and passes through a point in AB produced, 8 inches from B. Find the magnitudes of the two forces.

3. Two forces, one of 18 lb. wt. and the other of 30 lb. wt., act at a point of a body, and the angle between their directions is 60°. Find graphically the magnitude of their resultant and the angle its line of action makes with the larger of the two forces.

4. A particle is acted on by forces 1, 2, 3, 4, 5, 6 lb. wt. in directions parallel to the sides of a regular hexagon, taken in order. Find graphically the magnitude and direction of the resultant.

5. A horizontal weightless beam AB, 20 ft. long, rests on two supports, one under the end A and the other under a point C, 15 ft. from A. The beam carries loads 2, 4, 6 and 8 tons at points respectively distant 4, 8, 12 and 16 ft. from A. Find the thrust on each support.

Find also the vertical downward force which must be applied at B in order to relieve the support A of its load, and the vertically upward force at B to relieve the support C of its load.

PAPER 9

1. Find the magnitude of the resultant of parallel forces 2, 5, 6, 7 lb. wt. acting in vertical lines at distances 1 foot apart in the same vertical plane, the forces 2 and 6 lb. wt. acting upwards and the other two downwards. What is the distance of the resultant from the force of 7 lb. wt. ?

2. Calculate the magnitude of the force acting parallel to a smooth inclined plane which will just support a weight of 1 ton, if the plane rises 1 ft. for each 10 ft. along the plane. What is the magnitude of the reaction of the plane ?

3. Two forces of 12 and 31 lb. wt. act at a point, the angle between their directions being 70°. Calculate the magnitude of the resultant.

4. A body weighing 1 ton is to be drawn up a smooth inclined plank by means of a rope parallel to the plank. The pressure on the plank is not to exceed 16 cwt. Calculate the least inclination of the plank to the horizontal consistent with this condition.

5. A square trap-door of side 3 feet, movable about a horizontal hinge, is maintained at an elevation of 30° by a chain connecting the middle point of the highest side with a hook, 6 ft. vertically above the middle point of the hinge. If the door is a metal plate of uniform thickness, weighing 2 cwt., find graphically the tension in the chain and the thrust on the hinge.

PAPER 10

1. Two forces of 10 and 15 lb. wt. respectively act at a point, the angle between their directions being 105°. Find, by calculation, the magnitude and direction of the force that will balance them.

2. Forces 10, 30, 50, 20 lb. wt. act at a point in directions E., N., N.W. and S.W. respectively. Find graphically the magnitude and direction of their resultant.

3. O is any point in the plane of a parallelogram $ABCD$. Show that the system of forces, acting at O, represented in magnitude and direction by AO, OB, CO, OD, is in equilibrium.

4. A body of weight W rests on a smooth plane inclined at 20° 20′ to the horizontal, and is kept from slipping down by a string making an angle 30° 30′ with the plane. Find, by Lami's Theorem, the ratio of the tension of the string to the weight of the body.

5. A light rod AB is hinged at A and supported in a horizontal position by a string, one end of which is attached to the rod at a point C, and the other end fixed at a point D vertically above A. A weight of 500 grams is suspended from B. If $AB=50$ cm., $AC=30$ cm., $AD=60$ cm., find graphically the tension in the string and the magnitude and direction of the reaction at the hinge.

PAPER 11

1. $ABCD$ is a string; the part AB is vertical, the angle ABC is 120°, CD is horizontal, and the ends A and D are held fixed. Find *graphically* the magnitude of the horizontal force at B required to keep the string in this position when a load of 6 lb. hangs from C. Find also the tension in AB.

2. Solve the above problem by means of Lami's Theorem.

3. Forces 3, 5, 7 lb. wt. act at a point in directions parallel to the sides of an equilateral triangle. Calculate the magnitude of their resultant.

4. A tapering spar AB of length 25 ft., whose C.G. is not at the middle point, rests horizontally on two supports at P and Q. P is 4 ft. from A and Q is 9 ft. from B. An upward vertical force of 120 lb. wt. at A is just sufficient to lift the spar off the support P. An upward vertical force of 80 lb. wt. at B just lifts the spar off the support Q. Determine the weight of the spar and the distance of its C.G. from A.

5. A uniform rod 3 ft. long rests entirely inside a smooth hemispherical bowl of radius 2 ft., making an angle of 30° with the horizontal. Find *graphically* the distance of its C.G. from its lower extremity.

PAPER 12

1. Two forces of 5 and 6 lb. wt. act at an angle of 130°. Find, by calculation, the magnitude of their resultant and the angle it makes with the greater force.

2. Three forces 8, 5, 10 lb. wt. act at a point in directions N. 70° E., N. 50° W., S. 10° E. Find, by calculation, the magnitude and direction of their resultant.

3. The ends A and D of a light string $ABCD$ are fixed. Weights of 5 lb. and 7 lb. are fastened to the string at B and C respectively. AB is inclined at 45° to the vertical, and BC is horizontal. Find *graphically* the inclination of CD to the vertical, and the tension in CD.

4. A bench, 10 ft. long, has supports 2 ft. from each end. The weight of the bench, which may be taken as acting at its middle point, is 20 lb. A boy is sitting on the bench, which may now be just upset by a man of 160 lb. weight seating himself at one end, or by a man of 200 lb. weight at the other end. Find the weight of the boy and his distance from one end.

5. A metal sphere weighing 10 lb. rests against a smooth vertical wall with a string equal in length to the radius of the sphere attached to a point of the wall and to a point on the surface of the sphere. Find *graphically* the tension of the string and the pressure of the sphere on the wall.

CHAPTER VII

VELOCITY

42. Average Speed. If a train travels 160 miles in 4 hours, we are all familiar with the statement that its *average speed* is 40 miles per hour. This statement does not imply that the train is always moving at 40 miles an hour; in the first place, it will have to get up speed, then, owing to gradients on the line, its speed will sometimes be more and sometimes less than 40 miles per hour; it may, moreover, stop at intermediate stations. If, however, the train had travelled at a constant speed of 40 miles per hour, it would have covered the 160 miles in exactly 4 hours.

$$\textbf{Def.} \qquad Average\ speed = \frac{total\ distance\ moved}{total\ time\ taken}.$$

If we consider the *direction* in which a body is moving as well as its rate of motion, then the expression *velocity* is usual instead of speed.

In either case we are dealing with the *rate of change of position*.

43. Uniform Velocity. A body moving with uniform velocity describes equal distances in equal times in a constant direction, no matter how small these intervals of time are. If a train is travelling at a uniform speed of 30 miles per hour, we mean that in every minute it passes over $\frac{1}{2}$ mile, or 880 yards, in every second it passes over $\frac{44}{3}$ yards, in every tenth of a second over $\frac{22}{15}$ yard, and so on. We shall express a speed of 30 miles per hour as 30 ml./hr.; a speed of 10 feet per second as 10 ft./sec.

44. Angular Velocity. In the case of a rotating body it is often convenient to express the rate of change of position by a different method. A place on the equator describes a circle of radius 3960 miles in 1 day, *i.e.* 24,880 miles a day, whereas a place in latitude 60° describes a circle of radius 1980 miles in 1 day, *i.e.* 12,440 miles a day; but each place *rotates* round the earth's axis through an angle of 360° in a day.

Similarly, the minute hand of a clock turns through 360° or 2π radians in 1 hour, while the hour hand turns through 360° or 2π radians in 12 hours, *i.e.* 30° or $\dfrac{\pi}{6}$ radians in 1 hour.

45. Ex. 1. *If a train travels 25 miles at 30 ml./hr. and 5 miles at 45 ml./hr., what is the average speed and the total time?*

Time taken for 25 miles $= \frac{25}{30} = \frac{5}{6}$ hr.,

   ,,   ,,   ,,   5 miles $= \frac{5}{45} = \frac{1}{9}$ hr. ;

$\therefore$ total time $= \frac{5}{6} + \frac{1}{9} = \frac{17}{18}$ hr. $= 56\frac{2}{3}$ min.

$$\text{Average speed} = \frac{\text{total distance}}{\text{total time}} = \frac{30 \times 18}{17} = 31\frac{13}{17} = 31\cdot 8 \text{ ml./hr.}$$

Ex. 2. *A body moves round the circumference of a circle, radius r ft., with uniform angular velocity ω radians per second. Find the velocity round the circumference.*

Suppose the body moves from **A** to **P** in t seconds, then the angle described is ωt radians,

$\therefore$ arc $\mathbf{AP} = r\theta = r\omega t$ feet.

But if the velocity round the circumference is v ft./sec.,

arc $\mathbf{AP} = vt$ ft. ;

$\therefore vt = r\omega t,$

i.e. $\mathbf{v} = \mathbf{r\omega}.$

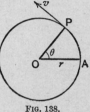

Fig. 138.

EXERCISE XVI

1. Reduce a velocity of (i) 30 ml./hr., (ii) 45 ml./hr., (iii) 25 ml./hr. to ft./sec.

2. Reduce a velocity of (i) 22 ft./sec., (ii) 30 ft./sec., (iii) 50 ft./sec. to ml./hr.

3. If a man runs a mile in 6 minutes, what is his average speed in ml./hr. ?

4. If the speed of a train is uniform for 5 minutes and the magnitude of the speed 30 ml./hr., how far will it travel in this 5 minutes ?

5. A body moves at the rate of 12 kilometres in 1 hour ; what is the speed expressed in metres per minute ?

6. If a man walks for 10 minutes at 5 ml./hr. and 15 minutes at 4 ml./hr., what is his average speed in ml./hr. ?

7. Find the average speed in ml./hr. if a man walks for 35 minutes at 4 ml./hr. and 45 minutes at $3\frac{1}{2}$ ml./hr.

8. A train travels 20 miles at 40 ml./hr., 50 miles at 30 ml./hr., and 10 miles at 60 ml./hr. What is its average speed, and how long does it take to make the journey ?

9. A man motors for 25 miles at 30 ml./hr., has a stop of half an hour, and then travels 20 miles at 32 ml./hr. Find his average speed,

10. If a man motors for 15 miles at 32 ml./hr., walks 5 miles at 4 ml./hr., and travels by train a distance of 12 miles at 25 ml./hr., what is his average speed ?

11. A boat travels 2 miles in a N.E. direction and then 2 miles in a N.W. direction, and takes 40 minutes. What is the average speed through the water, and the average speed due N. ?

12. A body moves through a ft. in x seconds and then b ft. in y seconds. Find the average speed.

13. A man walks at the rate of u ml./hr. for a hours, and v ml./hr. for b hours. Find his average speed.

14. If a man walks 15 miles in 4 hours, find his average speed. If the average speed for the first 5 miles is 4 ml./hr., calculate his average speed for the remaining 10 miles.

15. If a point revolves round a circle of radius 5 ft. five times in a second, find its angular velocity in (i) degrees per second, (ii) radians per second. (iii) Also find its velocity round the circumference in ft./sec.

16. If a point describes a circle of radius 10 ft. with angular velocity of 2 radians per sec., find its velocity round the circumference.

17. If a wheel of radius 5 ft. is rotating 12 times a second, find the velocity of (i) any point on the circumference, (ii) a point 2 ft. from the centre. (Assume $\pi = \frac{22}{7}$.)

18. If a disc of radius 3 ft. is turning about its centre so that any point on the rim is moving with a velocity of 25 ft./sec., calculate the angular velocity in radians per sec.

19. Calculate the angular velocity in radians per sec., due to rotation about the axis, of a point on the earth's surface situated on (i) the equator, (ii) the parallel of latitude 35° N. (iii) If the earth is considered a sphere of radius 3960 miles, what are the corresponding velocities in ml./hr. ?

20. A man standing behind a gun hears the report of the gun and sees the discharged shell burst at the same moment, the shell, gun and man being in the same straight line. He finds he was 2000 yd. from the gun and that the range of the gun was 5000 yd. Having given that sound travels at 1100 ft. per sec., find the average horizontal velocity of the shell.

46. Distance-time Graph.

If a body is moving with uniform velocity, its motion may be represented graphically by measuring *time* (*t*) along a horizontal axis and the corresponding *distance* (*s*) vertically.

Thus if a body is moving at 10 ft. per sec., it will pass over 10 ft. in 1 sec., 20 ft. in 2 sec., 30 ft. in 3 sec., etc., and the various points obtained will lie upon a straight line **OA** through the origin.

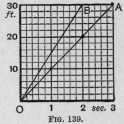

FIG. 139.

Similarly, if the velocity is 15 ft. per sec., the various points will lie on a steeper straight line **OB**.

In all cases where the *s*, *t* curve is *a straight line* through the origin, we conclude that the motion is one of *uniform velocity* and that the **gradient gives the magnitude of the velocity,** the gradient being the ratio of the ordinate of any point of the line to the corresponding abscissa.

47. Variable Velocity.

In actual practice, the velocity of a body is hardly ever uniform. A familiar instance of variable velocity is the motion of a motor car, the movement of the hand on the dial of the speedometer indicating the variations that take place.

If a body is moving with variable velocity and at some particular instant we find the average velocity for a very small interval of time including the instant, we obtain some idea of what is meant by the phrase *velocity at an instant.*

Def. Velocity at an instant equals *the limiting value of the average velocity during a small interval of time including the instant, when the small interval is indefinitely diminished.*

If the connection between the distance and time is given in the following table :

t (sec.)	0	0·5	1	1·5	2
s (ft.)	0	1	5	11	20

and a graph is drawn, then a curve is obtained. (Fig. 140.)

Since equal distances are not moved over in equal times, it follows that the velocity is not uniform.

Suppose it is required to find the velocity at the end of 1 second ; consider the average velocity during an interval of time extending from 0·5 to 1·5 sec., *i.e.* including the given instant of 1 second ;

$$\text{average velocity} = \frac{\text{distance}}{\text{time}} = \frac{QM}{RM} = \frac{10}{1} = 10 \text{ ft./sec.}$$

= gradient of chord RQ.

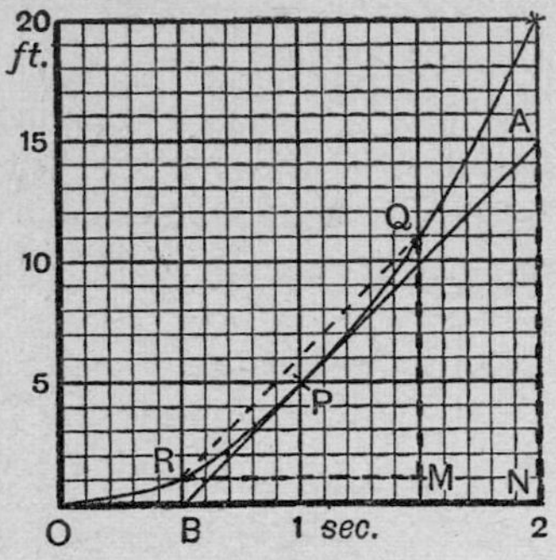

FIG. 140.

If now the points Q and R approach the point P and eventually coincide with it, the average velocity becomes the velocity at the end of 1 sec., and the chord RQ becomes the tangent at P,

∴ velocity at end of 1 sec.
= gradient of tangent at P
$$= \frac{AN}{BN} = \frac{14·6}{1·5} = 9·7 \text{ ft./sec.}$$

It follows that if the *t*-axis is taken horizontally, the **velocity at any instant is represented by the gradient of the tangent to the curve at the corresponding point.**

EXERCISE XVII

1. Corresponding values of distance (*s*) and time (*t*) are given in the following table :—

t (sec.)	0	1	2	3	4	5
s (ft.)	1	3	9	19	33	51

Illustrate graphically and thence determine the velocity when *t* = 3·4 sec.

2. Read off from the graph in Fig. 141 the velocity during the first 5 seconds, and also the velocity between the 10th and 15th seconds. What happens between the 5th and 10th seconds ?

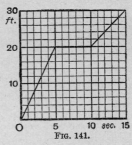

FIG. 141.

3. The movement of a motor car on a track is found to be that given in the annexed table, in which the distance s corresponding to a given time t is recorded :—

t (sec.)	3	4	5	6	7	8
s (ft.)	58	73	92	115	142	173

Plot these values on a distance-time graph and thence determine the velocity of the car at the end of the 4th and 7th seconds.

4. The distances of a moving body from a fixed point were observed at intervals of 0·5 sec. with the following results :—0, 31, 62, 83, 84, 65, 26 ft. Illustrate graphically and read off its position at the end of 2·25 sec.

Does the speed appear to have been constant during any part of its motion and, if so, during which part ?

Estimate the velocity at the end of 2 sec.

5. A point moves in a straight line, and its distance from a given point in the straight line is x ft. after an interval of t sec. measured from a given instant. Corresponding values of x and t are shown in the following table :—

t	0	0·5	1·2	1·9	2·5	3·2	3·5
x	0	0·5	7	27	63	147	132

Show the relation between x and t by means of a graph, and thence determine (i) the value of x, (ii) the velocity, when $t = 1·15$.

6. Plot the following values of t (sec.) and s (ft.) :—

t	0	1	2	3	4	5	6
s	2	5	14	29	47	65	83

Find the velocity when $t=1$, 2, 3, 4, 5, 6 seconds. What conclusion do you draw from the results obtained ?

7. If the connection between the distance in feet and time in seconds is given by the formula $s=3t^2$, plot a graph for s and t, and thence find the velocity when $t=3\cdot3$ sec.

8. Suppose a body to have fallen h feet in t seconds from rest according to the law $h=16\cdot1t^2$. (i) Find how far it falls between the times $t=3$ and $t=3\cdot1$; between $t=3$ and $t=3\cdot01$; between $t=3$ and $t=3\cdot001$. (ii) Thence find the average velocity in each of these intervals of time. (iii) What do these results suggest as to the probable velocity when $t=3$ sec. ?

9. The following is a time-table of a train from London to York, together with the distances of the stations from King's Cross :—

	MILES.	ARRIVE.	DEPART.
King's Cross . .	—	—	11.45
Hitchin . .	32	12.36	12.39
Peterboro' . .	$76\frac{1}{4}$	1.37	1.42
Grantham . .	$105\frac{1}{4}$	2.27	2.31
Newark . .	120	2.50	2.52
Retford . .	$138\frac{1}{2}$	3.18	3.21
Doncaster . .	156	3.46	3.50
Selby . . .	$174\frac{1}{4}$	4.13	4.15
York . . .	188	4.35	—

Draw a graph connecting time and the distance from King's Cross, and thence determine the two consecutive stations between which the train shows the greatest average velocity, and find the magnitude of this velocity.

48. Velocity-time Graph.

(i) In the case of *uniform* velocity, if the values of time (t) and velocity (v) are plotted, the graph is a straight line **AB** parallel to the t-axis, since v must always have the same value.

If **OA** represents the velocity and **OC** the time, then

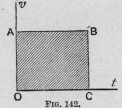

FIG. 142.

$$distance = v \times t = \mathbf{OA} \times \mathbf{OC} = area \text{ of rect. } \mathbf{AC}.$$

It must be noted that the length of **OA** is determined in terms of the scale on the v-axis, and the length of **OC** in terms of the scale on the t-axis.

(ii) If the body is moving with *variable* velocity, let the v, t curve be that shown in Fig. 143, and suppose the distance passed over in time **OC** is required.

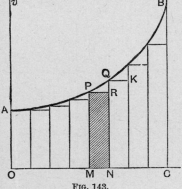

FIG. 143.

Divide **OC** into a number of equal intervals of time and describe rectangles as shown.

As the time increases from **OM** to **ON**, the velocity increases from **MP** to **NQ**; if it had remained constant and equal to **MP**, then the distance passed over would have been represented by the area of the rectangle **PN**.

Similarly, if during the next interval the velocity remains constant and equal to **NQ**, the distance passed over is represented by the area of the rectangle **NK**; and so on for all the intervals. Consequently, if these intervals of time are small, the total distance passed over does not differ very much from the sum of all the rectangles of the type **PN**; and the sum of all the rectangles is approximately the area of the figure bounded by the curve, the t-axis, and the ordinates **OA**, **CB**.

Thus in the limit, when the small intervals of time are diminished indefinitely,

the velocity varies continuously instead of by jerks, and the *distance* is *represented* by the limit of the sum of the rectangles,

i.e. by the area of the figure **OABC**.

The method of finding the area by using mid-ordinates will be illustrated by an example.

Ex. *The velocity of a train for the first minute of its motion is given by the table :—*

Time (sec.)	0	5	10	20	30	40	50	60
Velocity (ft./sec.)	0	8·5	14·6	23	29·2	33·6	37	39

Find the distance travelled in the first minute.

The values given in the table are plotted with the scales shown on the two axes and the curve **OA** obtained.

The distance passed over is represented by the area of the figure **OBA**.

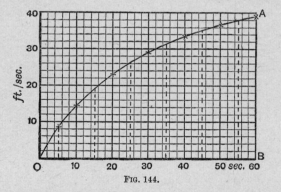

Fig. 144.

(i) Let **OB** be divided into a number of equal convenient distances, in this case six, and an ordinate erected at. the middle point of each distance. The average ordinate (*i.e.* the average velocity)

$$= \tfrac{1}{6}(8·5 + 19 + 26·2 + 31 + 35 + 38) = \tfrac{1}{6} \times 157·7$$
$$= 26·3 \text{ ft. per sec.}$$

∴ distance = average velocity × time = 26·3 × 60 ft. = 1578 ft.

(ii) Another method is to count the number of small squares in the area **OBA**, and this number is 394 ; since one small square represents the distance passed over in 2 sec. at the rate of 2 ft. per sec., *i.e.* 4 feet, it follows that 394 small squares represent 1576 ft.

EXERCISE XVIII

1. From observation on a moving body it is found to have velocities of 3, 6, 9, 12, 15 ft./sec. at the end of consecutive seconds. Find graphically the distance it passes over in the 5 seconds.

2. The velocity-time graph of a moving body is given in Fig. 145. Find the distance passed over in 40 seconds.

3. If the velocity-time graph of a car is shown in Fig. 146, find the distance passed over in 80 minutes.

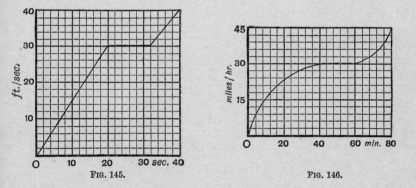

FIG. 145.   FIG. 146.

4. The relation between the time and velocity of a moving body is given by the following values :—

t (sec.)	0	1	2	3	4	5	6	7
v (ft./sec.)	0	0·2	0·55	1·1	1·7	2·5	3·5	4·8

Draw a curve and deduce the distance passed over in 3 and 6 sec. from rest.

5. A motor car starts from rest. After t sec. from the start, the speed is v ml./hr. The following table gives corresponding values of v and t.

v	0	3·2	6·4	8·5	10·4	12·7	13·2	13·8	14·4
t	0	4	8	11	14	19	20	22	25

Draw a curve to represent these data and estimate in feet the distance travelled in the first 25 sec.

6. The velocity of a train for the first minute of its motion is given by the table

t (sec.)	0	5	10	20	30	40	50	60
v (ft./sec.)	0	8·5	14·6	23	29·2	33·6	37	39

Find the distance travelled in the first minute.

7. A tube train gets up its maximum speed of 40 ft./sec. in 1 minute. The speed at various times from the start is given in the following table :—

t (sec.)	0	5	10	20	30	40	50	55	60
v (ft./sec.)	0	1·5	4	13	23	32	37·5	39	40

Plot these values and thence deduce the distance gone in 1 minute.

8. A tramcar is travelling at 14 ml./hr. when the brake is applied, and the subsequent relation between the velocity and time is given by the following table :—

t (sec.)	0	1	2	3	4	5	6	7	8	9	10
v (ml./hr.)	14	10·5	8·4	6·9	5·8	5	4·4	3·8	3·4	3·1	2·75

Plot a velocity-time curve and deduce the distance the car has covered in these 10 seconds.

CHAPTER VIII

ACCELERATION

49. If a body is moving with variable velocity, then its *rate of change of velocity* is called its **acceleration.**

If at the end of successive seconds the velocity of a body moving in a straight line is 10 cm./sec., 15 cm./sec., 20 cm./sec., etc., then we conclude the velocity is increasing at the rate of 5 cm. per sec. every second, and the acceleration is 5 cm. per sec. per sec.; this result being more conveniently expressed as 5 cm./sec.^{2}

In just the same way that velocity may be uniform or variable, so acceleration may be uniform or variable; in the subject of Elementary Dynamics, we are usually dealing with the effect of a constant force on a body, and in such cases the acceleration is uniform.

If, instead of increasing, the velocity of a body is diminishing, then the acceleration is negative and is spoken of as the *retardation*.

$$Average\ acceleration = \frac{total\ increase\ of\ velocity}{time\ taken}.$$

50. Velocity-time Graph.

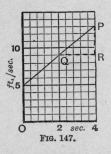
FIG. 147.

(i) If a body is moving in a straight line with a velocity at a particular instant of 5 ft./sec. and the acceleration is *uniform* and equal to 2 ft./sec.^{2}, then its velocity at the end of 1, 2, 3, 4 sec. is 7, 9, 11, 13 ft./sec. If these values are plotted, it is obvious that *a straight line graph* is obtained; and given any such straight line, the acceleration may be obtained by reading off the *gradient* of the line by taking any two convenient points P and Q and finding the value of $\frac{RP}{QR}$. If the line slopes downwards, then the acceleration is negative.

(ii) In the case of a body moving with *variable* acceleration, then the acceleration at any instant equals the limiting value of the average acceleration during a small interval of time including the instant, when the small interval is indefinitely diminished.

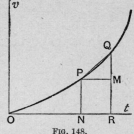

Fig. 148.

Since *velocity* is rate of change of *distance*,
and *acceleration* ,, ,, ,, *velocity*,

it follows that what has been given in connection with the graphical representation of velocity from the *s, t* curve may be adapted for the representation of acceleration from the *v, t* curve.

If P and Q are two points on the curve, then NP, RQ represent velocities, and ON, OR the corresponding times.

The average acceleration during the interval of time NR

$$=\frac{\text{change of velocity}}{\text{time taken}}=\frac{MQ}{NR}=\text{gradient of } PQ.$$

The smaller the time NR becomes, the more nearly will this average acceleration become the actual acceleration, and in the limit, when Q coincides with P, PQ becomes the tangent at P, and

the acceleration at the time represented by ON becomes the **gradient of the tangent to the curve** at P.

51. Suppose that when we first consider the motion of a body, its velocity is *u* ft./sec., and that the acceleration is *a* ft./sec.², then at the end of the

first second, the velocity will be $(u+a)$ ft./sec.,
second ,, ,, ,, $(u+2a)$ ft./sec.,
third ,, ,, ,, $(u+3a)$ ft./sec., etc. ;

and generally, if *v* ft./sec. is the velocity at the end of *t* sec.,

$$\mathbf{v=u+at.}$$

Ex. 1. *The acceleration of a body is 5·7 cm./sec.²   Calculate the original velocity, if, after 5 seconds, the velocity is 40 cm./sec.*

Since $v=u+at,$
$$\therefore\ 40=u+(5\cdot7\times5),$$
$$\therefore\ u=11\cdot5 \text{ cm./sec.}$$

52. Acceleration-time Graph.

(i) In the case of *uniform* acceleration, if the values of time (t) and acceleration (a) are plotted, the graph is a straight line parallel to the t-axis, since a has a constant value. (Fig. 149.)

If **OA** represents the acceleration and **OC** the time, then

$$\text{increase of velocity} = a \times t = \mathbf{OA} \times \mathbf{OC}$$
$$= \textit{area of rect. } \mathbf{AC}.$$

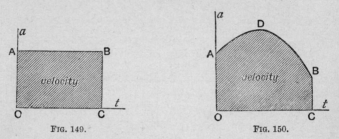

FIG. 149.   FIG. 150.

(ii) If the body is moving with *variable* acceleration (Fig. 150), then, for small intervals of time, using the fact that

$$\text{increase of velocity} = a \times t,$$

instead of, $$\text{distance} = v \times t,$$

we have, as in Art. 48,

$$\text{increase of velocity} = \textit{area of the figure } \mathbf{OADBC}.$$

53. The differences between the following diagrams should be noted :—

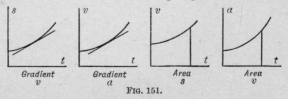

Gradient   Gradient   Area   Area
v a s v

FIG. 151.

EXERCISE XIX

1. Find the average acceleration of a body which, starting from rest, acquires a velocity of 20 ft./sec. in 15 seconds.

2. If a train reduces its velocity from 40 ml./hr. to 30 ml./hr. in 2 minutes, what is the retardation in ml./hr.^{2} ?

3. An acceleration is 11 ml./hr.²

    Express this in (i) ft. per hour per hour, (ii) ft. per sec. per hr., (iii) ft. per sec. per sec.

4. Express in ft.-sec. units an acceleration of 4 ml./hr.²

5. Express an acceleration of 32 ft./sec.² in yd. min. units.

6. The velocity of a body, starting from rest, is increased by 12 ft./sec. in 3 sec. ; what will be its velocity at the end of 2 minutes ?

7. If the velocity of a body increases from 5 cm./sec. to 11·4 cm./sec. in 7 sec., what is the acceleration ?

8. If a body moving with a velocity of 8 ft./sec. is subject to an acceleration of 2 ft./sec.², in what time will the velocity increase to 13·5 ft./sec. ?

9. The acceleration of a body is 3·2 ft./sec.² ; if the velocity is 18 ft./sec. after 4 sec., calculate the original velocity.

10. A body moving with a velocity of 10·2 cm./sec. is subject to an acceleration of 0·4 cm./sec.² ; what is its velocity after 11 sec. ?

11. If the velocity of a body is reduced from 15 ft./sec. to 12 ft./sec. in 1 minute, what is the retardation ?

12. In Fig. 152 what is the acceleration during the time OM, and the retardation during the time MN ?

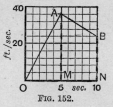

Fig. 152.

13. Corresponding values of velocity (ft./sec.) and time (sec.) are given in the following table :—

t	0	1	2	3	4	5	6
v	0	2	8	18	32	50	72

    Trace the curve and deduce the value of the acceleration when $t = 2·4$ sec.

14. Draw a velocity-time graph from the following values :—

t (sec.)	0	2	3	5	6	7	8
v (ft./sec.)	0	8	12	20	28·8	39·2	51·2

    What change takes place at 5 seconds ? Find the acceleration at 3 and 6·5 seconds.

15. If $v=1+2t^2$, find the average acceleration between $t=2$ sec. and $t=(2+x)$ sec., if the unit of length is 1 cm.

    By gradually diminishing x, what is the acceleration when $t=2$ sec. ?

16. The velocity of a point at times 0, 2, 5, 7, 10, 14, 16 sec. is observed to be 6, 14, 26, 34, 45, 60, 65 ft./sec. Calculate the average acceleration during each interval between observations and draw an acceleration-time graph. Does the acceleration appear to be uniform during any part of the motion, and does it finally increase or decrease ?

17. While a revolving flywheel was slowing down, the following observations of the speed were made at half-minute intervals :—

Time (sec.)	0	30	60	90	120	150
Revolutions per min.	370	240	146	80	33	0

    Plot a graph connecting these values. Deduce the retardation in rev. per min. per sec. at the time 70 sec.

18. The following is a distance-time table for a train slowing up :—

t (sec.)	0	5	9	11	15	17
s (yd.)	0	65	105	121	145	153

Assume that $\dfrac{\text{distance}}{\text{time}}$ for any interval represents the velocity at *half-time* for that interval, and plot a velocity-time graph. Find the retardation in ft./sec.², the velocity at zero-time and the time at which the velocity becomes zero.

19. A body starting from rest moves in a straight line and the following observations are taken :—

t (sec.)	0	0·2	0·4	0·6	0·8	1·0	1·2	1·4	1·6
s (cm.)	0	0·55	2·1	4·8	8·5	13·2	18·5	23·7	29·0

Plot a distance-time curve. Determine approximately the velocities of the body in cm./sec. at the middle of each interval of time. What conclusions do you draw as to the nature of the motion ?

20. The relation between time and acceleration for an electric tram-car starting from rest is given in the table :—

t (sec.)	0	10	20	30	40	50	60	70
a (ft./sec.²)	0·4	0·9	1·1	0·4	−0·4	−0·55	−0·57	−0·4

Plot the acceleration-time curve and deduce the velocity at the end of 20 and 60 sec.

21. A train takes 5 min. between two stations 2 miles apart. It runs at maximum speed for 3 minutes. Assuming that acceleration and retardation are constant, indicate the form of the velocity-time graph, and find the maximum speed.

54. Formulae. (i) If a body moves from rest with *uniformly* accelerated motion, then, from Art. 50, the t, v graph is a *straight line passing through the origin.*

If **OA** (Fig. 153) represents the time and **AB** the corresponding velocity, then the distance passed over is represented by the area of **OAB**,

$$\therefore \; \mathbf{s} = \tfrac{1}{2}\mathbf{OA} \cdot \mathbf{AB}$$
$$= \tfrac{1}{2}\mathbf{vt} \quad . \quad . \quad . \quad . \quad . \quad \text{(i)}$$

Also, $\qquad\qquad\qquad s = \text{average velocity} \times \text{time},$

$$\therefore \; \text{average velocity} = \tfrac{1}{2}v,$$

i.e. *if a body moves from* rest *under constant acceleration,*

average velocity = half the final velocity.

(ii) If the body has an initial velocity u, then the t, v graph is a straight line not passing through the origin.

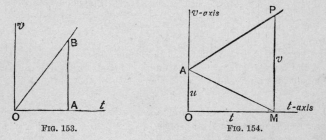

FIG. 153.   FIG. 154.

If **OM** (Fig. 154) represents the time, **MP** the corresponding velocity v, **OA** the initial velocity u, then the distance passed over is represented by the area of **OAPM**,

$$\therefore \; \mathbf{s} = \text{area of } \mathbf{OAM} + \text{area of } \mathbf{APM}$$
$$= \tfrac{1}{2}\mathbf{OA} \cdot \mathbf{OM} + \tfrac{1}{2}\mathbf{MP} \cdot \mathbf{OM}$$
$$= \tfrac{1}{2}ut + \tfrac{1}{2}vt = \tfrac{1}{2}(\mathbf{u}+\mathbf{v})\mathbf{t} \quad . \quad . \quad . \quad \text{(ii)}$$

Also, $\qquad\qquad\qquad$ since $s = \text{average velocity} \times \text{time},$

$$\therefore \; \text{average velocity} = \tfrac{1}{2}(u+v),$$

i.e. if a body moves under constant acceleration,

average velocity = half the sum of original and final velocities.

From   (i) since $\quad v = at, \qquad\qquad \therefore \; s = \tfrac{1}{2}at^2,$

$\qquad$ (ii) since $\quad v = u + at, \qquad \therefore \; s = \tfrac{1}{2}(u+u+at)t = ut + \tfrac{1}{2}at^2.$

Also $\qquad\qquad 2s = (u+v)t,$

$$\therefore \; 2as = (u+v)at = (u+v)(v-u) = v^2 - u^2,$$

i.e. $\qquad\quad v^2 = u^2 + 2as.$

We have thus established the following formulae :—

Initial Velocity u	*Initial Velocity zero*
$v = u + at.$	$v = at.$
$s = \frac{1}{2}(u + v)t.$	$s = \frac{1}{2}vt.$
$s = ut + \frac{1}{2}at^2.$	$s = \frac{1}{2}at^2.$
$v^2 = u^2 + 2as.$	$v^2 = 2as.$

55. Ex. 1. *A carriage slipped from a train is uniformly retarded by the brakes and stops in $1\frac{1}{2}$ min. If the train by this time is 990 yards away from the carriage, what is the speed of the train, supposing it to remain constant ?*

Let u ft./sec. be the speed of the train ; since $1\frac{1}{2}$ min. $= 90$ sec.,

distance moved by carriage $= \frac{1}{2}u \times 90$ ft., $\qquad$ ($s = av.\ vel. \times time$)

  „   „   train $= u \times 90$ ft. ; $\qquad$ ($s = vel. \times time$)

$\therefore\ 90u - 45u = 3 \times 990,$

$\therefore\ u = 66$ ft./sec. $= 45$ ml/hr.

Ex. 2. *A body moving with uniform acceleration describes 19 ft. in the first second, and 27 ft. in the third second. Find its acceleration and initial velocity.*

If u ft./sec. is the initial velocity, and a ft./sec.^{2} the acceleration, then

$$19 = u + \tfrac{1}{2}a\ ;\quad\ \cdot\quad\ \cdot\quad (i)\qquad (s = ut + \tfrac{1}{2}at^2)$$

the distance in the 3rd sec. $=$ distance in first 3 sec. $-$ distance in first 2 sec. ;

$$\therefore\ 27 = (3u + \tfrac{9}{2}a) - (2u + 2a)$$
$$= u + \tfrac{5}{2}a\quad\ \cdot\quad\ \cdot\quad (ii)$$

Subtracting (i) from (ii), $\qquad 2a = 8\ ;$

$\therefore\ a = 4$ ft./sec.^{2} ;

Substituting in (i), $\qquad\qquad u = 19 - 2 = 17$ ft./sec.

EXERCISE XX

1. A body is moving with a velocity of 30 ft./sec. and is stopped in 8 seconds. How far has it travelled in this time ?

2. If a car running at 25 ml./hr. is stopped in 18 yards, find the time taken to stop it.

3. If a train running at 45 ml./hr. is stopped in 4 minutes, find the distance it runs before it stops.

4. If a body, which starts from rest, covers 25·45 cm. in the first 5 seconds, find the velocity at the end of the 5 seconds, and the acceleration.

5. If the explosive force in a gun is constant, find the time taken by shell to travel 20 ft. along the barrel, if the muzzle velocity is 160 ft./sec.

6. If a body starts from rest with an acceleration of 4·5 cm./sec.², wha will be its speed, and what will be the distance traversed in 6 seconds

7. If a particle is projected with a velocity of 30 ft./sec., and if there is constant retardation of 1⅔ ft./sec.², for what distance and for how long will it move till it is instantaneously at rest ?

8. A body starts with a velocity of 10 ft./sec., and moves with unifor acceleration. After 2½ minutes it has gone 3750 ft. What has bee its acceleration, and what is its velocity at the end of the period ?

9. What acceleration (in foot-second units) is needed to increase a velocit of 10 ml./hr. to 30 ml./hr. (i) in half a minute, (ii) in half a mile ?

10. A train moving with uniform acceleration increases its speed from 10 ml./hr. to 20 ml./hr. in a quarter of a mile. Where and when wi its speed be 30 ml./hr. ?

11. A train moving with constant acceleration passes a point A at 15 ml./hr and a point B at 30 ml./hr. The distance AB is ¼ mile. Find th acceleration of the train in ft./sec.²

12. A point, whose initial velocity is 10 ft./sec., moves for 6 seconds wit acceleration 4 ft./sec.², and then with retardation 8 ft./sec.² How fa will it have gone before it comes to rest ?

13. If an aeroplane and a railway train start at the same moment from the same place and travel in the same direction, the former at 75 ml./hr and the latter at 45 ml./hr., how far will the aeroplane be in fror of the train after 50 minutes ?

14. A body starting from rest and moving with uniform acceleration trave 165 ft. in the 8th second. Find the acceleration.

15. A body starts with a velocity of 32 ft./sec., and moves in a straigh line with uniform acceleration. It describes 400 ft. in 10 second How many feet does it describe in the first 5 seconds ?

16. A body moving from rest with constant acceleration acquires a spee of 30 ft./sec. in 3 minutes. The acceleration remaining unaltere what distance will it move in the next minute ?

17. A motor car is travelling with a velocity of 28 ml./hr. when the brak are put on, and in 10 yards the speed is reduced to 20 ml./hr. Ho much farther will the car run before being reduced to rest ?

18. Find the acceleration (in ft./sec.²), assumed constant, of a train, that decreases in speed from 60 ml./hr. to 30 ml./hr. in a quarter of a mile. How much farther (in miles) would the train travel before coming to rest if the retarding force acting upon it continued the same ?

19. A train moving at 10 ml./hr. increases its speed to 30 ml./hr. in a distance of half a mile, the acceleration being uniform. How long did it take over this distance, and what was its speed at half-distance ?

20. A train is observed to run 64 ft. in the first second after the brakes are applied, and 60 ft. in the next. What was the original speed, and how far will the train run in coming to rest, assuming that the retardation is constant ?

21. A tram-car starts from rest and is uniformly accelerated for 10 seconds to a speed of 12 ml./hr. It maintains this speed for 1 minute and is then brought to rest in 5 seconds by a uniform retardation. Find the acceleration and retardation in ft./sec.², and also the distance, in yards, between the two stopping places.

22. In running a race, a man's greatest speed, which he maintains when once attained, is 10 yd./sec., and he runs 200 yards in 21 seconds when he starts from rest. If the first part of the race is uniformly accelerated, prove that he runs 10 yards before reaching the greatest speed.

23. An electric car travelling between two stopping places, distant 500 yd. apart, is uniformly accelerated for the first 10 sec., during which period it covers 100 ft. It then runs with a constant velocity until it is finally retarded uniformly in the last 50 ft. Calculate the maximum velocity and the time taken over the journey.

24. At a certain instant a particle is moving at the rate of 30 ft./sec., and in the next 8 sec. it describes a distance of 720 ft. Find the velocity with which it was moving at the end of the fifth second.

25. A point moving in a straight line with uniform retardation describes 7 ft. in the fifth second of its motion and 5 ft. in the seventh second. Prove that it will be at rest at the end of $11\frac{1}{2}$ seconds.

CHAPTER IX

ACCELERATION OF FALLING BODIES

56. Galileo, who published his results in 1638, was the first to show that heavy and light bodies, if dropped from the same height, reach the ground in the same time. He conducted his experiment from the top of the leaning tower at Pisa, a height of 179 feet above the ground ; the fact that the tower is some 14 ft. out of the perpendicular made it particularly suitable for this demonstration.

Exp. 16. We can easily show that a lead ball falls at the same rate as a wood one, by placing two balls of the same size in a box arranged so

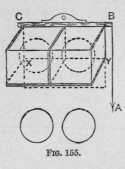

FIG. 155.

that, on pulling the string **AB**, the lever **BC**, which is pivoted at **B**, rises at **C** and releases a piece of metal attached to the bottom of the box; the result is that the bottom of the box turns down round a hinge **XY** at the back, and the two balls are liberated from the box at the same moment, and reach the floor at the same instant.

If a lead ball and a feather are allowed to fall in air from the same height, the lead ball will certainly reach the ground first, but this is owing to the more effective action of the resistance of the air on the feather; if each of the bodies is attached to a small piece of steel and suspended in a tall glass vessel by means of electro-magnets, and the air then pumped out of the vessel, it will be found, on breaking the electric current, that the two bodies fall at the same rate and reach the ground at the same moment.

57. Galileo first imagined that the velocities of falling bodies varied as the distances fallen through. This he eventually rejected and proceeded to demonstrate that the *velocity varied as the time* and was able to argue that this being true, it followed that *distance varied as the square of the time*.

The second result we can deduce from the formulae we have proved. For with bodies moving with constant acceleration,

$$v = at, \qquad i.e. \qquad v \propto t,$$
and
$$s = \tfrac{1}{2}at^2, \qquad i.e. \qquad s \propto t^2.$$

Galileo came to his conclusion that $s \propto t^2$, by allowing a body to roll down an inclined plane, assuming that the law would be the same as that for falling bodies, the only difference being that the velocities would be diminished. Distances 1, 4, 9, 16 . . . units were marked off along the plane from the starting point, and it was necessary to prove that these distances were passed over in 1, 2, 3, 4 . . . units of time. As a time measurer, he took a vessel of water with a large cross-section and a small orifice, which he could close with his finger, so that, the water running out slowly, the level of water in the vessel altered very slowly, and consequently the speed at which the water issued was practically constant.

At the same instant, he withdrew his finger and allowed the ball to run down the plane, the water which issued being collected in a glass beaker. When the unit distance was traversed by the rolling body, the orifice was closed and the water in the beaker weighed. The experiment was then repeated, the body being allowed to roll down the plane a distance of 4 units, and again when it had rolled 9 units, and so on, the weight of water being obtained in each case. These weights of water were proportional to the times, as the water was issuing from the orifice with the same speed for all the experiments.

He found that the weights of water were proportional to 1, 2, 3, 4 . . . and since

$$2^2 = 4, \quad 3^2 = 9, \quad 4^2 = 16, \; . \; . \; .$$

it followed that the

distances varied as the squares of the times.

A variation of the experiment can be conducted in the laboratory, either by allowing a ball to roll down a groove in an inclined plane, or down a glass tube, various distances being marked on the plane or tube and the times obtained with a stop-watch ; or, using a metronome, the distances passed over on a graduated plane can be observed for an exact number of ticks of the metronome. On plotting values of s and t^2, it is found that a straight line through the origin is obtained, and therefore $s \propto t^2$.

We have already seen that if a body starts from rest and is subject to constant acceleration, then $s = \tfrac{1}{2}at^2$; it follows, that when a body rolls down an inclined plane it is subject to constant acceleration.

By gradually making the inclined plane steeper and steeper, we eventually arrive at the result that, with bodies falling vertically, the acceleration is constant.

58. With modern apparatus, it has been determined that at Greenwich the acceleration of a falling body in a vacuum is 32·19 ft./sec.² or 981·17 cm./sec.² This acceleration is denoted by the symbol g, and for most purposes it will be sufficient to take its value as 32 ft./sec.² or 981 cm./sec.²

Thus, $g = 32$ ft./sec.² $= 981$ cm./sec.²

The value of g differs slightly at different places on the earth's surface ; it is least at the equator and greatest at the poles where the distance from the earth's centre is least.

Exp. 17. The value of g may be obtained in an ordinary laboratory by a simple experiment with a pendulum **DE** swinging about a knife-edge at **D**. A string is fastened to a hook at **C** and, passing over two pegs at **B** and **A**, supports a small weight **W**, which hangs in such a position that it will touch the rod if the latter is in a vertical position.

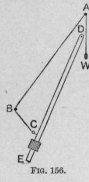

FIG. 156.

A piece of paper should be fastened on the side of the pendulum nearest **W**, which is slightly blackened. If the string is burnt, **W** falls and the pendulum starts swinging at the same instant, **W** striking the pendulum when it is in a vertical position and has just completed a quarter of a complete oscillation.

If the position of **W** before it starts falling and the mark made on the pendulum are noted, we have the distance it falls in a quarter of an oscillation ; the time of an oscillation can be calculated by timing 10 or 12 complete oscillations.

If **W** falls s cm. in t seconds, then since $s = \frac{1}{2}at^2$ it follows that

$$g = \frac{2s}{t^2} \text{ cm./sec.}^2.$$

59. Ex. 1. *Calculate the greatest height to which a body rises, if it takes 7 seconds to reach this point.*

Let the original *upward* velocity be u ft./sec., then since the final velocity is zero, and the *retardation* 32 ft./sec.²,

$$0 = u - 32 \times 7, \qquad\qquad [v = u + at]$$
$$\therefore\ u = 224 \text{ ft./sec.}$$

The average velocity is $\frac{1}{2} \times 224 = 112$ ft./sec.,

$$\therefore\ s = 112 \times 7 \qquad\qquad [s = \text{av. vel.} \times t]$$
$$= 784 \text{ ft.}$$

Ex. 2. *A stone is dropped from the top of a tower 128 ft. high, and at the same instant another stone is thrown up from the bottom of the tower. Find the velocity of projection of the second stone if the two meet at a height of 47 ft.*

If the second stone rises 47 ft., the first falls 81 ft.

Let the velocity of projection of the second stone be u ft./sec., and let the stones meet after t sec.

Considering the first stone,

$$81 = 16t^2, \qquad\qquad [s = \tfrac{1}{2}gt^2]$$
$$\therefore\ t = \tfrac{9}{4} \text{ sec.}$$

Considering the second stone,

$$47 = \tfrac{9}{4}u - 16(\tfrac{9}{4})^2, \qquad\qquad [s = ut - \tfrac{1}{2}gt^2]$$
$$\therefore\ u = \tfrac{512}{9} = 56\tfrac{8}{9} \text{ ft./sec.}$$

EXERCISE XXI

[Assume $g = 32$ ft./sec.$^2 = 981$ cm./sec.^{2}]

1. If a stone, dropped from a railway bridge, reaches the track in 2·5 seconds, from what height was the stone dropped ?

2. If a stone is dropped from a height of 144 ft., how long does it take to reach the ground, and with what velocity does it strike the ground ?

3. A stone is thrown down a pit shaft with a velocity of 40 ft./sec. If the depth is 200 ft., find with what velocity the stone will reach the foot of the shaft. Find also the time taken.

4. A stone is thrown vertically upwards with a velocity of 192 ft./sec. Calculate its velocity after 4 seconds and also after 8 seconds.

5. A stone was thrown vertically upwards so as to reach a height of 300 metres. Find the initial velocity of the body.

6. A stone is thrown vertically downwards from the top of a tower 120 ft. high, and reaches the ground with a velocity of 88 ft./sec. ; with what speed was it projected from the top of the tower ?

7. If a body is projected vertically upwards with a velocity of 20 metres/sec., find the height to which it rises and the time before it reaches the ground again.

8. A cricket ball was thrown straight up and was observed to remain in the air 5·6 sec. How high did it rise and with what velocity was it thrown ? Suppose that instead of rising freely, it had struck a wire 30 ft. up, find the time when it struck the wire and its velocity at that time.

9. The final velocity with which a parachute reaches the ground is about 15 ft./sec. Show that the shock to the parachutist on meeting the ground is practically that received by jumping on to the ground from a table 3½ ft. high.

10. A balloon rises with an acceleration of 4 ft./sec.² What is its velocity and height at the end of 20 seconds from the start? If a stone is then let go over the edge of the car, how far will it rise from the ground?

11. A stone is dropped over a cliff 100 ft. high. With what downward velocity must a stone be projected 1 second later in order to reach the ground at the same time?

12. If a stone is thrown vertically upwards with a velocity of 50 ft./sec., calculate the time at which it is at a height of 30 ft., (i) going up, (ii) coming down.

13. A stone is dropped from the top of a building and is observed to pass a window ledge 20 ft. above the ground with a velocity of 40 ft./sec. Find the height of the building and the velocity with which the stone strikes the ground.

14. Two stones are thrown vertically upwards from the same point at an interval of 5 sec., the first with a velocity 128 ft./sec., and the second with double that velocity. Find when they will meet, and at what height above the point of projection.

15. Two balls are dropped from rest at the same point, one two seconds before the other. Owing to their different air resistances, the first one dropped has an acceleration $\frac{5}{6}g$, and the second one has an acceleration $\frac{4}{5}g$. After what time will the second overtake the first?

16. A body is projected vertically upwards, and during the first second of its motion moves twice as far as it does during the next second of its motion. Find the velocity of projection and the whole height ascended.

17. A stone is thrown upwards from the foot of a tower 60 ft. high with a velocity of 45 ft./sec. At the same instant another stone is let fall from the top of the tower. Find their height above the ground when they meet.

18. An elastic ball dropped from a height h strikes the ground and rises to a height $\frac{2}{3}h$. Find the ratio of the velocity with which the ball leaves the ground to the velocity it had when it struck the ground.

19. A body is thrown vertically upwards with velocity v ft./sec. from a point A, and at the same instant another body is thrown vertically downwards with velocity $3v$ ft./sec. from a point at height h ft. vertically above A. Find the height at which they will meet.

20. A stone is dropped down a well. What will be the speed of the stone on reaching the surface of the water 121 ft. below ? What time will elapse before the sound of the splash reaches the top of the well ? The speed of sound may be taken as 1100 ft./sec.

21. A stone falls vertically from rest for 3 seconds, and another is then thrown straight down after it from the same point with a velocity of 160 ft./sec. Show that the second stone will overtake the first at a point 441 ft. below the starting point, and find the velocity of each stone at the instant of overtaking.

22. A ball thrown up is caught by the thrower 7 seconds afterwards. How high did it go, and with what speed was it thrown ? How far below its highest point was it 4 seconds after its start ?

23. Two bodies are thrown vertically upwards with the same velocity at an interval of $1\frac{1}{2}$ seconds. If they meet 6 seconds after the first body starts, what is the velocity of projection ?

24. A body which is dropped from the top of a tower is observed to strike the ground $1\frac{1}{2}$ seconds after passing a window whose height is 84 ft. above the ground. Find (i) the height of the tower, (ii) the velocity of the body when it passes the window.

25. A particle is projected vertically upwards with a velocity of 88 ft./sec. ; to what height will it rise ? One second later, another particle is projected vertically upwards with a velocity v ft./sec. If the two particles are at the same height $2\frac{1}{2}$ seconds after the first is projected, find the value of v, and the height of the second particle when the first reaches the point of projection.

CHAPTER X

FORCE AND ACCELERATION

60. We deduce from Newton's First Law, that if a body travels in a straight line with uniform velocity, then the resultant of all the forces acting on it is zero; and if the velocity is uniform then the acceleration is zero.

In Chapter IX we found that if a body is acted on by its own weight only, then the acceleration is uniform and its value is approximately 32 ft./sec.²

We shall now consider the effect of forces of various magnitudes upon the same body.

Exp. 18. Support a Fletcher's trolley with a vibrating spring on an inclined plane by means of a string passing over a pulley **A** at the top of the plane, a weight of **P** lb. being attached to the other end of the string; adjust **P** so that the trolley, on being started by hand, runs down the plane with uniform velocity; when this is the case, we know that the *resultant force* on the trolley, parallel to the line of greatest slope of the plane, must be *zero*. (Fig. 157.)

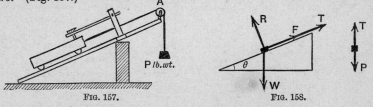

FIG. 157.　　　　FIG. 158.

The forces on the trolley are (Fig. 158)

    its weight **W** lb. vertically downwards,
    the normal reaction of the plane **R** lb. wt.,
    the friction **F** lb. wt. up the line of greatest slope,
    the tension of the string **T** lb. wt.

Resolving down the plane, since the resultant force is zero,

$$W \sin \theta - F - T = 0.$$

Since the weight **P** lb. is also moving uniformly upwards, it follows that the resultant force acting on it is also zero,

$$\therefore \ \mathbf{T} - \mathbf{P} = 0 \ ;$$
$$\therefore \ \mathbf{W} \sin \theta - \mathbf{F} = \mathbf{P}.$$

Now remove the string and let the trolley run down with increasing velocity under the influence of its own weight and friction, so that the resultant force on it down the plane is

$$\mathbf{W} \sin \theta - \mathbf{F} \ ;$$

this resultant force is numerically equal to **P**, and in the particular experiment performed,

$$\mathbf{P} = 72 \cdot 5 \text{ gm.}$$

A series of waves similar to those shown in Fig. 159 is produced on the paper pinned on the trolley, if the vibrating spring is set in motion ; the

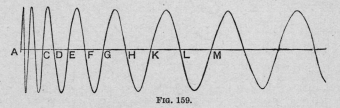

Fig. 159.

time occupied by the trolley in passing over distances **CE, EG, GK . . .**, corresponding to complete waves, being usually $\frac{1}{5}$ second.

Suppose the following table gives the wave-lengths passed over from rest by the trolley in the 1st, 2nd, 3rd . . . complete vibrations :—

Wave-lengths (cm.)	0·8	2·8	4·9	7·0	8·9	11·0

The average *velocities* in successive vibrations will be

0·8, 2·8, 4·9, 7·0, 8·9, 11·0 cm. per vibration ;

now all the times being small, the average velocities cannot differ much from the actual velocities at the middle instant of each successive vibration, and consequently may be taken as the *velocities* of the trolley at those middle instants. It follows that the average *increases of velocity* for every successive vibration will be

2·8−0·8, 4·9−2·8, 7·0−4·9, 8·9−7·0, 11·0−8·9,

i.e. 2·0, 2·1, 2·1, 1·9, 2·1 cm. per vibration.

These values are approximately equal, indicating that the *acceleration* is constant, and may be taken to be the mean of the above values, *i.e.* 2·04 cm. per vibration per vibration. If the experiment is repeated with the same trolley on the same plane at different slopes, then different values of P will be obtained.

P (gm. wt.)	72·5	58·3	45·1
Acceleration	2·04	1·57	1·27

The successive values of $\dfrac{a}{P}$ are 0·028, 0·027, 0·028 ; we thus see that when acting on the same body

resultant force ∝ acceleration ;

also,

Forces are equal if they produce the same acceleration in the same body.

61. If a body weighs W lb. and is acted on by its own weight only, then the acceleration is g ft./sec.², so that if a force of F lb. wt. produces in it an acceleration of a ft./sec.²,

$$\frac{a}{F}=\frac{g}{W}, \qquad i.e. \qquad \frac{F}{W}=\frac{a}{g}.$$

In using this equation, F and W must be measured in the same units, since we are expressing the ratio of F to W. If a number of forces are acting on a body, then F will represent the resolved part of the resultant in *any* direction we please, and a the acceleration in the *same* direction.

This result is equivalent to Newton's Second Law of Motion which was expressed in a different form in terms of Momentum and is considered subsequently.

62. Ex. 1. *If a body weighing 100 lb. is acted on by a force of 150 lb. wt., what acceleration is produced ?*

$$\frac{150}{100}=\frac{a}{g}, \qquad\qquad \left[\frac{F}{W}=\frac{a}{g}\right]$$

$$\therefore\ a\ =\tfrac{3}{2}g=48 \text{ ft./sec.}^2$$

Ex. 2. *An airship weighing 5 cwt., whose machinery is damaged, falls with constant acceleration, and descends 90 feet in 6 seconds. Find the retarding pressure of the air on the ship, supposing it to be constant.*

If a ft./sec.^{2} is the acceleration,

$$90 = \tfrac{1}{2}a \times 36, \qquad [s = \tfrac{1}{2}at^2]$$

$$\therefore \; a = 5 \text{ ft./sec.}^2$$

The forces acting on the airship are

      5×112 lb. wt. vertically downwards,

      R lb. wt. resistance vertically upwards.

Since the acceleration is 5 ft./sec.^{2} vertically *downwards*, the resultant force must be measured vertically *downwards*, and is $(560 - R)$ lb. wt.,

$$\therefore \; \frac{560 - R}{560} = \frac{5}{g}, \qquad \left[\frac{F}{W} = \frac{a}{g}\right]$$

$$\therefore \; R = 560\left(1 - \frac{5}{g}\right) = \frac{560 \times 27}{32}$$

$$= 472\cdot5 \text{ lb. wt.}$$

R *lb. wt.*

560 *lb. wt.*
FIG. 160.

Ex. 3. *A boy in a toboggan slides down a perfectly smooth hill whose inclination is 1 in 20. At what rate will he be going when he has travelled 100 yards from rest?*

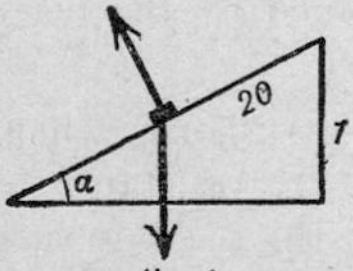

m lb. wt.
FIG. 161.

If the boy and toboggan weigh m lb., then the forces acting are

    m lb. wt. vertically downwards and the resistance at right angles to the plane.

Since the acceleration is a ft./sec.^{2} *down the plane*, the resultant force must be *down the plane*, and is $m \sin \alpha$ lb. wt.

$$\therefore \; \frac{m \sin \alpha}{m} = \frac{a}{g}, \qquad \left[\frac{F}{W} = \frac{a}{g}\right]$$

i.e. $\qquad\qquad a = g \sin \alpha = \tfrac{1}{20}g.$

If v ft./sec. is the velocity after travelling 100 yd.,

$$v^2 = 2 \times \tfrac{1}{20}g \times 300 = 960; \qquad [v^2 = 2as]$$

$$\therefore \; v = \sqrt{960} = 31\cdot0 \text{ ft./sec.}$$

EXERCISE XXII

1. Find the acceleration produced if a body of weight 5 lb. is acted on by forces of (i) 10 lb. wt., (ii) 5 lb. wt., (iii) 4 lb. wt.

2. Calculate the magnitude of a force which produces an acceleration of 12 ft./sec.² in a body of weight 10 lb.

3. What acceleration in ft./sec.² is produced in a body of weight 4 Kg. by a force of 10 Kg. wt. ?

4. If a force of 33 lb. wt. acting on a body produces an acceleration of 66 ft./sec.², what is the weight of the body ?

5. A force acting on a weight of 100 grams produces an acceleration of 150 cm./sec.² Find the magnitude of the force in grams wt.

6. A balloon weighs 1½ tons. Assuming that the air exerts a constant vertical lifting force of 2 tons wt., find (i) the acceleration, (ii) the time the balloon will take to rise 300 ft. from rest, (iii) its velocity at this height.

7. Find the time in which a force equal to the weight of 28 lb. generates a velocity of 5 ft./sec. in a body of weight 4 cwt.

8. A balloon, which weighs 1 ton, is drifting horizontally, and 20 lb. of ballast are thrown out. With what acceleration will the balloon begin to ascend ?

9. A horizontal force of 8 lb. wt. is applied to a body of weight 5 lb. lying on a smooth horizontal table. Find the speed attained by the body at the end of 6 seconds.

10. A truck of weight 10 tons is moved along a level track by a horse, which pulls steadily with a horizontal force of 120 lb. wt., the resistance to motion being 50 lb. wt. How far can the horse pull the truck in half a minute from rest ?

11. A train of weight 150 tons is running at 45 ml./hr. What is the magnitude of the frictional force which brings it to rest in 40 seconds ?

12. A cage weighing 2000 lb. is hoisted up a mine shaft by means of a rope. It starts from rest at the bottom and is uniformly accelerated for the first 135 ft., which it covers in 15 sec. What is the pull in the rope during this time ?

13. A car moving 30 miles an hour is brought to rest in a distance of 10 yards. Find the ratio of the force necessary to do this, to the weight of the car.

14. A bullet, weighing $\frac{1}{2}$ oz., moving with a speed of 800 ft./sec., hits a target and penetrates it to a depth of 8 inches. Calculate, in lb. wt., the resistance offered by the target, assuming it is constant.

15. A truck weighing 8 tons has a velocity of 12 ft./sec. Find, in tons wt., the force required to stop it (i) in 25 seconds, (ii) in 25 ft.

16. If a train runs freely from rest down an incline of 1 in 180, find its speed in ml./hr. after running for 1 mile.

17. If a body slides down a smooth plane of length 100 ft. inclined at 40° to the horizontal, find the time of describing the lower half.

18. What force would be necessary to pull a train of 200 tons up a smooth incline of 1 in 250 with an acceleration of 3 ft./sec.² ?

19. A train of weight 180 tons on an incline of 1 in 120 is pulled downhill by an engine which exerts a draw-bar pull of 5 tons weight. Find the acceleration of the train, neglecting all resistances.

20. A piston is $1\frac{1}{2}$ sq. ft. in cross-section and the steam pressure is 1 oz. wt. per sq. in. ; if the weight of the piston is 25 lb., find its velocity after it has moved through $2\frac{1}{2}$ ft.

21. A weight of 150 lb. is moved vertically by a chain. Find the tension in the chain when the weight is moved with
    (i) an acceleration of 4 ft./sec.² upwards,
    (ii) uniform velocity,
    (iii) an acceleration of 2 ft./sec.² downwards.

22. A locomotive draws a load of 200 tons. Find the pull needed
    (i) at a constant speed, if the friction is 0·05 of the load,
    (ii) if the friction is the same, and the speed rises from 30 ft./sec. to 60 ft./sec. in 1 minute.

23. A body slides from rest at A down a smooth plane AB, which is inclined so that it rises 1 ft. vertically for 3 ft. along the plane. If $AB = 24$ ft., find the velocity at B. If the body after reaching B moves horizontally and is subject to a retardation of 6 ft./sec.², how far will it move from B in 2 sec. ? Assume that one-tenth of the velocity is lost through the sudden change of direction at B.

24. A railway wagon moves freely down an incline, which falls 1 ft. per 200 ft. of rail, with uniform velocity ; find, in lb. wt. per ton, the total resistance to the motion. If the wagon is started up the incline with a velocity of 15 ml./hr., find how far it travels before coming to rest, the resistance being the same as before.

25. A bullet is fired horizontally with a velocity of 1800 ft./sec. It is assumed that the path of the bullet is a horizontal straight line, and that the air resistance is equivalent to a force equal to 20 times the weight of the bullet. Find how long the bullet takes to travel 450 ft.

26. A truck weighing 1000 lb. is hauled up a slope rising 1 ft. in 20 ft. along the slope. The truck starts from rest. The acceleration is uniform and the velocity after 10 seconds is 15 ft./sec. Prove that the pull on the truck is about 97 lb. wt.

27. A train is moving along a level track with a constant acceleration of $\frac{1}{2}$ ml./min.^{2} At what angle to the vertical will a plumb-line, suspended in the train, hang ?

28. A car weighing 1 ton, and travelling at 50 ml./hr., was brought to rest, by applying the brakes, in 231 ft. What was the frictional force, in lb. wt., exerted on the tyres by the road ?

29. A balloon, weighing 768 lb., is descending with a constant acceleration of $1\frac{1}{2}$ ft./sec.^{2}, when 54 lb. of ballast is suddenly thrown out. Find the resulting acceleration upwards.

If the velocity of the balloon downwards was 5 ft./sec. when the ballast was thrown out, find how far the balloon falls before it begins to rise.

30. When 1 foot was cut off the muzzle of a 6 in. gun, the velocity dropped from 1490 to 1330 ft./sec. If the shell weighed 100 lb., calculate the pressure on the base of the shell in tons wt./sq. in., assuming it uniform. (Assume $\pi = \frac{22}{7}$.)

63. Newton's Third Law of Motion.

To every action there is an equal and opposite reaction.

This result has already been studied when dealing with a body at rest and its truth illustrated by means of spring-balances ; its truth, however, is not so obvious when the bodies are in motion.

We may take an illustration from the action of the heavenly bodies on one another. If we consider the earth and moon, then the earth attracts the moon with a force which is equal and opposite to that with which the moon attracts the earth. Astronomical calculations are based on this assumption, and knowing how careful these calculations are, and how exactly they are verified by observation (as in the case of the discovery of Neptune by calculation by Prof. Adams), we can have no doubt that the law is true.

Various problems have from time to time been propounded which, at first sight, appear to contradict the law. For instance, if a horse pulls a cart with a certain force, and the cart pulls the horse back with the same force, how can the combination move ? When the horse moves along a road he exerts a backward push on the road and his hoofs have a tendency to slip *backwards*, so that the equal and opposite force of the earth on the horse has a horizontal component (F_1) *forwards*.

The traces exert a *backward* force on the horse and an equal *forward* force (T) on the cart, which, for simplicity, we will consider to be without wheels like a sledge.

The friction between the road and the sledge (F_2) retards the motion of the sledge and acts *backwards* on the sledge.

If we represent the forces in a diagram, let H signify the horse and S the sledge, then

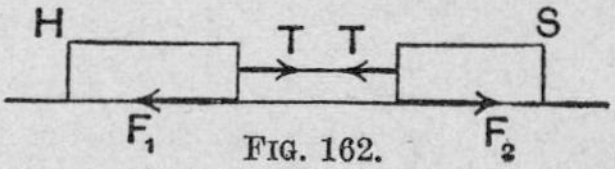

FIG. 162.

the resultant force on the horse is $F_1 - T$ forwards,

,,   ,,   ,, sledge is $T - F_2$ forwards,

and if $F_1 > T$ and $T > F_2$, the horse and sledge will move forwards ; or considering the combination of the horse and sledge, it is necessary that $F_1 > F_2$, the tension of the traces being an internal force ;

i.e. the friction between the horse and road must be greater than that between the sledge and road.

64. Driving Wheels of a Locomotive.

In the given diagram, the *driving wheels* are made to rotate counter-

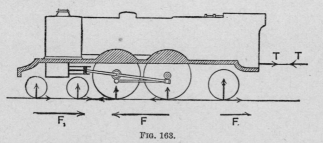

FIG. 163.

clockwise by the pistons and connecting rods, and if the rails were smooth, the points of contact of these wheels would slip and the wheels skid, the

engine remaining stationary ; the fact that the rails are rough and tha
the wheels roll, means that *friction* prevents the skid and acts *forwards*.

As far as all the *other wheels,* both of the engine and train, are concerned
they would merely slide along the rails if the track were smooth ; the *friction*
acting *backwards,* causes them to rotate in a counter-clockwise direction.

If F is the friction on the driving wheels forwards,

    F_1 ,,   total friction on the other wheels backwards,

    T ,,   tension in the couplings,

then the resultant forward force on the engine is $F - F_1 - T$; and if F_2
the friction backwards on the rest of the train, the resultant force forwar
on the engine and train is $F - F_1 - F_2$.

Ex. *A man weighing* 12 *stone stands on the floor of a lift which* (i) *move
with uniform velocity,* (ii) *ascends with an acceleration of* 2 *ft./sec.*², (iii) *descend
with an acceleration of* 2 *ft./sec.*²   *Find, in each case, the pressure he exert
on the floor.*

Let the pressure on the floor be R lb. wt., then the pressure on the ma
is R lb. wt. *upwards.*

(i) If there is no acceleration, the total force upwards is zero,

$$\therefore \quad R - 168 = 0,$$

$$i.e. \qquad R = 168 \text{ lb. wt.} = 12 \text{ stone.}$$

(ii) The acceleration is 2 ft./sec.² *upwards,* and the resultant force
$(R - 168)$ lb. wt. *upwards,*

$$\therefore \quad \frac{R - 168}{168} = \frac{2}{32},$$

$$R - 168 = \frac{21}{2},$$

$$\therefore \quad R = 178\tfrac{1}{2} \text{ lb. wt.}$$

(iii) The acceleration is 2 ft./sec.² *downwards* and the resultant force
$(168 - R)$ lb. wt. *downwards,*

$$\therefore \quad \frac{168 - R}{168} = \frac{2}{32},$$

$$168 - R = \frac{21}{2},$$

$$\therefore \quad R = 157\tfrac{1}{2} \text{ lb. wt.}$$

EXERCISE XXIII

1. If a weight of 32 lb. is placed on a platform which is made to ascend with a uniform acceleration of 2 ft./sec.², find the pressure on the platform.

2. A cylindrical vessel containing 50 lb. of water is being raised vertically with an acceleration of 1 ft./sec.² Find the pressure on the bottom of the vessel. What is the pressure when the vessel is falling, but the fall is being retarded at the rate of 1 ft./sec.² ?

3. Find the resultant pressure exerted by a stone weighing ½ cwt. on the floor of a lift when it is ascending with an acceleration of 4 ft./sec.²

4. A horse, which exerts a constant horizontal force of 300 lb. wt. moves a truck of weight 2 tons from rest through a distance of 10 ft. in 5 seconds. Find, in lb. wt., the force resisting the motion of the truck.

5. A man in a lift holds a spring-balance with a 7 lb. weight hanging from it. The lift descends (i) with a downward acceleration of 4 ft./sec.², (ii) with uniform speed of 6 ft./sec., (iii) with a retardation of 2 ft./sec.² What are the readings of the spring-balance in each case ?

6. A man weighing 140 lb. is being drawn up a mine shaft in a cage weighing 340 lb. If at a certain moment the acceleration of the cage is 4 ft. sec.², what is the tension in the rope, and what is the pressure between the man's feet and the floor of the cage ?

7. A man weighing 160 lb. stands in a large iron bucket weighing 128 lb., which is being hauled up a mine shaft with acceleration 2 ft./sec.² Find the tension in the rope, and also the pressure between the man and the bottom of the bucket.

8. A youth weighing 112 lb. stands on the floor of a lift which is moving upwards. The lift starts with a uniform acceleration of 3 ft./sec.², then moves with uniform speed, and finally is brought to rest with a uniform retardation of 2 ft./sec.² Find the pressure of the youth on the floor of the lift in each of the three stages of motion.

9. A man lifts a 20 lb. wt. vertically from rest through 6 ft. In doing so, he lifts the weight through the first 4 ft. in 1½ seconds with uniform acceleration. Through the next 2 ft., he lifts it without acceleration, with the velocity which it has acquired after rising the first 4 ft. Find the force exerted by the man during each stage of the lifting.

10. In a locomotive cylinder, the steam pressure on the piston is 50 cwt., the weight of the piston and rod 5 cwt., and the thrust in the connecting rod 1400 lb. wt. Find the acceleration of the piston.

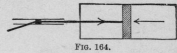

Fig. 164.

11. In one of the cylinders of an engine, the diameter is 15 inches and the boiler pressure 225 lb. wt. per sq. inch. If the weight of the piston is 220 lb., its acceleration 0·12 ft./sec.² and the pressure in the cylinder 80% of the boiler pressure, calculate the thrust in the connecting rod. (Assume $\pi = 3\cdot14$.)

12. A weight of 2 lb. is hanging by a string from the roof of a railway carriage which is moving with an acceleration of 4 ft./sec.² ; what angle will the string make with the vertical ?

13. The envelope, car, passengers, etc., of a balloon weigh 600 lb.; its capacity is 20,000 cu. ft. of coal gas, the density of which is 0·45 that of air. Assuming that, under the atmospheric conditions prevailing at the time of the ascent, 1 cu. ft. of air at the earth's surface would weigh 0·08 lb., find the acceleration with which the balloon will begin to rise.

65. We will now consider a type of problem where it is necessary to consider the motion of more than one body ; in such cases we must consider the forces on each body and measure the resultant force in the same direction as the acceleration.

Ex. 1. *Two scale-pans, each of weight 4 lb., are connected by a string passing over a smooth pulley. If a weight of 1 lb. is placed in one pan, find the tension of the string and the pressure between the 1 lb. wt. and the scale-pan.*

Let the tension be T lb. wt. and the common acceleration a ft./sec.²

The *downward* force on the right is $(5-T)$ lb. wt.,

the *downward* acceleration a ft./sec.²,

$$\therefore \frac{5-T}{5} = \frac{a}{g}, \qquad \left(\frac{F}{W} = \frac{a}{g}\right)$$

$$\therefore 5-T = \frac{5a}{g}. \quad \cdot \quad \cdot \quad \cdot \quad \cdot \quad \cdot \quad (i)$$

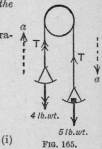

4 lb.wt.

5 lb.wt.

Fig. 165.

The *upward* force on the left is $(T-4)$ lb. wt.,

the *upward* acceleration a ft./sec.²

$$\therefore \quad \frac{T-4}{4} = \frac{a}{g},$$

$$\therefore \quad T-4 = \frac{4a}{g}. \qquad . \quad . \quad . \quad . \quad . \quad . \quad \text{(ii)}$$

Adding (i) and (ii), $\quad 1 = \dfrac{9a}{g}, \qquad \therefore \ a = \tfrac{1}{9}g,$

substituting in (ii), $\quad T = 4 + \tfrac{4}{9} = 4{\cdot}44$ lb. wt.

If R lb. wt. is the pressure between the scale-pan and the 1 lb. wt., then

the *downward* force on the 1 lb. wt. is $(1-R)$ lb. wt.,

the *downward* acceleration is a ft./sec.²,

$$\therefore \quad \frac{1-R}{1} = \frac{a}{g},$$

$$\therefore \quad R = 1 - \frac{a}{g} = 1 - \tfrac{1}{9} = \tfrac{8}{9} = 0{\cdot}89 \text{ lb. wt.}$$

R *lb.wt.*

a

1 *lb.wt.*
FIG. 166.

N.B.—In Fig. 165, the forces on the left and right are distinguished by single and double arrows.

Ex. 2. *A weight of 3 lb., hanging freely at the end of a string, pulls a body of weight 4 lb. up a smooth inclined plane of 30°. Find the tension of the string and the distance the body moves up the plane in 3 seconds from rest.*

Let the tension of the string be T lb. wt. and the acceleration of the two weights a ft./sec.², that of the 4 lb. wt. being up the plane, and that of the 3 lb. wt. vertically downwards.

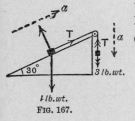

a

T

a

$\uparrow$ T

30°

3 *lb.wt.*

4 *lb.wt.*
FIG. 167.

Considering the vertical motion of the 3 lb. wt.,

the resultant force is $(3-T)$ lb. wt. *downwards*,

the acceleration is a ft./sec.² *downwards*,

$$\therefore \quad \frac{3-T}{3} = \frac{a}{g}, \qquad \left(\frac{F}{W} = \frac{a}{g}\right)$$

i.e. $\quad 3-T = \dfrac{3a}{g}. \qquad . \quad . \quad . \quad . \quad . \quad \text{(i)}$

Considering the 4 lb. wt.,

the resultant force *up the plane* is $T-4\sin 30°$,   *i.e.* $(T-2)$ lb. wt.,

the acceleration *up the plane* is a ft./sec.²,

$$\therefore \quad \frac{T-2}{4}=\frac{a}{g},$$

i.e. $T-2=\dfrac{4a}{g}.$.   .   .   .   (ii)

Adding (i) and (ii), $1=\dfrac{7a}{g},$ $\therefore \ a=\frac{1}{7}g.$

Substituting in (ii), $T=2+\frac{4}{7}=2\cdot57$ lb. wt.

If s ft. is the distance moved up the plane in 3 seconds,

$$s=\tfrac{1}{2}\times\tfrac{1}{7}g\times 9=\tfrac{9}{14}g=20\cdot6 \text{ ft.} \qquad (s=\tfrac{1}{2}at^2.)$$

N.B.—Note particularly that the tension in the vertical string is *not* 3 lb. wt. as it would be if the system were at rest, or moving with uniform velocity.

EXERCISE XXIV

1. Two weights of 7 and 9 lb. are connected by a string passing over a smooth peg. Find the tension in the string.

2. Weights of 8 and 11 lb. are connected by a string passing over a smooth pulley ; find their common acceleration and the tension of the string. Find also the resultant pull on the pulley.

3. Weights of 2 and 6 oz. are connected by a string which passes over a fixed smooth pulley and the system is allowed to move from rest. Find the tension of the string and the distance traversed by each weight in the first half-second.

4. Two scale-pans, each of weight 3 lb., are connected by a string which passes over a smooth pulley. A weight of 2 lb. is placed in one pan, and motion ensues. Find the tension of the string and the pressure between the extra weight and the scale-pan.

5. A light cord, hung over a smooth pulley, has at one end a pail whose weight is 2 lb., and at the other end a weight of 5 lb. If a stone of weight 10 lb. is placed in the pail, find the tension of the cord and the pressure which the stone exerts on the pail in the ensuing motion.

6. A weight of 9 lb. lies on a smooth table and is connected by a string with a weight of 5 lb., which hangs over the edge of the table. Find the acceleration of the weights and the tension in the string.

FIG. 168.

7. A weight of 10 lb. lies on a smooth horizontal table and a string connects it to another weight, hanging over the edge, which is let go. If the two weights move through 1 ft. in half a second, find the second weight and the tension in the string.

8. A body weighing 1 lb. is at the centre of a smooth table ; a string passes from it over a smooth pulley at the edge of the table, and is attached to a weight of 3 lb. Find the velocity of the descending weight after motion has ensued for half a second.

9. A body of weight 2 lb., hanging freely at the end of a string, pulls a body of 3 lb. up a smooth inclined plane of 35°. Find the tension of the string and the distance the body moves up the plane in 2 seconds.

10. Weights of 3 lb. and 1 lb. are fixed to the ends of a string hanging over the opposite edges of a smooth horizontal table, and a weight of 2 lb. attached to the string rests on the table. Calculate the tension of each string and the acceleration of the system.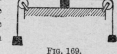

FIG. 169.

11. A 3 lb. wt. is placed on a smooth plane inclined at an angle of 30° to the horizontal. How long will it take to slide 10 ft. down the plane ?

If it is attached to one end of a string which, after passing through a smooth ring at the top of the plane, hangs vertically with a weight of 1 lb. attached to the other end, show that the 3 lb. wt. will take twice as long as before to travel the same 10 ft.

12. A weight of 9 lb. draws up a weight of 3 lb. by means of a string passing over a smooth fixed pulley ; if the string be cut at the end of 4 seconds from rest, for how long afterwards will the lighter weight continue to rise ?

13. Two weights of 2 and 3 lb. are connected by a string passing over a smooth pulley. After they have been moving from rest for 3 seconds, the heavy weight is stopped and then immediately released. Find how long it will be before the string becomes taut again.

14. A weight of 56 lb. is placed on a smooth table at a distance of 8 ft. from the edge, and is connected by a string passing over the edge with a weight of 10 lb. hanging freely. What time will elapse before the former weight leaves the table ?

15. Two bodies A and B, each of weight 7 lb., are attached to the ends of a light string passing over a smooth pulley. A body C, of weight 2 lb., is suspended from B by a string BC. B is held still, and is then allowed to fall. After 1 second, C reaches the ground, so that the string BC becomes slack ; after another second, B reaches the ground. Find the length of the string BC.

16. Weight of 16 and 17 oz. are connected by a string passing over a smooth pulley. With what acceleration does the greater weight descend ?

After descending 1 ft. from rest, this weight is brought to rest on reaching the ground. What interval elapses before the string again becomes taut ?

17. Two weights of $15\frac{1}{2}$ oz. and $16\frac{1}{2}$ oz. are connected by a string passing over a smooth pulley, and starting from rest, they are in motion for 2 seconds ; $1\frac{1}{2}$ oz. is then suddenly removed from the heavier weight, the motion being uninterrupted. How long will it be before the motion is reversed ?

18. A string passes over a fixed pulley, then under a free pulley and is afterwards fastened to a beam. Weights of 100 gm. are attached to the free end of the string and to the movable pulley.

    (i) If the movable pulley rises 1 ft., how far does the free end of the string descend ?

    (ii) Find the tension in the string, the acceleration of the movable pulley, and the acceleration of the 100 gm. at the free end of the string.

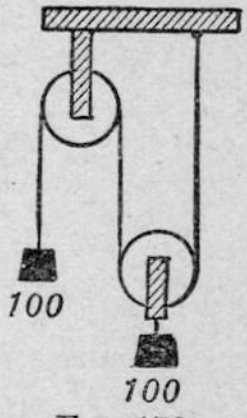

FIG. 170.

19. Two bodies A and B, of weights 1 lb. and 2 lb. respectively, are connected by a short string, and both rest on a smooth horizontal table. If horizontal forces of 3 and 2 lb. wt. act on A and B in the directions shown in Fig. 171, find the common acceleration of A and B and the tension in the string.

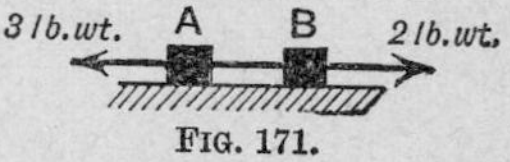

FIG. 171.

REVISION PAPERS

Velocity and Acceleration

PAPER 13

1. If a body moves at the rate of 10 kilometres per hour, what is its velocity in metres per second ?

2. A boat sails 3 miles from A to B in a direction N. 20° E. at 5 ml./hr., then 6 miles from B to C in a direction N. 30° W. at 7 ml./hr. If it had travelled straight from A to C in the same time, what would have been the average velocity ?   (Solve graphically.)

3. If a man shouts in front of a vertical cliff and hears the echo after 5 seconds, what is his distance from the cliff if the velocity of sound is 1100 ft./sec. ?

4. If the connection between the distance in feet and time in seconds of a moving body is given by the formula $s = 5t^2$, plot a graph for s and t and thence find the velocity when $t = 4 \cdot 7$ sec.

5. If a shell takes $\frac{2}{19}$ sec. to travel along the barrel of a gun of length 31 ft., what is its acceleration ?

PAPER 14

1. A man motors 20 miles at 25 ml./hr., rests for $\frac{3}{4}$ hour and then travels 15 miles at 28 ml./hr. Find his average speed in ml./hr.

2. If a point describes a circle of radius 12 ft. with angular velocity of 3 radians per second, find its velocity round the circumference.

3. Plot the values of t (sec.) and s (ft.) for a moving body :—

t	1	2	3	4	5
s	1	8	21	42	65

Find the velocity when $t = 2 \cdot 5$, $4 \cdot 5$ seconds.

4. A train which is being uniformly retarded has its velocity reduced from 30 ml./hr. to 24 ml./hr. while it moves a distance of 22 yards. Find the retardation in ft./sec.^{2}

5. A body is thrown vertically upwards with a velocity of 50 ft./sec. Find (i) when its velocity will be 25 ft./sec., (ii) when it will be 25 ft. above the point of projection.

PAPER 15

1. If a disc of radius 2 ft. is rotating round its centre so that any point on the rim is moving with a velocity 14 ft./sec., calculate the angular velocity in radians/sec.

2. The relation between the time and velocity of a moving body is given by the table

t (sec.)	0	1	2	3	4	5
v (ft./sec.)	0	1	6	15	28	45

Plot a curve and deduce the distance passed over in the first 5 seconds.

3. A train starts from rest with uniform acceleration, and after travelling for 1 mile reaches its maximum velocity of 30 ml./hr. Find the acceleration in ft./sec.^{2}

Show also that the distance passed over in the third minute after starting is 550 yards.

4. The greatest height attained by a particle projected vertically upwards is 225 ft. Find how soon after projection the particle will be at a height of 176 ft.

5. A stone projected downwards from the top of a tower with a velocity of 40 ft./sec. reaches the ground in one second less time than a stone which is simply let fall without initial velocity. Find the height of the tower.

PAPER 16

1. If a point revolves round a circle of radius 4 ft. three times a second, find its angular velocity in (i) degrees per second, (ii) radians per second. (iii) Also find its velocity round the circumference in ft./sec. (Assume $\pi = 3 \cdot 14$.)

2. Draw a graph for v and t from the following values :—

t (sec.)	0	1	2	3	4	5	6
v (ft./sec.)	5	6	9	14	21	30	41

Thence find the acceleration when $t = 2$ and 4 sec.

3. A cyclist, starting from rest at the top of a hill, free-wheels down a straight road on the hillside. After free-wheeling 5000 ft. his velocity is 20 ft./sec. At the bottom of the hill, his velocity is 30 ft./sec. Find his acceleration, the length of the road and the total time taken.

4. Express in ml. hr. units an acceleration of 50 ft./sec.²

5. A balloon is rising vertically with a velocity of 60 cm./sec. when a stone is dropped from the car. Describe the motion of the stone.

It is found that the stone strikes the ground 6 seconds after being dropped. Find the height of the balloon at the instant the stone is dropped. (Assume $g = 981$ cm./sec.²)

PAPER 17

1. A train is running at 40 ml./hr. when the steam is shut off. Friction produces a retardation of $29\frac{1}{3}$ ft./sec.² How long will it be before the train comes to rest ?

2. A stone is released from rest from a point 2·25 ft. vertically above the top of a window 6·75 ft. high, and falls freely under gravity. How long will it take to pass the window, and with what velocity will it reach the ground 3·25 ft. below the window-sill ?

3. A train moves from rest to rest; it covers the first third of its journey with uniform acceleration, the middle third with constant speed v, and the final third with uniform retardation. Prove that its average speed is $\dfrac{3v}{5}$.

4. A lift is descending with an acceleration of $\frac{1}{2}$ ft./sec.^{2} and, at the instant when its velocity is 3 ft./sec., a particle is let fall from a point 5 ft. above the lift. When will it reach the lift? What is its velocity at that moment? How far has the particle fallen through space?

5. Plot the velocity-time graph for a moving body from the following table :—

v (ft./sec.)	2	3·8	5·6	7·4
t (sec.)	0	3	6	9

Find (i) the acceleration, (ii) the distance of the body from its position at zero time at the end of 4 and 7 sec. respectively.

PAPER 18

1. If a balloon is rising at the rate of 35 ft./sec., and a stone let fall from it reaches the ground in 15 seconds, how high was the balloon when the stone was dropped?

2. A body is dropped from the top of a tower, 100 ft. high, and at the same instant another body is shot up vertically from the foot of a tower with a velocity of 50 ft./sec. How far from the ground will the bodies be when they meet?

3. A car moving at 20 ml./hr. can be pulled up in 25 ft. Assuming that the retardation is constant, find the distance in which the car could be pulled up if its velocity was 40 ml./hr.

4. A train passes another on a parallel track; the first is running at a uniform speed of 40 ml./hr., and the second is running at a speed of 10 ml./hr., with an acceleration of $\frac{1}{2}$ ft./sec.^{2} How long will it be before the second train catches the first again, and how far will the trains run in the interval?

5. Two motorists, *A* and *B*, are travelling side by side in the same direction at 30 ml./hr. *A* puts on his brakes, which cause a uniform retardation, and comes to rest in 220 yards. How long after *A* puts on his brakes does he come to rest, and how far will *B* then be ahead ?

(Including Force)

PAPER 19

1. What force must act upon a weight of 65 lb. to increase its velocity from 32 to 33 ft./sec. in passing over 50 ft. ?

2. Two men exerting together a force of 90 lb. wt. put a railway wagon into motion. The wagon weighs 6 tons and the resistance to motion is 10 lb. wt. per ton. How far does the wagon advance in 1 minute ?

3. A fine string passes over a smooth peg and has its ends attached to weights of 4 lb. and 6 lb. respectively. Find the acceleration of the system and the resultant thrust on the peg.

4. A balloon is at rest at a height of 100 ft. above a railway line ; a stone, which is dropped from the balloon when the front of a passing train is vertically below it, just strikes the end of the last carriage. If the train is 110 ft. long, what is its speed ?

5. A car is timed to cover 220 yd. in 15 sec., and the next 220 yd. in $11\frac{2}{5}$ sec. Assuming constant acceleration, find the average speed of the car in ml./hr., and its acceleration in ft./sec.^{2}

PAPER 20

1. A rough plane 5 ft. long is propped up so that the upper end is 3 ft. higher than the lower end. A weight is placed on the plane at the top and it slides down to the bottom in 2 seconds. Find the acceleration and the frictional force up the plane if the body weighs 10 lb.

2. Find the tension in a rope which is raising a weight of 112 lb. with a vertical acceleration of 2 ft./sec.^{2}

3. A weight of 7 lb. is drawn along a smooth horizontal table by a string which passes over the edge of the table and is attached to another weight of 3 lb. which is descending vertically. Find the acceleration of the system.

4. A man throws a stone directly upwards with a velocity of 79 ft./sec., his hand being 5 ft. above the ground when the stone leaves it. Find after how many seconds the stone will be at a height of 93 ft. above the point of projection. Find also its velocity when it reaches the ground.

5. A body is moving in a straight line. Its distances from a fixed point noted at intervals of one-fifth of a second are 5·1, 5·5, 6·7, 8·7, 11·5 cm. Plot graphs showing (i) distance and time, (ii) distance and square of time. Do these indicate either constant speed or constant acceleration? Deduce the acceleration at the end of 1 sec.

PAPER 21

1. By pushing a sleigh weighing 200 lb. with a force of 26 lb. wt., a man finds he can give it an acceleration of 4 ft./sec.² What resistance does the ice offer to the motion of the sleigh?

2. Assuming the resistance to the motion of a train with the brakes on to be 154 lb. wt. for every ton the train weighs, how long would it take for the speed of the train to be reduced from 45 ml./hr. to 20 ml./hr.?

3. A car, travelling along a level road at 24 ml./hr., comes to an incline of 1 in 40. How far will it travel up the incline before coming to rest, assuming all the forces acting on it, except that due to the incline, to remain the same as before?

4. A train, starting from rest and moving with uniform acceleration, travels 480 yards in the first two minutes of its motion. Find its velocity at the end of this time, and the distance in miles it has gone when its speed reaches 60 ml./hr.

5. A particle starts from a point O with uniform velocity 4 ft./sec., and after 2 seconds another particle leaves O in the same direction with a velocity of 5 ft./sec. and subject to an acceleration of 3 ft./sec.² Find when and where it will overtake the first particle.

PAPER 22

1. A train whose weight is 400 tons is acted on by a force equal to the weight of 5 tons. Find its velocity in ml./hr. one minute after it starts from rest.

2. A body of weight of 5 lb. rests on a smooth horizontal table ; a string attached to it passes over a smooth pulley fixed at the edge of the table and carries a weight of 2 lb. at the other end. Find the acceleration when the system is left to itself, the tension in the string, and the time the 2 lb. weight takes to fall 2 ft.

3. A man weighing 150 lb. is descending in a lift weighing 9 cwt. Find the tension of the rope and the pressure exerted by the man on the floor, (i) when the lift is starting with an acceleration of 4 ft./sec.^{2}, (ii) when it is stopping at the same rate.

4. A stone A is thrown vertically upwards with a velocity of 96 ft./sec. How high will it rise ?

   After 4 seconds from the projection of A, another stone B is let fall from the same point. Prove that A will overtake B after 4 seconds more.

5. A train, under constant acceleration, is observed to travel $49\frac{1}{2}$ ft. and $60\frac{1}{2}$ ft. respectively in two consecutive seconds. Find, in ft./sec., the velocity of the train at the end of the first second. Find also the acceleration in ft./sec.^{2}

PAPER 23

1. A train of 600 tons is uniformly accelerated from a speed of 15 ml./hr. to 45 ml./hr. in running a mile. What force, in tons wt., must be applied ?

2. A string, passing over a light pulley, carries weights of 5 and 7 kilograms at its extremities. When the bodies move, find the tension in the string and the total pressure produced on the pulley.

3. A weight of 4 lb., hanging at the end of a string, pulls a weight of 5 lb. up a smooth inclined plane of angle 25°. Find the tension of the string and the distance the body moves up the plane in 3 seconds from rest.

4. A train moves from one stopping place to another, a distance of 1 mile, in 3 minutes. During the first 44 sec. the motion is uniformly accelerated, and during the rest of the time it is uniformly retarded. Find the acceleration and retardation in ft./sec.^{2}, and the maximum velocity in ml./hr.

5. The velocity of a motor car on a level road is noted every ten seconds after starting, and the following readings are obtained :—

Time (sec.)	0	10	20	30	40	50	60
Velocity (metres/sec.)	0	8·7	13·2	16·3	18·5	19·3	19·7

Draw the velocity time curve and from it deduce the acceleration of the car after 35 seconds in cm./sec.²

If the car weighs 500 Kg., find the resultant force it must have experienced at this instant.

PAPER 24

1. A motor car, whose weight is 8 cwt., is moving at the rate of 15 ml./hr. ; the motor is thrown out of action and the car brought to rest by the brakes alone in 10 yards. Find the average force exerted.

2. A train, of weight 200 tons, starts from rest and is uniformly accelerated so that it reaches a speed of 30 ml./hr. in 7 min. 20 sec. If the various resistances to motion are equivalent to a retarding force of 1·5 tons wt., find the pull exerted by the engine.

3. A weight of 5 lb., descending vertically, draws up a weight of 3 lb. by means of a light string passing over a smooth pulley. At the end of half a second from rest the string breaks ; find how much higher the 3 lb. weight will go.

4. Weights of 4 lb. and 2 lb. are fixed to the ends of a string hanging over the opposite edges of a smooth horizontal table, and a weight of 1 lb. attached to the string rests on the table. Calculate the tension of each string and the acceleration of the system.

FIG. 172.

5. The speedometer of a car reads 30, 29, 27, 23, 17, 15, 18, 26, 30 ml./hr. at intervals of 15 sec. when ascending a hill. Draw a graph showing how the speed varies with the time. Find from the graph, the length of the hill in yards between the first and last reading, and state the times when the retardation is greatest and when the acceleration is greatest.

CHAPTER XI

FRICTION

66. In Chapter I. smooth bodies were defined to be such that if placed in contact and an effort made to slide one along the other, then the reaction of the one on the other would be at right angles to their common surface of contact. No bodies, however, are really perfectly smooth, and a certain amount of effort is required to slide one body along another ; if this force is small, the body does not move, the force being balanced by the friction ; as the force increases, the friction increases, until at length the body moves. We thus see that the frictional force is variable and gradually increases, trying to prevent motion, but a stage is at length reached when the frictional force attains its maximum value and if the external force is increased beyond this, it overcomes the friction and the body moves.

The maximum frictional force is called the **Limiting Friction.**

It can be shown by experiment that the least value of the force necessary to start motion is greater than the force required to maintain motion after the body has once started to move.

67. Exp. 19. A rectangular block of pine-wood **A** is placed on a mahogany board **B** and attached, by means of a string passing over a smoothly running pulley, to a scale-pan **C.** The block having been previously weighed and the weight of the scale-pan known, weights are added to the scale-pan until, on just starting the block, it moves with steady motion.

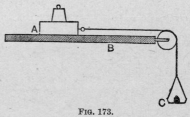

FIG. 173.

Extra weights are then placed on the block **A** and additional weights put in the scale-pan, until steady motion is once more produced. Neglecting the friction of the pulley, the weight of the scale-pan and its contents gives the value of the *friction* called into play, while the weight of **A** and the extra weight give the *normal reaction* between the block and board.

125

In an experiment tried, the block weighed 170 grams, and additional weights, each of 100 grams, were put on it. The following results were obtained :—

Normal Reaction R.	Friction F.	$\dfrac{F}{R}$.
170	49·9	0·29
270	70·4	0·26
370	91·4	0·25
470	113·4	0·24
570	135·4	0·24
670	156·4	0·23

It will be noticed that the values of $\dfrac{\text{Friction}}{\text{Normal Reaction}}$ are approximately the same.

This constant fraction is called the **Coefficient of Friction** between the two substances and is usually represented by the symbol μ.

Thus　　　　　　　　$F = \mu R$, approximately.

Another experiment can be tried in which the areas of the surfaces of the two substances in contact can be varied. Since the grain of wood varies on different faces, it is advisable to try glass on iron, or iron on iron, etc. ; we shall then find that the limiting friction does not depend on the amount of surface in contact, but merely on the normal reaction.

We can now summarise the laws of sliding friction as follows :—

(i) The frictional force acts in a direction opposite to that in which the body is urged to move.

(ii) The limiting frictional force is directly proportional to the total normal reaction.

(iii) The coefficient of friction depends only on the nature of the two substances in contact, and does not depend on the area of the surfaces in contact nor on the velocity of the body.

These results were obtained by *Morin* in 1831-4.

68. The coefficient of friction between a body made of one substance, and an inclined plane made of another, may be obtained *experimentally* by placing the body on the plane, and gradually increasing the inclination until the body slips.

Suppose slipping occurs when the inclination is α; then if **R** is the normal reaction and μ**R** the friction, resolving up the plane,

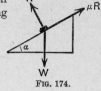

$$\mu\textbf{R} - \textbf{W} \sin \alpha = 0 ;$$

resolving at right angles to the plane,

$$\textbf{R} - \textbf{W} \cos \alpha = 0.$$

$$\therefore \ \mu = \frac{\mu\textbf{R}}{\textbf{R}} = \frac{\textbf{W} \sin \alpha}{\textbf{W} \cos \alpha} = \tan \alpha.$$

Fig. 174.

69. The **total reaction** of a body on a plane is the resultant of the normal reaction and friction.

If the body is in *limiting* equilibrium, the friction has its maximum value

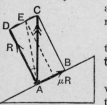

Fig. 175.

and equals μ**R**, and in Fig. 175 the direction of the total reaction is **AC**.

The angle **CAD**, which the total reaction makes with the normal to the plane, is called the **Angle of Friction** (λ).

If the equilibrium is *not limiting* then the friction will be less than μ**R**, *i.e.* less than **AB**, and consequently the total reaction, represented by **AE**, will make with the normal an angle less than the angle of friction. In other words, the maximum angle which the total reaction can make with the normal to the plane is λ.

Ex. 1. *A body of weight 6 kilograms rests on a rough plane inclined at an angle of $10°$ to the horizontal. Find the force of friction.*

Since the body has a tendency to slide *down* the plane, it follows that the frictional force **F** acts up the plane; the other forces are the normal reaction **R** at right angles to the plane, and the weight 6 Kg. vertically downwards.

Fig. 176.

Resolving up the plane for equilibrium,

$$\textbf{F} - 6 \sin 10° = 0,$$

$$\therefore \ \textbf{F} = 6 \times 0{\cdot}1736 = 1{\cdot}04 \text{ Kg. wt.}$$

Ex. 2. *A weight of 14 lb. is just sustained on a rough plane inclined at an angle of 30° to the horizon by a force of 7 lb. wt. which acts at an angle of 30° with the inclined plane. Determine the coefficient of friction.*

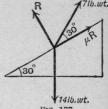

FIG. 177.

R is the normal reaction, and since the body is on the point of sliding *down* the plane, the frictional force μ**R** acts *up* the plane.

Resolving up the plane,

$$\mu R + 7 \cos 30° - 14 \cos 60° = 0 \quad . \quad . \quad . \quad (i)$$

Resolving at right angles to the plane,

$$R + 7 \cos 60° - 14 \cos 30° = 0 \quad . \quad . \quad . \quad (ii)$$

From (i), $\mu R = 14 \cos 60° - 7 \cos 30° = 0·938$;

„   (ii), $R = 14 \cos 30° - 7 \cos 60° = 8·624$.

$$\therefore \quad \mu = \frac{0·938}{8·624} = 0·109.$$

EXERCISE XXV

1. A horizontal force of 5 lb. wt. acts on a body of weight 12 lb. and keeps it in steady motion on a horizontal plane. What is the frictional force called into play, and what is the coefficient of friction ?

2. What horizontal force is required to push a body of weight 10 lb. steadily along a horizontal plane if the coefficient of friction is 0·4 ?

3. If the weight on the driving wheels of a locomotive is 35 tons, find the greatest pull the engine can exert if the coefficient of friction between the wheels and rails is 0·21.

4. A book, held vertically, is grasped between the fingers ; what pressure must be exerted if the book weighs 4 lb. and the coefficient of friction is 0·27 ?

5. A body of weight 10 lb. rests on a rough inclined plane of angle 15°. Find the magnitude of the frictional force.

6. If a body rests on a horizontal plane and is acted on by a force of 20 lb. wt. making an angle of 25° with the plane, what frictional force is called into play ?

7. A block of stone, of weight 200 lb., stands on a rough horizontal floor ; the coefficient of friction is $\frac{1}{2}$. Find the force necessary to make the block slide if the force is applied (i) horizontally, (ii) at an angle of 30° with the horizontal.

8. A man of 11 stone is pulling a packing-case along a floor ; what is the greatest horizontal pull he can exert, if the coefficient of friction between his boots and the floor is 0·5 ?

9. A brake presses against a wheel with a force of 12·5 lb. wt. and the coefficient of friction is 0·45. What is the force of friction tending to stop the wheel ?

10. A body rests on a horizontal table, and is pulled by a string which is inclined at 45° to the vertical. If the coefficient of friction is $\frac{1}{4}$, prove that the body will just slip when the tension in the string slightly exceeds 0·28 times the weight of the body.

11. A weight of 10 lb., placed on an inclined plane, is just on the point of sliding down when the inclination of the plane is 15°. What is the coefficient of friction ?

    What is the magnitude of a horizontal force which will keep the body from sliding down if the angle of the plane is increased to 30° ?

12. A weight of 10 lb. on a slope of 30° is just on the point of slipping. What push applied (i) up the slope, (ii) horizontally, will just move it up the slope ?

13. A load of 50 lb. resting on a plane begins to slip when the plane is tilted to an angle of 30° with the horizontal. What force up the plane will be necessary to keep the load from slipping if the angle of slope is increased to 45° ?

14. A body of weight 5 lb. rests on a plane of angle 10°. What force, acting at an angle of 50° to the plane, is just sufficient to move the particle up the plane, if the coefficient of friction is 0·5 ?

15. A boat weighing 2 tons rests on a slip at 25° to the horizontal. The coefficient of friction between boat and slip is 0·6. Find the least force needed to move the boat (i) up the slip, (ii) down the slip, assuming that the force is applied parallel to the slip.

16. If a weight of 12 lb. is placed on an inclined plane and the coefficient of friction is 0·45, find at what angle the weight will begin to slip.

17. A weight W rests on a rough plane inclined at 45°, being supported by a horizontal force P. When $P = \frac{1}{5}W$, the weight is on the point of slipping down the plane. Find the coefficient of friction, and determine the value of P for which the weight would be on the point of slipping up the plane.

18. Two bodies of equal weight are connected by a string passing over a smooth pulley at the top of two equally rough inclined planes (angles 30° and 60°) placed back to back. Find the coefficient of friction if they are on the point of motion.

19. A wedge has as its section the triangle ABC, where $\angle A = 30°$, $\angle B = 90°$, and the wedge is held fixed with AC horizontal. A weight of 10 lb. resting on AB and a weight W resting on BC are connected by a string passing over B. Find the greatest value W can have, consistent with equilibrium, if the coefficient of friction between each weight and the plane on which it rests is $\frac{3}{4}$.

20. Two weights, 6 lb. and 12 lb., connected by a light rigid bar, are placed on a rough plane, inclined at an angle α to the horizontal, where $\tan \alpha = \frac{5}{12}$, the connecting bar being parallel to a line of greatest slope. If the weights are just about to slip and the coefficient of friction of the 6 lb. weight is 0·5, find the magnitude of the stress in the bar and the coefficient of friction between the 12 lb. weight and the plane.

CHAPTER XII

WORK AND MACHINES

71. If a force overcomes a resistance, then, from a mechanical point of view, it is said to do work ; this work may be such as is commonly expended in raising a heavy object from one level to another, that done in kicking a football, or in overcoming various resistances when a mowing machine is pushed over a lawn.

The practical **unit of work** is that used in raising a weight of 1 lb. vertically through 1 ft., and is called a **Foot-pound.** In the Metric System, the work done in lifting the weight of 1 gram through 1 cm. is called a **Centimetre-gram.**

The work done in lifting 50 lb. through 1 ft. is clearly fifty times that expended in raising 1 lb., and if the weight is raised 8 ft. instead of 1 ft., again the work will be eight times as much, thus the total amount of work done is 50×8 ft.-lb. If the weight has been lifted slowly and steadily, the force exerted must have been 50 lb. wt., so that the work done is measured by the product of the number of units of force and the number of units of displacement in the direction of the force.

This result is perfectly general, and the force may act in any direction, so that if a force of **F** moves a body from **A** to **B** in its *own direction*, then

FIG. 178.

$$\text{work done} = \mathbf{F} \times \mathbf{AB}.$$

72. A force does no work if it is acting on a body which is moving at right angles to its own direction ; the weight of a man who is sitting in a railway carriage in motion does not help to move the carriage forward.

If several forces act on a body, then the point of application of one particular force **F** may move from **A** to **B** in a direction making an angle θ with **F**. If the force **F** is resolved into $\mathbf{F} \cos \theta$ along **AB** and $\mathbf{F} \sin \theta$ at right angles to **AB**, $\mathbf{F} \cos \theta$ will help to move the body, whereas $\mathbf{F} \sin \theta$ will be ineffective.

FIG. 179.

The work done by $F \cos \theta = F \cos \theta \cdot AB$
$$= F \cdot AB \cos \theta$$
$$= F \cdot AC,$$
where BC is perpendicular to the direction of F,
while the work done by $F \sin \theta$ is zero.

It is important to notice that the work is not measured by $F \cdot AB$.

Generally, *the work done by any force is measured by the product of the number of units in the force and the number of units in the projection of the displacement of its point of application along the direction of the force.*

73. Horse-Power. An agent is said to be working at the rate of 1 Horse-Power when it performs 33,000 ft.-lb. of work per minute, or 550 ft.-lb. per second.

This unit was introduced by Watt, and he derived his estimate from experiments conducted at Barclay and Perkins' brewery in 1784 with large horses ; a horse was made to raise a weight from the bottom of a deep well by means of a horizontal rope passing over a pulley and then hanging vertically. He found that the greatest power on which he could rely was 22,000 ft.-lb. per minute and he added 50 per cent. to allow for loss in friction.

The time in which an engine does a particular amount of work is naturally of great practical importance, and the shorter the time, the more effective is the engine. It should be recognised that the horse-power (H.P.) of an engine is a variable quantity, and as in the case of a petrol engine of a motor car, it depends on the speed at which the car is moving ; a nominal 16 H.P. car will often develop as much as 40 H.P. when going at high speed. The theoretical value, called the Indicated Horse-Power (I.H.P.), can be determined from the size of the cylinders, length of stroke and pressure of petrol vapour ; but the useful horse-power is less than this, since some of the work is used in overcoming friction and moving the various parts of the machine ; this useful horse-power is called the Brake Horse-Power (B.H.P.).

Energy is defined to be the capacity for doing work.

74. Ex. 1. *A train is moving at the rate of 30 miles per hour and weighs 120 tons ; if the average pull on it is 10 lb. wt. per ton, what is the horse-power exerted ?*

The total pull $= 10 \times 120$ lb. wt. ;
$$30 \text{ ml./hr.} = 44 \text{ ft./sec.} ;$$
$\therefore$ distance moved over in 1 sec. $= 44$ ft.,
$\therefore$ work done in 1 sec. $=$ pull $\times$ distance
$$= 1200 \times 44 \text{ ft.-lb.}$$
$$\therefore \text{ H.P.} = \frac{1200 \times 44}{550} = 96.$$

Ex. 2. *Find the work done in pumping* 10,000 *cu. ft. of water from a rectangular tank in which the water is* 10 *ft. deep, and delivering it at a height of* 30 *ft. above the bottom of the tank.*

Weight of water = 10,000 × 62·3 lb. = 623,000 lb.

Now we shall show, in the Chapter on Centre of Gravity, that the work done in raising a number of particles from one position to another is the same as that done in raising the total weight, supposed collected at the centre of gravity, from the first to the second position of the centre of gravity.

In this problem, the C.G. of the water is raised from a distance of 5 ft. above the bottom of the tank to 30 ft., *i.e.* through a distance of 25 ft. ;

∴ work done = 623,000 × 25 = 15,575,000 ft.-lb.

EXERCISE XXVI

1. What is the work done in riding a bicycle for 7 miles against an average resistance of 13·5 lb. wt. ?

2. A weight of 2 tons has to be raised from the bottom of a shaft 300 ft. deep ; how many ft.-lb. of work will be done ?

3. If the resistance to traction on a level road is 170 lb. wt. per ton, how many ft.-lb. of work are done in drawing 5 tons through 100 yards ?

4. A chain, 600 ft. long, weighing 15 lb. per ft., is wound up. What work is done ?

5. A cage weighing 4 cwt., at the bottom of a mine, is wound up by a chain 500 ft. long weighing 3 lb. per ft. What is the work done ?

6. Find the work done in bringing the soil obtained from digging a shaft 150 ft. deep to the surface ; the section of the shaft is 75 sq. ft., and the soil may be taken to weigh 145 lb. per cu. ft.

7. A circular well contains water, the surface of which always remains at the same depth of 75 ft. Find the work done in pumping 20,000 gallons to the level of the ground. Assume 1 gallon of water weighs 10 lb.

8. What is the H.P. of an engine necessary to maintain in a train a speed of 50 ml. per hr. against a resistance of 2400 lb. wt.

9. A box weighing 1 ton is being dragged along the surface of a frozen pond by means of a horizontal rope. Calculate the work done in moving it 25 yards. Assume coefficient of friction $= \frac{1}{40}$.

10. A motor car develops 10 H.P. when running at 10 ml. per hr. What is the magnitude of the force propelling it ?

11. What is the H.P. of an engine which keeps a train going at the rate of 45 ml./hr. against a resistance equal to 1500 lb. wt. ?

12. A man riding a bicycle at 10 ml./hr. finds that on account of the wind he has to work harder to the extent of $\frac{1}{8}$ H.P. Find the force due to the wind.

13. Assuming that the forces opposing the motion of a train are equivalent to a force equal to the weight of half a ton, and that the engine cannot do more than 49,000 ft.-lb. of work per second, find the greatest velocity with which the train can move.

14. Twelve tons of water per minute fall 64 ft. over a waterfall. Calculate the available H.P. of a machine worked by the waterfall, if 75 per cent. of the energy supplied is converted into useful work.

15. In what time will an engine of 20 H.P. empty a tank $60 \times 40 \times 8$ cu. ft. filled with water, the average lift being 40 ft. ? Assume 1 cu. ft. of water weighs 62·3 lb.

16. A 20-horse-power engine is employed to pump water from the bottom of a mine 100 ft. deep. How many cu. ft. of water will it raise in 24 hours. Assume 1 cu. ft. of water weighs 62·3 lb.

17. A cage weighing 15 cwt. is raised through a height of 200 ft. by means of a rope weighing 2 lb. per ft. in 90 seconds. Find the H.P. of the engine required for the work.

18. The section of a stream is 15 sq. ft., and the average velocity 3 ft./sec. The average available mean fall of the particles of water is 30 ft. ; what is the H.P. available ? Assume 1 cu. ft. of water weighs 62·3 lb.

19. In a steam engine, the steam exerts a pressure of 200 lb. wt./sq. in. on a piston 7 in. in diameter. At each stroke the piston moves through a distance of 16 in. What is the work done per stroke in ft. tons ? If the piston makes 30 strokes a minute, what is the H.P. of the engine ? Assume $\pi = 3·14$.

20. A cylindrical well is 90 ft. deep, and has a diameter of 4 ft., and is two-thirds full of water. Find the H.P. of an engine which, delivering the water at the surface, empties the well in 25 minutes. Assume $\pi = 3.14$ and 1 cu. ft. of water weighs 62·3 lb.

21. A dock 600 ft. long and 120 ft. wide, with a depth of water 36 ft., has to be pumped dry in 6 hours, all the water being lifted to a level of 2 ft. above the original water level of the dock. If the useful H.P. exerted by the pumping engines is constant, calculate what it must amount to, and show that it takes $1\frac{3}{4}$ hr. to empty the last 6 ft. of water in the dock. Assume 1 cu. ft. of water weighs 62·5 lb.

Machines

75. In a machine we have an arrangement by means of which a force called the **Effort** is used to overcome a **Resistance** or **Load**, and in order that such a machine may be of advantage in performing a certain piece of work, it must be constructed so that a small effort will overcome a large resistance, and moreover so that the effort can be applied in a convenient direction. When an effort is applied to a machine, it not only overcomes the resistance, but overcomes the internal friction, and in some cases raises or lowers certain parts of the machine, and in so doing work is expended.

By the Principle of the Conservation of Energy (Art. 113), we know that the total energy of a system is a quantity which can neither be increased nor diminished by any action between the parts of the system, though it may be changed into any of the forms of which energy is susceptible.

Applying this principle to machines, it follows that the work put into a machine by the effort cannot be lost ; part is used in raising the load, part in overcoming friction, and part in moving portions of the machine.

If we assume, as we shall in some cases, that there is no friction, and that the parts of the machine are weightless, then

the work done by the effort = work done on load or resistance.

In a real machine, in which there is friction, we shall naturally get less *useful* work out of it than the amount put in by the effort, and

$$\text{the efficiency of the machine} = \frac{\text{useful work done}}{\text{work put in}}.$$

Since the amount of useful work done is always less than the total amount of work put in by the effort, it follows that the efficiency is always less than unity.

$$\text{The } \textbf{velocity ratio} = \frac{\text{distance moved by effort}}{\text{distance moved by load}} \text{ ;}$$

this ratio is *constant* for a particular machine and does not depend on the magnitude of the load overcome; its value depends on the dimensions of the various parts of the machine.

$$\text{The } \textbf{force ratio} \text{ or mechanical advantage} = \frac{\text{load}}{\text{effort}}.$$

It should be noticed that

$$\text{efficiency} = \frac{\text{work done on load}}{\text{work done by effort}} = \frac{\text{load} \times \text{distance moved by load}}{\text{effort} \times \text{distance moved by effort}}$$
$$= \frac{\text{force ratio}}{\text{velocity ratio}}.$$

The efficiency of a machine is not a constant quantity, for since the work done in lifting the dead weights of the machine does not increase with the load, it follows that the *efficiency increases with the load.*

76. The Inclined Plane.

(i) Suppose a body of W lb. wt. is being pulled steadily at a uniform rate up a plane of length l ft. and height h ft.; then if the plane is smooth, the work done by the effort will equal the work done on the load.   (Fig. 180.)

FIG. 180.

The work done by the effort = P × displacement in direction of P

$$= \text{P}l \text{ ft.-lb. ;}$$

the work done on the load = W × displacement in direction of W

$$= \text{W} \times h \text{ ;}$$

∴ by the Principle of Work,

$$\text{P}l = \text{W}h, \qquad i.e. \text{ P} = \text{W} \cdot \frac{h}{l}.$$

(ii) If the plane is rough, suppose a force of P lb. wt., acting parallel to the line of greatest slope, draws a body of weight W lb. slowly and steadily *up* the plane. If R is the normal reaction, the friction μR will act *down* the plane.

Since there is no motion at right angles to the plane, resolving in this direction we have

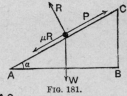
FIG. 181.

$$R - W \cos \alpha = 0.$$

In this case, work done by P = work done against W + work done against friction,

$$\therefore P . AC = W . BC + \mu R . AC$$
$$= W . BC + \mu W \cos \alpha . AC ;$$
$$\therefore P = W . \frac{BC}{AC} + \mu W \cos \alpha$$
$$= W (\sin \alpha + \mu \cos \alpha).$$

In a similar manner it can be proved that if Q lb. wt. is the force which just allows the body to slide steadily *down* the plane,

$$Q = W(\sin \alpha - \mu \cos \alpha) ;$$

it follows that

$$P - Q = 2\mu W \cos \alpha = 2\mu R$$
$$= \text{twice the frictional force.}$$

Ex. *Find the efficiency when a force of 64 lb. wt. drags a weight of 250 lb. up a rough incline of 10° with uniform speed.*

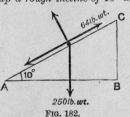
FIG. 182.

If the body is moved from A to C,

useful work done = 250 × BC ft.-lb.,

work done by effort = 64 × AC ft.-lb.,

$$\therefore \text{efficiency} = \frac{250 \; BC}{64 \; AC} = \frac{250}{64} \sin 10° = 0.68.$$

This is sometimes expressed by saying that the efficiency is 68 per cent.

EXERCISE XXVII

1. A horse drags a barge along a canal, parallel to the bank, by means of a rope making an angle of 10° with the bank. If the pull in the rope is 75 lb. wt., what work is done in dragging the barge 100 yards ?

2. A roller is pushed up a plane from *A* to *B* by a horizontal force of 25 lb. wt. If *BC* = 10 ft. and the inclination of the plane 35° find the work done by the force.

FIG. 183.

3. A smooth incline has a height of 1 foot and sloping length 12 ft. What work is done in pulling 12 lb. up 10 ft. along the slope ?

4. A man whose weight is 11 stone walks up a hill of 1 in 11 at the rate of 3 ml./hr. ; at what H.P. is he working ?

5. On a smooth incline it is found that a horizontal force will move 20 lb. up 10 ft. of the incline rising 1 in 5. What is the work done ? Find also, by the Principle of Work, the force parallel to the plane which will just support the weight.

6. Find the work done in drawing a load of 15 lb. wt. 10 ft. up an incline of 25°, the coefficient of friction being 0·2.

7. Find the work done in pulling 10 cwt. up to the top of an incline which is 100 ft. long and 25 ft. high, the coefficient of friction being 0·4. Find also the work done in pulling it down again.

8. To drag a packing-case of 120 lb. wt. up an incline of 1 in 5 requires a force of 85 lb. wt. parallel to the plane. Calculate the force of friction.

9. A lifting machine has a velocity ratio 15, and a load of 110 lb. wt. is raised by an effort of 8 lb. wt. Find the force ratio and efficiency.

10. The efficiency of a machine is 0·6 and the velocity ratio 4. Find the load raised by an effort of 50 lb. wt.

11. Find the effort required to raise a weight of 120 lb. in a machine, if the velocity ratio is 5 and the efficiency 70 per cent.

12. The efficiency of a machine is 0·75 and an effort of 25 lb. wt. raises a load of 124 lb. Find the velocity ratio.

13. Find the efficiency of a machine if the velocity ratio is 8 and the force ratio 5.

14. Find the efficiency when a weight of 200 gm. is pulled with uniform speed up an incline of 20° by a force of 124 gm. wt. acting along the plane.

15. Given that the efficiency is 0·58, find what effort, acting parallel to the plane, will be required to pull a body weighing 55 kilograms with uniform speed up an incline of 1 in 150.

16. In a machine, a weight of 100 lb. falling through 80 ft. lifts a weight of 60 lb. to a height of 90 ft. How many units of work are done against the frictional resistances, and what is the efficiency ?

17. A man's hand, on the handle of a crane, moves 120 ft. when the weight is lifted 1 ft. ; 35 per cent. of the total work done by the man is wasted in friction. A load of 1·5 tons is being lifted. Find (in lb. wt.) the force exerted by the hand.

18. Find the pull on the draw-bar exerted by a locomotive which develops 600 H.P. when travelling at 60 ml./hr., the mechanical efficiency of the locomotive being taken as 60 per cent.

19. In a certain lifting tackle, the law connecting the effort P lb. wt. and the load W lb. wt. is $P = 0.045W + 3.5$. Find the value of P when $W = 350$, and if the velocity ratio is 20, calculate the efficiency.

20. In a machine used for hoisting loads, the velocity-ratio is 42, and it is found that an effort of 32 lb. wt. is required to raise a weight of 350 lb. at a steady speed. Find the efficiency at this load.

    If in the above machine the effort P and the load W are connected by the law $P = a + bW$, and an effort of 2·2 lb. wt. is required just to move the machine when there is no load, find a and b.

21. In a certain machine, the connection between the load W lb. wt. and the effort P lb. wt. is given by the formula $P = 3.7 + 0.058W$, and the velocity-ratio is 30. Determine the efficiency when W has the values 10, 20, 40, 50, 100, and thence draw a curve connecting efficiency and load ; and deduce the efficiency if $W = 65$.

22. The relation between the force P and the load W is given by the equation $P = a + bW$, when a and b are constants. If in a machine, in which the velocity-ratio is 15, a force of 30 lb. wt. will lift a weight of 130 lb., and a force of 40 lb. wt. will lift a weight of 200 lb., find the weight that a force of 80 lb. wt. will lift, and the efficiency of the machine under this load.

77. Pulleys. One advantage of any system of pulleys is that it easily enables us to change the direction of a force. The great advantage of a pulley in comparison with a fixed peg for changing the direction of a force is that with a pulley the rope surrounding it does not slip, and consequently the friction at the circumference is small, whereas with a peg the rope slides over it and considerable friction is produced.

    In the case of a *single movable pulley* (Fig. 184), if we *neglect friction*, the tension throughout the rope will be the same. If the pulley and load of **W** lb. wt. rise 1 ft., there will be 1 ft. of rope to spare on each side of it, and consequently

FIG. 184.

the effort **P** lb. wt. applied at **A** will rise 2 ft. ; it follows that the velocity ratio is 2.

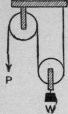

The work done by the effort = **P** × 2 ft.-lb.,

    „   „   on the load = **W** × 1 ft.-lb. ;

$$\therefore\ 2\mathbf{P} = \mathbf{W}.$$

If the weight w lb. of the pulley is taken into consideration,

$$2\mathbf{P} = \mathbf{W} + w.$$

The effort would be more conveniently applied by passing the rope over a fixed pulley and pulling downwards as in Fig. 185.

P

W

Fig. 185.

78. Greater mechanical advantage is obtained by passing the rope round a series of pulleys, one set being in the upper fixed block, and another set in the lower movable block, as in the ordinary *block and tackle* system.

If the ropes are considered to be parallel and there is *no friction*, the tension throughout will be equal to the effort **P**, and if there are n vertical pieces of rope passing to the lower block, then if the load **W** rises a distance x, the effort **P** will descend a distance nx, so that the velocity ratio is n.

The work done by the effort = **P** × nx,

    „   „   on the load = **W** × x ;

$$\therefore\ \mathbf{P} \cdot nx = \mathbf{W} \cdot x,$$

i.e. $\qquad n\mathbf{P} = \mathbf{W}.$

If the weight w of the lower block is taken into consideration,

$$n\mathbf{P} = \mathbf{W} + w.$$

An *alternative* method of solution is to note that since there are n strings supporting the lower block, and that the tension in each is **P**, resolving vertically,

$$n\mathbf{P} = \mathbf{W}.$$

Fig. 186.

79. Exp. 20. In an experiment performed in the laboratory with 3 pulleys in each block, and consequently with a velocity-ratio of 6, the values of load (**W** gm. wt.) and effort (**P** gm. wt.) given in the following table were obtained. From these were calculated the corresponding values of the force ratio and efficiency.

The fact that the *efficiency increases with the load* is illustrated by the values obtained.

If a curve is drawn illustrating the connection between load and effort, we obtain a series of points on a straight line, and consequently the formula connecting **P** and **W** will be of the first degree. Let the equation be

$$P = aW + b.$$

Substituting for **P** and **W** any corresponding pairs of values,

$$49 \cdot 6 = 227a + b,$$
$$90 \cdot 9 = 454a + b,$$
$$\therefore \ 41 \cdot 3 = 227a, \quad i.e. \ a = 0 \cdot 18,$$
$$b = 8 \cdot 3.$$

W	P	Force Ratio	Efficiency
227	49·6	4·58	0·76
273	57·8	4·71	0·79
318	66·3	4·79	0·80
363	74·7	4·86	0·81
409	82·7	4·94	0·82
454	90·9	4·99	0·83

Thus the *Law of the Machine* is **P = 0·18W + 8·3.**

80. Ex. 1. *An ordinary block and tackle has two pulleys in each block.* (i) *If the system were frictionless, what force would have to be exerted to lift a load of* 400 *lb. wt.?* (ii) *What force would be required to lift the* 400 *lb. wt. if the efficiency for this load is* 0·4?

Since there are 4 strings to the lower block, the velocity ratio is 4; suppose the load rises 1 ft.

(i) If **P** lb. wt. is the effort, then

$$\text{work done by effort} = P \times 4 \text{ ft.-lb.,}$$
$$\text{useful work done on load} = 400 \times 1 \text{ ft.-lb.,}$$
$$\therefore \ 4P = 400, \quad i.e. \ P = 100 \text{ lb. wt.}$$

(ii)
$$0 \cdot 4 = \text{efficiency} = \frac{\text{useful work done on load}}{\text{work done by effort}} = \frac{400}{4P};$$
$$\therefore \ P = \frac{100}{0 \cdot 4} = 250 \text{ lb. wt.}$$

Ex. 2. *A man weighing 11 stone raises 12 stone by means of an ordinary block and tackle with two pulleys in each block. What will be his thrust on the ground when he pulls vertically downwards, the system being frictionless?*

Let the pull in the rope be **P** stone weight; this force will act *downwards on the pulley system*, and *upwards on the man*; let the reaction of the ground *upwards* on the man be **R** stone weight.

[Double arrows are used to represent the forces on the pulley system, and single arrows for those on the man.]

(i) The velocity ratio of the pulley system is 4; if the load of 12 stone rises 1 ft.,

work done by effort = $P \times 4$ ft. stone,

useful work done on load = 12×1 ft. stone,

$$\therefore \quad 4P = 12, \quad i.e. \ P = 3 \text{ stone weight.}$$

(ii) Considering the equilibrium of the man,

$$P + R - 11 = 0, \quad \therefore R = 11 - P = 8 \text{ stone weight.}$$

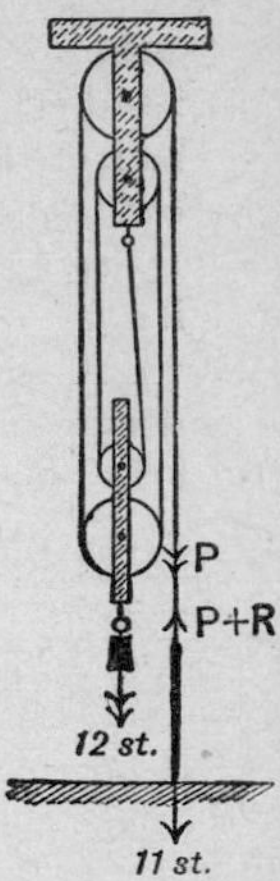

FIG. 187.

Ex. 3. *A pulley block and tackle has two sheaves in each block, the lower block weighing 20 lb. Each time the rope passes round a sheave, its tension diminishes by 10 per cent. Calculate the efficiency of the machine when used to raise loads of 1 cwt., 2 cwt., 3 cwt.*

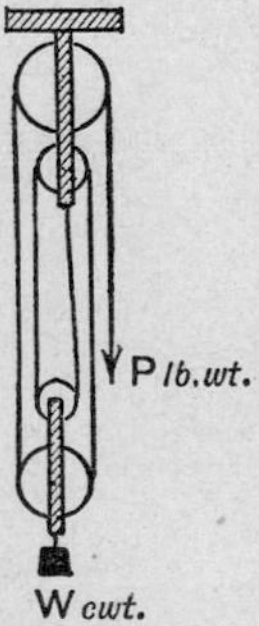

If the effort is **P** lb. wt. and the load **W** cwt., then the tensions in the four ropes supporting the load are respectively $\frac{9}{10}P$, $\left(\frac{9}{10}\right)^2 P$, $\left(\frac{9}{10}\right)^3 P$, $\left(\frac{9}{10}\right)^4 P$ lb. wt.

$$\therefore \ [0·9 + (0·9)^2 + (0·9)^3 + (0·9)^4]P = 112W + 20,$$
$$3·095P = 112W + 20,$$
$$\therefore \ P = \frac{112W + 20}{3·095}.$$

For loads of 1, 2, 3 cwt., the values of **P** are 42·65, 78·84, 115·0 lb. wt.

Since the velocity-ratio is 4,

$$\text{efficiency} = \frac{112W}{4P} = 0·66, \ 0·71, \ 0·73 \text{ respectively.}$$

P lb.wt.

W cwt.

FIG. 188.

EXERCISE XXVIII

1. A block and tackle has two sheaves in each block, one end of the string being attached to the upper block. The weight of the lower block is 6 lb. Find the pull required to support a weight of 18 lb. attached to the lower block. (Neglect friction.)

2. A block and tackle has the rope attached to the lower block (Fig. 189). What is the velocity-ratio ? Find the weight of the lower block if an effort of 15 lb. wt. is required to hold it at rest. What effort would be required to raise a load of 96 lb. ? (Neglect friction.)

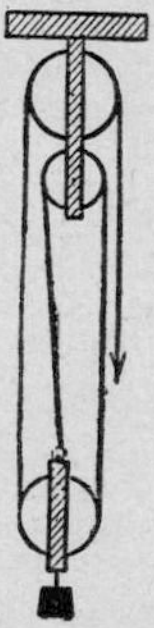

3. In a continuous string system of pulleys, the weight of the lower block is 5 lb., and it requires an effort of 7 lb. wt. to raise a weight of 30 lb. ; find what weight could be raised by an effort of 10 lb. wt. (Neglect friction.)

FIG. 189.

4. Find the velocity-ratio in a hoisting tackle with three pulleys in the upper block and two in the lower. What force is necessary to support a weight of 3 cwt. if the lower block weighs 19 lb. ? (Neglect friction.)

5. In a block and tackle, the upper block is fixed and contains two sheaves, while the lower is a single movable pulley ; the two blocks weigh 10 lb. each. What force is necessary to support a weight of 120 lb., and what will be the pressure on the point of support of the upper block ? (Neglect friction.)

6. In a block and tackle in which the rope passes round three pulleys in each block, find the weight which a force of 5 lb. wt. can support if there is no friction.

   If there is friction, this force can only raise a weight of 24 lb.; calculate the percentage efficiency of the machine.

7. In a block and tackle the upper block contains three pulleys and the lower two. If the weight to be raised and the lower block together weigh 200 lb., and if a force of 70 lb. wt. has to be used to raise this weight, find (a) the work done by the operator when the weight is raised through 2 ft., (b) the work done on the weight and block, and (c) the work done against friction.

8. In a pulley tackle the velocity-ratio is 8, and the friction of the tackle is such that only 55 per cent. of the force applied is usefully employed in lifting the weight. Find what force would have to be exerted to raise a load of $\frac{1}{4}$ ton by this pulley tackle.

9. A system of pulleys has a velocity-ratio of 8 and an efficiency of 75 per cent. Determine the force necessary to lift a load of 300 lb. wt.

10. In the continuous string system of block and tackle, there are three pulleys in each block. A force of 100 lb. wt. raises 4 cwt., and the lower block weighs 14 lb.; what fraction of the work done is wasted in overcoming friction?

11. In a continuous string system of block and tackle, there are three pulleys in the upper block and two in the lower.

(i) If there is no friction, calculate the effort required to raise a load of 200 lb. wt.

(ii) Assuming that, owing to friction, the tension on one side of a pulley is $\frac{4}{5}$ of the tension on the other side of the pulley, prove that the force required to raise the load must be increased to over 74 lb. wt.

12. In a continuous string block and tackle, each block contains two pulleys. Assume that, owing to friction, each time the rope passes round a pulley, the tension is reduced in the ratio 4 : 5. Calculate the efficiency of the tackle.

13. The following method can be employed to tear down a barbed wire entanglement :—A grapnel, with a rope attached to it, is thrown into

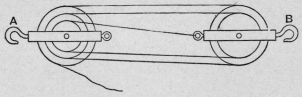

Fig. 190.

the entanglement. A tackle consisting of two pulley blocks is made fast by one end to a stake or a tree and by the other to the grapnel rope, so that a great force may drag the grapnel.

Suppose you have for the purpose a pair of pulley blocks in which the rope is rove as in Fig. 190. Would it make any difference which end (A or B) you attach to the grapnel rope and which to the stake? Give reasons.

With the tackle fastened as you suggest, if its efficiency as a machine was 70 per cent., what force would you get in the grapnel by exerting a pull of 600 lb. wt. on the rope of the tackle ?

14. A crane, in which the velocity-ratio is 40, gave the following results :—

Load lifted (W lb. wt.)	100	300	500	700
Force applied (P lb. wt.)	8·5	17·0	25·6	34·2

Plot a curve showing the relation between P and W, on a W base, and, on the same base, plot a curve of efficiency. Thence find the percentage efficiency for a load weighing 350 lb.

15. In a certain machine in which the velocity-ratio is 8, the loads (in cwt.) and corresponding efforts (in lb. wt.) are given in the following table :—

Load (W)	2	3	4	5	6	7	8
Effort (P)	50	70	88	112	128	150	170

Draw a graph and thence find the law of the machine in the form $P = a + bW$. Thence calculate the percentage efficiency with loads of 4 and 7 cwt.

16. A man, whose weight is 10 stone, sits in a loop suspended from the lower block of a system of pulleys with a continuous rope, and supports himself by holding the free end of the rope. There are three pulleys in each block, and each block weighs 7 lb. If there is no friction, find what force he must apply, and the stress on the beam from which the system is hung.

17. In a system in which one rope passes round all the pulleys, a man weighing 12 stone stands on the ground and by means of the pulleys supports a weight of half a ton. There are nine ropes at the lower block and its weight is 14 lb. Find the pressure of the man on the ground in lb. wt. (Neglect friction.)

81. Wheel and Axle.

If a is the radius of the wheel, and b that of the axle, then in one complete revolution of the wheel and axle,

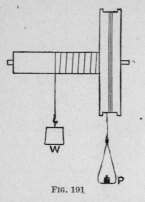

P descends a distance $2\pi a$,

W rises   ,,   ,, $2\pi b$;

(i) If there is no friction,

$$P \times 2\pi a = W \times 2\pi b,$$

$$\therefore \quad P = \frac{b}{a} W.$$

(ii) If friction is taken into consideration,

$$\text{efficiency} = \frac{\text{useful work done on load}}{\text{work done by effort}}$$

$$= \frac{W \times 2\pi b}{P \times 2\pi a} = \frac{Wb}{Pa}.$$

Fig. 191.

82. Differential Wheel and Axle.

In this arrangement the axle consists of two parts of different diameters and is attached rigidly to the wheel. The rope supporting the load passes under a movable pulley and is wound on the two parts of the axle in opposite directions, the part on the smaller axle being wound in the same direction as the rope round the wheel.

Let a, b be the radii of the smaller and larger axle, and R the radius of the wheel, then if the wheel turns once, the effort P descends a distance $2\pi R$; the rope supporting the load would be shortened by a length $2\pi b$ if the smaller axle did not revolve, and would be lengthened by $2\pi a$ if the larger axle did not revolve ; since both axles are moving, the rope is shortened

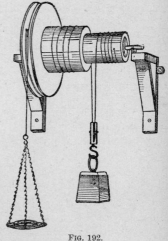

Fig. 192.

$2\pi(b-a)$, and since the load hangs from a loop surrounding the pulley, it follows that the load rises a distance $\pi(b-a)$.

The work done by the effort $= P \times 2\pi R$,

the useful work done on load $= W \times \pi(b-a)$.

(i) If there is no friction,

$$\therefore \quad P \times 2\pi R = W \times \pi(b-a),$$

$$\therefore \quad P = \frac{b-a}{2R}W.$$

(ii) If friction is considered,

$$\text{efficiency} = \frac{\text{useful work done on load}}{\text{work done by effort}}$$

$$= \frac{W \times \pi(b-a)}{P \times 2\pi R} = \frac{W(b-a)}{2PR}.$$

83. Differential Pulley.

In this machine the upper fixed block contains two pulleys of slightly different diameters fixed together, while the lower movable block contains one pulley. An endless chain passes round the larger pulley of the upper block, under the movable pulley, and then round the smaller pulley of the upper block, the grooves of the pulleys being provided with notches so that the chain cannot slip.

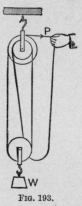

Suppose the chain at which the effort is applied is pulled down such a distance that the pulleys in the upper block turn round once, then if R and r are the radii of these pulleys, a length $2\pi R$ is wound round the larger pulley and $2\pi r$ off the smaller pulley, so that the chain supporting the lower block is shortened by $2\pi(R-r)$; since the load is suspended from the loop of the chain, it follows that it rises half this distance,' $i.e.$ $\pi(R-r)$, while the effort P descends $2\pi R$.

The work done by the effort $= P \times 2\pi R$,

the useful work done on load $= W \times \pi(R-r)$.

FIG. 193.

(i) If there is no friction,

$$P \times 2\pi R = W \times \pi(R-r),$$

$$\therefore \quad P = \frac{R-r}{2R}W.$$

(ii) If friction is taken into consideration,

$$\text{efficiency} = \frac{\text{useful work done on load}}{\text{work done by effort}}$$

$$= \frac{W \times \pi(R-r)}{P \times 2\pi R} = \frac{R-r}{2R} \cdot \frac{W}{P}.$$

The friction in this machine being considerable, it does not **overhaul** or run backwards when the hand supplying the effort is withdrawn. Whenever the efficiency of a machine is less than 50 per cent., then the work necessary to overcome friction is greater than the work required to raise the load, so that if the load tried to descend of its own accord, it could not do enough work to overcome friction.

It should also be noticed that the velocity-ratio is $\dfrac{2R}{R-r}$ and since R is only slightly greater than r, and consequently $(R-r)$ is small, it follows that the velocity-ratio is a large quantity, and the load only rises slowly though the effort may move through a considerable distance.

84. Ex. *In a wheel and differential axle, the diameters of the axle are 5 in. and 7 in. and the diameter of the wheel is 28 in. Find the velocity-ratio of the machine. The relation between the effort P lb. wt. and the load W lb. wt. is $P = aW + b$, where a and b are constants. If the efficiency is 0.2 when $W = 20$ lb. wt. and 0.6 when $W = 400$ lb. wt., find a and b.*

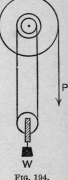

If the wheel makes one revolution,

     P descends 28π in.,

the loop containing the movable pulley is shortened by $\pi(7-5) = 2\pi$ in.,

     $\therefore$ W rises π in. ;

     $\therefore$ velocity-ratio $= \dfrac{28\pi}{\pi} = 28.$

        Efficiency $= \dfrac{W \times 1}{P \times 28} = \dfrac{W}{28(aW+b)}$;

FIG. 194.

     $\therefore$ $0.2 = \dfrac{20}{28(20a+b)}$ and $0.6 = \dfrac{400}{28(400a+b)}$;

     $\therefore$ $20a+b = \tfrac{25}{7}$ and $400a+b = \tfrac{500}{21}$;

     $\therefore$ $380a = \tfrac{425}{21}$,   *i.e.* $a = 0.053$;

        $b = \tfrac{25}{7} - 20a = 2.51.$

EXERCISE XXIX

1. What is the velocity-ratio in a wheel and axle if R is the radius of the wheel and r the radius of the axle, given that

    (i) $R=20$ in., $r=2$ in.,   (ii) $R=36$ in., $r=3$ in.,

    (iii) $R=2$ ft., $r=2\frac{1}{2}$ in.,   (iv) $R=3\frac{1}{2}$ ft., $r=4\frac{1}{2}$ in. ?

2. Four men work at a capstan, each exerting a force of 20 lb. wt. at a distance of 4 feet from the central axis. If the rope is wound on a drum 1 ft. in diameter, find the pull on the rope which balances the pressure on the handles. (Neglect friction.)

3. In a wheel and axle, the diameter of the wheel is 3 ft. and that of the axle 1 ft. If the efficiency is 56 per cent., find the effort necessary to raise a load of 200 lb. wt.

4. A windlass is used to hoist a block of 6 cwt. by a rope round a barrel of 8 in. diameter, turned by handles 20 in. long at each end. If 25 per cent. of the work done is lost by friction, etc., what force must each of the men working the handles exert ?

5. A bucket of water, weighing 36 lb., is drawn out of a well by a windlass. The drum on which the rope is wound is 9 in. diameter, and the handle which winds it moves in a circle of 30 in. diameter. Find (i) the force required to raise the bucket if there is no friction, (ii) the amount of energy used up in overcoming friction if the actual effort is 14 lb. wt. and the handle is turned five times. (Assume $\pi = \frac{22}{7}$.)

6. In a wheel and axle, the velocity-ratio is 5. The connection between various loads and the corresponding efforts is shown in the accompanying table :—

Load (W lb. wt.)	10	20	35	40	50	55	64	75
Effort (P lb. wt.)	9·25	11·75	15·5	16·77	19·23	20·53	22·72	25

    Find the law of the machine, and calculate the percentage efficiency for a load of 40 lb. wt.

7. In a differential wheel and axle, if the radius of the wheel is R, and that of the two parts of the axle a and b respectively, find the velocity-ratio if

    (i) $R = 20$ in., $a = 5$ in., $b = 4$ in.,
    (ii) $R = 3$ ft., $a = 6$ in., $b = 4\frac{1}{2}$ in.

8. In a differential wheel and axle, the diameter of the wheel is 12 in., and the diameters of the two parts of the axle $4\frac{1}{2}$ and 4 in. respectively. It is found that an effort of 50 lb. wt. is necessary to support a load of 10 cwt. ; calculate the percentage efficiency of the machine.

9. In a differential wheel and axle, the diameter of the wheel is 35 in. and the diameters of the two portions of the axle 10 and 8 in. respectively. If the efficiency of the machine is 55 per cent. for a load of 200 lb. wt., find the tangential force which must be applied to the wheel to raise a weight of 200 lb.

10. In a differential wheel and axle, in which the efficiency is 45 per cent. for a given load, the diameter of the wheel is 42 in., and the diameters of the two portions of the axle 9 in. and 8 in. respectively. What is the above load which can be raised by an effort of 15 lb. wt. ?

11. In Weston's differential pulley the radii of the upper wheels are $3\frac{1}{2}$ in. and 3 in. ; what is the velocity-ratio ?

12. In the differential pulley, find at what rate the chain must be hauled so that the load may rise at the rate of 4 ft. per min., the diameters of the pulleys in the upper block being 6 and 7 in. respectively.

13. In a differential pulley, the diameters of the two pulleys are 8 in. and $7\frac{1}{2}$ in. respectively, and it is found that a pull of 25 lb. wt. is sufficient to raise a weight of 240 lb. Find the percentage efficiency.

14. In a differential pulley, the radius of the larger pulley is $2\frac{1}{2}$ in. and that of the smaller 2 in. ; it is found that a pull of 12 lb. wt. on the leading side of the chain is required to lift a weight of 45 lb. Find the force-ratio and the percentage efficiency.

15. In a differential pulley the percentage efficiency for a load of 250 lb. wt. is 35. If the radii of the upper pulleys are $4\frac{1}{2}$ and 4 in. respectively, what is the necessary effort to raise the load ?

16. A differential pulley has a velocity-ratio of 16, and it is found that efforts of 9, 14, 24 lb. wt. are needed to lift loads of 28, 56, 112 lb. wt. Find the effort necessary to lift a weight of 100 lb., and plot a graph showing how the efficiency alters with the load. What is the probable efficiency with a load of 5 cwt., and how much work will be done against friction in lifting this load through 1 ft. ?

85. Screws. The screw consists of a cylinder on which is a special ridge or *thread* which fits into a corresponding groove on the nut. As the screw is rotated the thread slides through the groove and advances in the direction of the axis of the cylinder.

The shape of the spiral can be seen by taking a piece of paper in the shape of a right-angled triangle **ADE** and wrapping it round a cylinder so that

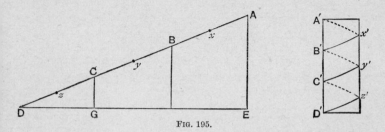

FIG. 195.

one side **AE** is parallel to the axis. The hypotenuse **A**x**B**y**C**z**D** then becomes the spiral **A'**x'**B'**y'**C'**z'**D'**.

The distance (**A'B'**), measured parallel to the axis, between the threads of a screw is called the **Pitch**.

A *right-hand screw* is one which on being turned clockwise, when viewed from the head, advances into the block or nut; a *left-hand* screw is rotated in the opposite direction.

If the screw is rotated once in the nut, it travels in the direction of its axis a distance d equal to the pitch, while if the effort **P** is applied at the end of a lever, of length a, perpendicular to the axis of the screw, it will move through a distance $2\pi a$.

$$\therefore \text{ work done by effort} = \mathsf{P} \times 2\pi a,$$

work done against resistance $\mathsf{R} = \mathsf{R} \times d$.

(i) If it is assumed that there is no friction,

$$\mathsf{P} \times 2\pi a = \mathsf{R} \times d.$$

(ii) If friction is taken into consideration,

$$\text{efficiency} = \frac{\text{useful work done}}{\text{work done by effort}} = \frac{\mathsf{R} \times d}{\mathsf{P} \times 2\pi a}.$$

86. Right- and left-handed screws are used in the couplings of railway carriages, and when the central nut is rotated by the lever, the two screws, and the carriages attached to them, are pulled towards one another. (Fig. 196.)

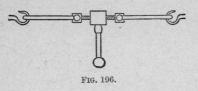

FIG. 196.

The *Screw-jack* is used extensively in workshops and garages for lifting heavy objects through a small distance.

FIG. 197.

In the bottle screw-jack (Fig. 197), the screw has a square thread which fits into a fixed nut **A** and is terminated by a spherical head **B**, which can be rotated by a lever placed through openings which it contains. An iron cap **C** rests on the head and rotates independently of it, and on **C** is placed the load to be lifted.

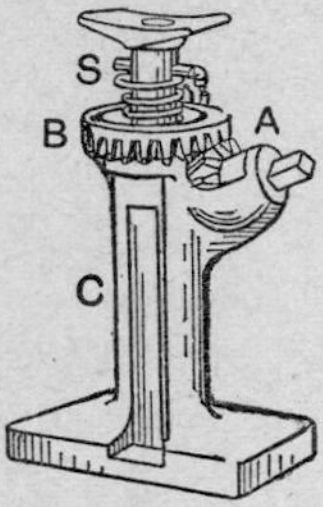

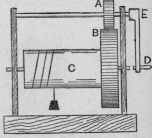

FIG. 198.

In the garage-jack (Fig. 198), the cog-wheel **A** is rotated by a lever at the end of a long rod, and this fitting into a second cog-wheel **B** which can rotate on the stand **C**, causes it to rotate also. The threads of a vertical screw **S** fit into the grooves inside **B**, and consequently as **B** revolves, the screw, which has a rectangular lower end and cannot rotate, moves vertically up or down and carries the car with it.

87. Toothed Wheels. An essential part of many machines consists of two or more cog-wheels, or toothed wheels, of different sizes, fitting into one another.

It can easily be shown that the *number of revolutions* of two cog-wheels which are in gear is *inversely proportional to their diameters*; for since the teeth are of the same size, the number of teeth are proportional to the diameters, and if one wheel has 20 teeth and the other 10, then the larger wheel revolves once while the smaller revolves twice.

Cog-wheels are used in the **Simple Winch** (Fig. 199); the effort applied at the handle **ED** rotates the small cog-wheel **A**, which being in gear with the larger wheel **B**, rotates it and with it the barrel **C**, to which

FIG. 199

...t is rigidly attached ; the result is that the load **W** ...ises owing to the rope being wound up on the ...arrel.

For some purposes a cog-wheel works into a straight ...ar containing teeth, as, for instance, in raising ...luice-gates. Such an arrangement is called a **Rack and Pinion**. A lever is attached to the pinion and ...he effort **P** applied at its extremity ; by this means ...he pinion is rotated and the rack raised.

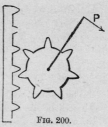

FIG. 200.

88. Ex. 1. *A screw-jack has a handle 20 inches long connected to a screw ...f 8 threads to the inch. What is the velocity-ratio ? A force of 20 lb. wt. ...pplied to the handle lifts 2·5 tons. What is the efficiency ?*

In one complete revolution of the handle, the effort moves $2\pi \times 20$ in., ...nd the load is lifted $\frac{1}{8}$ in. ;

$$\therefore \text{ velocity ratio} = \frac{40\pi}{\frac{1}{8}} = 320\pi = 1005.$$

$$\text{Efficiency} = \frac{\text{useful work done}}{\text{work done by effort}} = \frac{2\cdot5 \times 2240 \times 1}{20 \times 1005}$$

$$= \frac{56}{201} = 0\cdot28.$$

Ex. 2. *If the length of the handle in a simple winch* (Fig. 199) *is 18 inches, ...he number of cogs in* **A** *20, the number of cogs in* **B** *110, and the diameter of ...* **C** *10 inches, a force of 12 lb. wt. applied at the handle raises a load of 58 lb. ...What is the efficiency ?*

$$\frac{\text{The number of revolutions of } \textbf{A}}{,, \quad ,, \quad ,, \quad \textbf{B}} = \frac{\text{number of teeth in } \textbf{B}}{,, \quad ,, \quad ,, \quad \textbf{A}}$$

$$= \frac{110}{20} = \frac{11}{2} ;$$

$\therefore$ if the barrel **C** makes 1 revolution,

the cog-wheel **B** ,, 1 ,,

,, **A** ,, $\frac{11}{2}$,,

crank **ED** ,, $\frac{11}{2}$,,

It follows that when the load 58 lb. wt. rises $2\pi \times 5$ in.,

the effort 12 lb. wt. moves through $2\pi \times 18 \times \frac{11}{2}$ in. ;

$$\therefore \text{ efficiency} = \frac{\text{useful work done}}{\text{work done by effort}} = \frac{58 \times 10\pi}{12 \times 18 \times 11\pi} = 0\cdot24.$$

Ex. 3. *A pinion works into a straight rack used for lifting a sluice-gate. The pinion has a diameter of 4 inches and the lever handle is 8 inches long. If the weight of the gate and rack is 150 lb., what force must be applied at the end of the lever to raise the gate, supposing there is no friction ? If 30 per cent. of the force applied is absorbed in overcoming friction, what force will then be necessary ?*

If the pinion makes one revolution, the distance described by any one tooth will be 4π inches ; thus the gate will be lifted 4π inches. The effort **P** lb. wt., since it acts at the end of a lever 8 inches long, will move through a distance 16π inches.

(i) If there is no friction,

$$150 \times 4\pi = \mathbf{P} \times 16\pi,$$
$$\therefore \ \mathbf{P} = 37\tfrac{1}{2} \text{ lb. wt.}$$

(ii) If the efficiency is 70 per cent.,

$$\frac{7}{10} = \frac{150 \times 4\pi}{\mathbf{P} \times 16\pi},$$
$$\therefore \ \mathbf{P} = 53\tfrac{4}{7} \text{ lb. wt.}$$

EXERCISE XXX

(Assume $\pi = \tfrac{2\,2}{7}$.)

1. Why is it easier to drive a screw into a hard piece of wood with a large screw-driver rather than a small one ?

2. A lifting screw-jack has a screw with pitch $\tfrac{1}{6}$ inch. How many times must the screw be turned to lift the load 4 inches ?

3. A screw whose pitch is $\tfrac{1}{4}$ in. is turned by means of a lever 4 ft. long. Neglecting friction, find the effort which will raise 15 cwt.

4. The velocity-ratio of a screw-jack is 60 and its efficiency 30 per cent. What effort is needed to lift a load of 1 ton ? In raising the load $\tfrac{1}{2}$ in., how much work is done against friction ?

5. A vertical smooth screw is turned by a horizontal lever the length of which, measured from the axis of the screw, is 15 in. ; the pitch of the screw is $\tfrac{3}{8}$ in. What pressure will be produced at the end of the screw when a horizontal force of 20 lb. wt. is applied at the end of the lever ? (Neglect friction.)

6. A screw-jack required to lift a load of $5\frac{1}{2}$ tons is turned by a capstan rod. What force must be applied at a distance of $24\frac{1}{2}$ in. from the centre of the screw, if the pitch of the screw is $\frac{1}{2}$ in. and the efficiency 60 per cent. ?

7. In a screw-jack the pitch of the screw is 0·25 in., and a force of 35 lb. wt. is applied at right angles to the arm at a distance of 30 in. from the axis. What weight would be lifted if there was no friction ?

   If in actual practice the weight lifted is only one-fourth of the above, calculate how much energy is used up in overcoming friction, etc., during one complete turn of the screw.

8. A screw-press (Fig. 201) has plates 10 in. square. The screw has 6 threads to the inch and forces of 70 lb. wt. are applied to the ends of a handle 15 in. long. Find the pressure per sq. in. between the plates. (Neglect friction.)

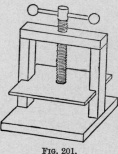

FIG. 201.

9. In the ordinary double screw-coupling of a railway carriage (Fig. 196), the pitch of each screw is $\frac{1}{2}$ in. and the lever arm 12 in. If a force of 40 lb. wt. is applied at the end of the arm, with what force will the carriages be pulled together if the efficiency is 40 per cent. ?

10. In a screw-jack the handle is 7 in. long and the pitch of the screw $\frac{1}{2}$ in. What is the velocity ratio ? What is the percentage efficiency if an effort of 5 lb. wt. will lift a load of 1 cwt. ? If the efficiency for heavier loads rises to 33 per cent., what effort will lift a ton ?

11. Two cog-wheels A and B with (i) 33 and 22 teeth respectively, (ii) diameters 13 in. and 9 in. respectively, are in gear. If A revolves once, how many times will B turn ?

12. A pinion (Fig. 200) has a diameter of 12 in. and gears with a straight rack of a sluice-gate. If the lever handle is 15 in., what force must be applied to lift the gate, if the weight of the sluice and rack is 120 lb. (Neglect friction.)

13. A press is worked by a rack and pinion (Fig. 200). The cogs are ¾ in. apart and there are 12 cogs on the wheel or pinion. The crank handle is 2 ft. long. If the efficiency is 60 per cent., what thrust is produced by an effort of 50 lb. wt. ?

14. In a simple winch (Fig. 199) the gear-wheels A and B have 20 and 85 teeth respectively; the drum C has a diameter of 10 in. and the handle DE is 18 in. long. Calculate the velocity-ratio of the machine and find the efficiency if a force of 28 lb. wt. is required to raise a load of 3 cwt.

15. In a simple winch (Fig. 199) the number of cogs in A and B are 25 and 135 respectively, and the diameter of C is 12 in. If the length of the handle is 20 in., find the load lifted by an effort of 18 lb. wt., if the efficiency of the machine is 25 per cent.

16. In a crab, worked by a worm and wheel, the axle of the wheel is 8 in. in diameter, the wheel has 35 teeth, and the handle is 20 in. long. If the efficiency is 30 per cent., find the weight lifted when an effort of 25 lb. wt. is applied at the handle.

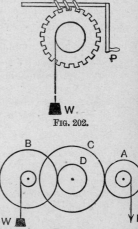

FIG. 202.

17. A train of 4 cog-wheels is arranged as in Fig. 203, drums being rigidly attached to the wheels A and B, and the wheels C and D rotating together. If the number of teeth in A, B, C, D are 10, 24, 26, 8 and the diameters of the drums are the same, what is the velocity-ratio ? If an effort of 25 lb. wt. raises a load of 94 lb. wt., what is the efficiency ?

FIG. 203.

18. In the double-purchase crab the arrangement of cog-wheels is similar to that shown in Fig. 203, but the effort P is applied at the end of a handle. If the number of cogs in A, B, C, D are 12, 28, 25, 9 respectively, the length of the handle 20 in. and the diameter of the drum attached to B 8 in., find the effort required to raise a load of 100 lb. wt., given that the efficiency with this load is 35 per cent.

19. A weight is lifted by a screw-jack, pitch ¼ in., the force being applied
at right angles to a lever 15 in. long.   The values of the loads in tons
wt. and the corresponding efforts in lb. wt. are :—

Load	1	2·5	5	7	8	10
Effort	24	32	46	57	63	73

Find the law of the machine, and calculate the efficiency under
loads of 4 and 9 tons wt.

20. Find the velocity-ratio in a screw-jack in which the pitch is ⅝ in. and
the length of the lever 18 in.   Find the law of the machine if an effort
of 32 lb. wt. overcomes a resistance of 1800 lb. wt. and one of 41 lb. wt.
overcomes a resistance of 2400 lb. wt.   If the resistance is 2800 lb. wt.,
what will be the effort, and what the efficiency ?

EXERCISE XXXI

(Miscellaneous)

1. If in a lifting machine the velocity-ratio is 25 and the efficiency is
64 per cent., find the effort necessary to raise half a ton.

2. In a block and tackle the velocity-ratio is 16.   Friction is such that
only 35 per cent. of the work done is usefully employed.   What force
is necessary to raise a load of 12 cwt. ?

3. An electrically driven pump raises 20,000 gallons of water per hour
through a vertical height of 80 ft.   If the efficiency of the plant is 0·65,
find the horse-power required, given that 1 gallon of water weighs
10 lb.

4. The tractive resistance of a train weighing 335 tons is 11 lb. wt. per
ton.   If the effective horse-power of the locomotive is 600, estimate
the uniform speed (in ml./hr.) attainable when ascending an incline
of 1 in 200.

5. A block and tackle with a continuous rope has two pulleys in each block ;
find the force necessary to raise a load of 350 lb. wt., if the efficiency
at this load is 65 per cent.

6. A weight is raised by means of a rope coiled round a drum which is rotated by a handle connected with the drum by a series of cog-wheels. The velocity-ratio is 10, and the effect of friction is equivalent to an additional load equal to two-thirds of the weight. Find the mechanical advantage and the efficiency.

7. Assuming the law of a machine to be $P = 1\cdot38 + 0\cdot182W$, and the velocity-ratio 16, find the mechanical advantage and efficiency for a load of 48 lb. wt.

8. In a crane the lifting force is applied to a handle which rotates in a circle of 3 ft. diameter, and it is found that when the handle makes 5 complete revolutions the load is lifted 1·46 ft. It is also found that with loads of 1 cwt., 3 cwt. and 5 cwt. respectively, the lifting forces required are 17·5, 26, and 35 lb. wt. respectively. Find the efficiency at each of these loads. (Assume $\pi = 3\cdot142$.)

9. In a Weston's differential pulley the diameters of the upper wheels are 5 and $5\frac{1}{2}$ in. respectively. If an effort of 50 lb. wt. raises a load of 465 lb. wt., what is the efficiency?

10. A bicycle is hung up clear of the ground and the pedal cranks are 7 in. long. What is the smallest weight which, hung from the rim of the back wheel of diameter 28 in., will balance a pressure of 10 lb. wt. at right angles to one of the cranks, assuming there is no friction. The back wheel makes 11 revolutions for 4 revolutions of the pedals. (Fig. 204).

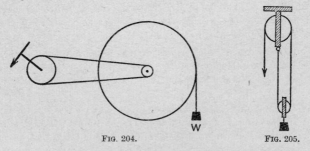

FIG. 204. FIG. 205.

11. What is the velocity-ratio in the arrangement of pulleys shown in Fig. 205? The movable pulley weighs 2 lb. and the load is 15 lb. Find the effort if (i) there is no friction, (ii) if the efficiency is 70 per cent.

12. In the arrangement of pulleys known as the *Barton*, what is the velocity-ratio ? If W is 30 lb. wt., and the efficiency is 75 per cent., find the value of P. (Fig. 206.)

13. In Fig. 207, each movable pulley is suspended in a separate string. If W rises 1 ft., how far do the next two pulleys rise, and what distance does P descend ?   If each of the movable pulleys weighs 1 lb., what load can be raised by an effort of 30 lb. wt., if there is no friction ?

14. With the arrangement shown in Fig. 207, find the efficiency if an effort of 20 lb. wt. raises a load of 95 lb. wt.

15. In the arrangement shown in Fig. 208, suppose the load W rises 1 ft., how far will the movable pulleys and the effort P descend ? If the efficiency for a load of 24 lb. wt. is 63 per cent., what is the effort ?

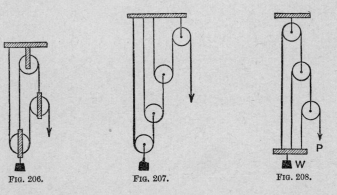

FIG. 206.   FIG. 207.   FIG. 208.

16. Water is drawn in a bucket from a well 50 ft. deep by a winding mechanism worked by a handle moving in a circle of 2 ft. diameter. The handle exerts a force of 2 lb. wt. and makes 40 revolutions while the empty bucket is being lowered. Find out how much water is being raised when a force of 8 lb. wt. is needed to turn the handle.

17. The screw of an ordinary bottle-jack has a pitch of $\frac{1}{2}$ inch. A man working this jack is able to exert a pull of 55 lb. wt. at the end of a lever. If the man's effective leverage is 33 inches, and he is able then to lift $1\frac{1}{2}$ tons wt., what is the efficiency ?

18. The screw of a screw-jack is rotated by a lever 30 in. long, and the pitch
of the screw is $\frac{1}{4}$ in. To lift a load of 1 ton wt. a force of 9 lb. wt.
is applied, and to raise a load of 2 tons wt. the force must be increased
to 15 lb. wt. Find the law of the machine in the form $P=aW+b$.
What force would be required to raise a load of 3 tons wt., and what
in this case is the efficiency of the machine ? (Assume
$\pi=\frac{2.2}{7}$.)

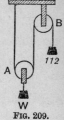

19. In Fig. 209, there is no friction in pulley A which weighs
3 lb., but in pulley B there is sufficient friction to cause
a loss of 10 per cent. in the tension of the string passing
round it. The weight 112 lb. is on the point of
descending. Calculate the weight W. What would be
the value of W if the 112 lb. had been on the point of
ascending ?

FIG. 209.

REVISION PAPERS

(Including Friction, Work, Machines)

PAPER 25

1. A ladder, 24 ft. long, whose centre of gravity is 8 ft. from one end, is being carried by its ends by two men. Find how much weight each is carrying, if the ladder weighs 60 lb.

   If the man at the lighter end shifts his position to a point of the ladder 6 ft. from that end, the other man supporting the heavy end as before, what now will be the weight carried by each ?

2. A crane consists of an upright post AB (with A uppermost) and two bars, AC inclined at 30° with the horizontal, and BC inclined at 60° with the horizontal, C being higher than A. A weight of 1 ton hangs from C. Find graphically the forces along the bars CA and BC.

3. Three forces of 25, 45, 65 lb. wt. act on the same particle in directions inclined at angles of 120° with one another. Find graphically the magnitude of the resultant and the angle it makes with the greatest force.

4. A weight of 14 lb. rests on a rough plane inclined at 30° to the horizontal. If the coefficient of friction is 0·8, find the least force which, acting directly down the plane, will just move the weight.

5. What must be the H.P. of an engine which just pulls a load of 200 tons up a smooth incline of 1 in 60 at a rate of 15 ml./hr. ?

PAPER 26

1. A cylindrical log AB, of length l, lies on the ground. A force P applied vertically upwards at A will just lift the end A from the ground ; a force Q applied vertically upwards at B will just lift the end B from the ground. Prove that the weight of the log is $P+Q$, and find the distance of the centre of gravity of the log from A.

2. Find by calculation the angle which the resultant of forces of 60 lb. wt. and 70 lb. wt., acting at a point and containing an angle of 60°, makes with the greater force.

3. A force of 10 lb. wt. acting along an inclined plane supports a heavy body resting on the plane and pressing against it with a force of 18 lb. wt. Find, by resolution, the weight of the body.

4. A force of 5 cwt. acting at an angle of 45° is found necessary to draw a block of stone weighing 9·265 cwt. over a rough horizontal surface. Find the coefficient of friction.

5. The weight of a boy and his bicycle is 140 lb. When cycling along a road, he comes to a hill which rises 1 ft. for every 50 ft. of its length. If the hill is half a mile long, how much work would he have to do against his weight in getting to the top ?

PAPER 27

1. A uniform beam AB, 15 ft. long and weighing 40 lb., is supported by a pier at C and a pier at D, where $AC=3$ ft., $AD=9$ ft. ; weights of 10, 14, 14 lb. are placed at the middle points of AC, CD and DB respectively. Find the reactions at the two piers.

2. Two forces, of magnitudes $4P$ and $5P$, act at a point in directions inclined at an angle of 50° to one another. Find, by calculation, the angle between the direction of their resultant and that of the smaller force.

3. Four forces act at a point O : a force of 9 lb. wt. due N., a force of 5 lb. wt. due E., a force of 4 lb. wt. S.E., and a force of 7 lb. wt. S.W. Find, by calculation, the magnitude and direction of the resultant force.

4. A weight of 2 lb. rests on a rough plane inclined at 25° to the horizontal. What force acting at an angle of 30° to the plane is just sufficient to move the particle up the plane, the coefficient of friction being 0·35 ?

5. A tram-car weighing 10 tons runs freely down an incline of 1 in 30 with a constant velocity of 15 ml./hr. What H.P. is required to drive it at the same speed up the same incline, the frictional resistance being the same in both cases ?

PAPER 28

1. A uniform rod ABC 4 ft. long, weighing 10 lb., rests in a horizontal position supported by two nails driven into a wall. One of the nails is at the end A and the rod passes underneath it. The other nail is at a point B 6 in. from A, and the rod passes over it. Find the force exerted on each nail when a weight of 2 lb. is suspended from the end C of the rod.

Find also the greatest weight which could be safely suspended from C if the nail at B is likely to collapse when the force on it exceeds 70 lb. wt.

2. A force of 10 lb. wt. is resolved into two components. One component is a force of 6 lb. wt. making an angle of 30° with the force of 10 lb. wt. Find the magnitude of the second component and the angle it makes with the force of 10 lb. wt.

3. A weight rests on a smooth plane of angle 35°. It is kept in equilibrium by a horizontal force of 15 lb. wt. and a force of 8 lb. wt. acting downwards parallel to the plane. Find, by resolution, the weight and the pressure on the plane.

4. Two bodies of equal weight are connected by a string passing over a smooth pulley at the top of two equally rough inclined planes (angles 25° and 40°) placed back to back. If the bodies are on the point of motion, find the coefficient of friction.

5. In a lifting machine, an effort of 26·6 lb. wt. just raises a load of 2260 lb. wt. What is the mechanical advantage ? If the efficiency is 75·5 per cent., what is the velocity-ratio ?

PAPER 29

1. A, C, B, O, D are points in order in a horizontal straight line with $AC=14$ in., $CB=70$ in., $BO=1$ ft., $OD=9$ ft. AB represents a 9-ton gun with its centre of gravity at C, and BD represents a lever with its fulcrum at O. The gun rests on a fixed support at A and on the end B of the lever BD. Prove that a force of $3\frac{1}{3}$ cwt., applied vertically downwards at D, will maintain equilibrium.

2. A rod AB, 8 ft. long, whose weight may be neglected, is hinged to a vertical wall at A and has a weight of 10 lb. suspended from the end B. It is kept in a horizontal position by a string CD attached to a point C in the rod 6 ft. from A and to a point D in the wall 3 ft. above A. Find the tension of the string and the force at the hinge. Solve graphically.

3. A string $ABCD$ is attached at one end to a point A, has a weight W suspended at B, passes over a small pulley at C, and carries at its other end D a weight of 100 lb. The points A, C are 5 ft. apart; C is 3 ft. higher than A, and AB is horizontal and equal to BC. Find graphically the value of W and the tension in AB. (Fig. 210.)

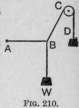

FIG. 210.

4. A weight is resting on a rough inclined plane of 30°, being supported by a string which makes an angle of 30° with the plane, and the coefficient of friction is tan 15°. Prove that the greatest possible value of the tension of the string for which equilibrium will be maintained is double the least possible value.

5. An ordinary winch is used to lift water out of a well. It is found that a load of 112 lb. wt. hanging on the rope can just be balanced by a force of 30 lb. wt. acting at the handle at right angles to it. If the length of the handle is 20 in. and the diameter of the winch 8 inches, calculate the efficiency.

PAPER 30

1. A uniform rectangular beam, 20 ft. long, whose weight is 400 lb., rests on two supports A and B, each of which can bear a load of 300 lb., and no more, without being crushed. If A is 6 ft. from the centre of the beam, how near the centre may B be placed? Show that if a, b are the distances of A and B from the centre, then one support will be crushed if $a < b/3$, or if $b < a/3$.

2. A man is slowly raising a weight of 28 lb. by means of a rope passing over a small pulley, the portion of the rope in the man's hand making an angle of 45° with the vertical. The pulley is suspended by a chain from a fixed point. Find the tension in the chain and the inclination of the chain to the vertical if the tension in the inclined part of the rope is greater by 30 per cent. than that in the vertical part.

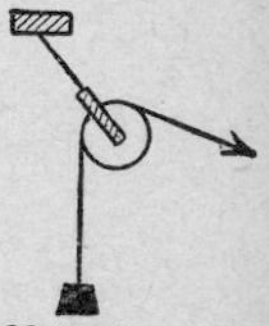

28 lb.wt.
FIG. 211.

3. From the bob of a simple pendulum another simple pendulum is suspended. The lower bob is drawn aside by a horizontal string, and when the lower pendulum makes an angle of 45° with the vertical, the upper is inclined at 30° to the vertical. If the lower bob weighs 10 lb., find graphically the weight of the upper.

4. A man is hauling a weight of 1 cwt. up an incline of $\sin^{-1} \frac{1}{6}$ by means of a rope. The coefficient of friction between the weight and incline is 0·25. What pull must the man exert when the rope is parallel to the incline ?

5. In a Weston pulley block, the diameters of the two pulleys are 9 in. and 8½ in. respectively. Find the percentage efficiency of the tackle if a pull of 20 lb. wt. is sufficient to raise a weight of 200 lb.

PAPER 31

1. The heavy bar (Fig. 212) AB, hinged at A, is held at 60° with the vertical by the light stay CD. C is 6 in. below A and the weight of the bar (10 lb.) acts at a point 12 in. from A. Find graphically the thrust in the stay and the magnitude and direction of the reaction at the hinge.

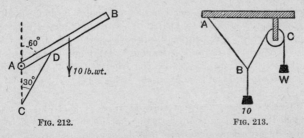

FIG. 212.   FIG. 213.

2. At an angle pole in a telegraph route, two wires run south and two 15° E. of N. Explain why a supporting stay to the pole should be fixed in a plane making an angle of 7½° with the east-west line. If the tension in each of the four telegraph wires is 40 lb. wt., and the stay makes an angle of 30° with the vertical, find the tension in the stay.

3. A weight of 10 lb. (Fig. 213) is suspended as shown. In the position of equilibrium, AB makes 40° with the vertical and BC makes 30° with the vertical. Find the tensions in AB and BC.

If the pulley C does not run quite smoothly, so that when in motion the tension in the part running off is 10 per cent. greater than the tension in the part running on to the pulley, find the limits within which the weight W must lie so as to keep the weight of 10 lb. in position.

4. In a screw-jack the pitch is $\frac{3}{4}$ in. and the effort is applied at the end of a horizontal arm of 15 in. What force must be exerted at the end of the arm if it is required to lift a load of 1 ton wt. ?

If only 25 per cent. of the work done by the force reappears as useful work, what must the pull be then ?

5. In a differential wheel and axle the diameter of the wheel is 12 in., and the diameters of the two parts of the axle $4\frac{1}{2}$ and 4 in. respectively. It is found that an effort of 50 lb. wt. is necessary to support a load of 10 cwt. Calculate the percentage efficiency.

PAPER 32

1. A straight rod of varying section has a string 5 ft. long fixed to it at two points P and Q, 3 ft. apart. This string is placed over a smooth peg, and when equilibrium is established, the peg divides the string into two parts 2 ft. and 3 ft. long. Find graphically the distance of the centre of gravity of the rod from P, and if the weight of the rod is 30 lb., find the tension of the string.

2. AB, BC, CD, DE are strings knotted at B, C, and D. A and E are attached to two points in the same horizontal line. Weights of 4, 2 and 6 lb. are suspended from B, C, D and the lengths of the strings are such that the angles BAE and DEA are each 45°. Find graphically the tension in each string and the inclinations of BC, CD to the vertical.

3. In a lifting tackle the lower movable block has two sheaves and the upper fixed one three. What is the velocity-ratio ? If a load of 2 cwt. is supported by an effort of 70 lb. wt., what is the efficiency ? Find also the number of ft.-lb. of work lost in friction when the load rises 1 foot.

4. The coupling between two railway carriages consists of a rod with a right-hand and left-hand screw cut at its opposite ends and turning in nuts attached to the carriages. The pitch of each screw is 0·25 in., and the rod is turned by a force of 56 lb. wt. at the end of a lever 15 in. long. Find the force with which the carriages are drawn together. (Assume $\pi = \frac{22}{7}$.) Neglect friction.

5. A man weighing 11 stone is suspended from the lowest of a system of 4 movable pulleys, each weighing 8 lb. and hanging in a separate rope, and supports himself by pulling the end of the rope which passes over the fixed pulley. Neglecting friction, find the force he exerts on the rope.

PAPER 33

1. A metal planing machine makes 5 backward and 5 forward strokes in a minute, each stroke being 5 ft. in length ; if the sliding table weighs 100 lb. and the coefficient of friction between the sliding surfaces is 0·08, find the number of ft.-lb. of work done per minute in moving the table.

2. If the axis of a smooth screw is vertical and the pitch 2 in., and a door of weight 100 lb. is attached to the movable screw, as to a hinge, find the work done in turning the door through a right angle.

3. In a system of 4 pulleys consisting of a fixed block which contains two of them, and a movable block containing the others, the same rope passes continuously round all the pulleys. From the movable block is suspended a basket containing a man, the weight of man and basket being W. If another man standing on the ground pulls the free end of the rope, what force must he exert to raise the man and basket ? If the free end of the rope is pulled by the man in the basket, what force must he exert for the same purpose ? (Neglect friction.)

4. A train of cog-wheels is arranged as in Fig. 203, drums being rigidly attached to the wheels A and B, and the wheels C and D rotating together. If the number of teeth in A, B, C, D are 12, 25, 27, 10 respectively, and the diameters of the drums are the same, what is the velocity-ratio ? If an effort of 20 lb. wt. raises a load of 63 lb. wt., what is the percentage efficiency ?

5. The machine (Fig. 214) is used for raising a load W. A rope is fastened to a fixed point A, passes round a pulley B from which the load is suspended, and is then coiled round a barrel C, 8 in. in diameter. A spur-wheel D has 60 teeth and is fixed to the same shaft as the barrel; a pinion E has 18 teeth and gears with D. The machine is driven by a handle F, fixed to the same shaft as the pinion E; F measures 14 in. from the shaft axis to the point of application of the effort P, which is applied at right angles to the handle. Calculate the velocity-ratio of the machine. If the effort P is 25 lb. wt. when W is 300 lb. wt., calculate the efficiency of the machine, and also the work done by the effort while raising the load 1 foot.

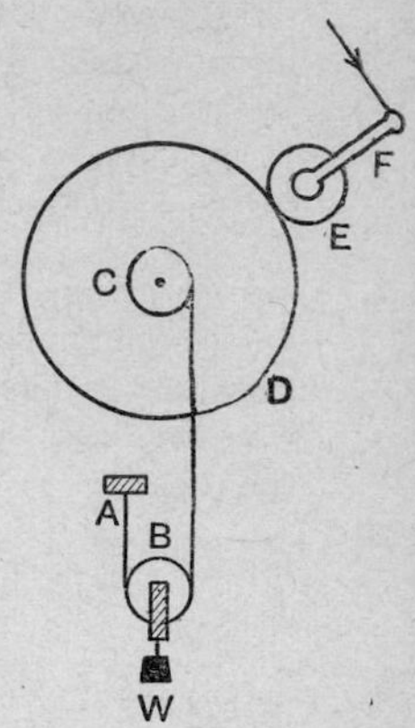

FIG. 214.

CHAPTER XIII

RESULTANT AND RELATIVE VELOCITY AND ACCELERATION

89. Successive Displacements.

Suppose a man is standing in a truck at **A**, and that the truck moves so that it travels from **A** to **A′**, and that *afterwards* the man walks across the truck from **A′** to **B**, then as far as his *final* position is concerned, the result is the same as if the man moved direct from **A** to **B**.

Fig. 215.

The displacement **AB** is the *resultant* of the two *successive* displacements **AA′** and **A′B**, and the two latter displacements are said to be *compounded* into a single displacement **AB**.

This result may be reversed, and if we start with a single displacement **AB** it may be *decomposed* into two others **AA′** and **A′B**.

90. Simultaneous Displacements.

In the example we have just considered, it makes no difference to the final position of the man if he starts moving across the truck *at the same moment* that the truck commences to move, provided the truck moves the same distance as before and the man walks to the same final position in the truck.

Thus we may compound simultaneous displacements in exactly the same way that we have compounded successive displacements.

91. Simultaneous Uniform Velocities.

Suppose the man moves with uniform velocity u ft./sec. relatively to the truck, while the truck moves with uniform velocity v ft./sec., **PQ** representing the displacement of the man relatively to the truck in **T** sec., and **QR** the displacement of the truck in the same time ; then $PQ = uT$ ft., $QR = vT$ ft., and **R** is the final position of the man.

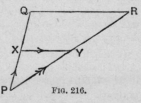

Fig. 216.

At some previous time, t sec. from the start, the man will have walked a distance PX relatively to the truck, while the truck will have moved a distance XY, so that if Y is the position of the man after t sec.,

$$PX = ut \text{ ft.,} \qquad\qquad XY = vt \text{ ft.,}$$

where XY is parallel to QR.

Now

$$\frac{PX}{XY} = \frac{ut}{vt} = \frac{u}{v} = \frac{uT}{vT} = \frac{PQ}{QR},$$

and since $\qquad P\hat{X}Y = P\hat{Q}R, \qquad\qquad \therefore \quad \triangle s. \text{ PXY, PQR are similar,}$

$\therefore \quad X\hat{P}Y = Q\hat{P}R, \qquad i.e. \quad$ P, Y, R are collinear.

Since we may take any value for t, it follows that the *man actually moves along the straight line* PR ; also, since X moves along PQ with uniform velocity, it follows that Y moves along PR with uniform velocity. If we take $t = 1$ sec., then PX will represent u, XY will represent v, and

PY will represent the resultant velocity.

We thus have the result known as the **Triangle of Velocities :**

If a body has simultaneously two velocities represented by the two sides OA, AB *of a triangle, taken in order, the resultant velocity is represented by the third side* OB.

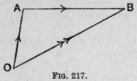

FIG. 217.

NOTE that the arrows representing the original velocities start at O, and the arrow representing the resultant velocity also starts from the same point O.

If we complete the parallelogram OABC, then since OC is equal and parallel to AB and therefore represents the second velocity in magnitude and direction, the result may be stated as the **Parallelogram of Velocities :**

If a body possesses simultaneously two velocities represented in magnitude and direction by the two sides of a parallelogram drawn from a point, then the resultant velocity is represented in magnitude and direction by the diagonal of the parallelogram drawn from the same point.

It should be observed that if we make use of the Triangle of Velocities, the arrows are drawn end to end, whereas with the Parallelogram, they radiate from the same point.

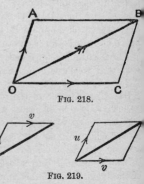

FIG. 218.

FIG. 219.

92. Formula for Resultant of Two Velocities.

Let **OC, OA**, drawn from the same point **O**, represent two simultaneous velocities u and v, and **OB**, drawn from the same point, the resultant velocity **V**, and let $\widehat{AOC}=a$.

From the extremity **B** of the diagonal, draw **BD** perp. to **OC** produced.

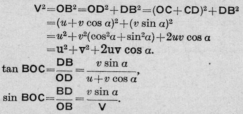

Fig. 220.

$$V^2=OB^2=OD^2+DB^2=(OC+CD)^2+DB^2$$
$$=(u+v\cos a)^2+(v\sin a)^2$$
$$=u^2+v^2(\cos^2a+\sin^2a)+2uv\cos a$$
$$=u^2+v^2+2uv\cos a.$$

Also, $$\tan BOC=\frac{DB}{OD}=\frac{v\sin a}{u+v\cos a},$$

or $$\sin BOC=\frac{BD}{OB}=\frac{v\sin a}{V}.$$

NOTE that all the results we have obtained for *velocities* are similar to those obtained for *forces* in Chapter IV.

93 Change of Velocity.

Suppose a body originally has a velocity represented by **OC**, and that a new velocity represented by **CB** is given to it, then the resultant velocity is represented by **OB**.

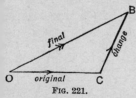

Fig. 221.

We may speak of the velocity represented by **CB** as being the *change of velocity*, when comparing the *original* velocity **OC** with the *final* or resultant velocity **OB**.

94. Resolved parts.

If a velocity **V**, represented by **OB**, is decomposed into two components at right angles, then these components along **OC** and **OA** are called the *resolved parts* of the velocity in these two directions.

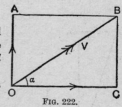

Fig. 222.

Since   **OC=OB** cos a,   **OA=CB=OB** sin a,   it follows that the resolved parts are

$$V\cos a \quad \text{and} \quad V\sin a.$$

The resolved part along **OA** may be written **V** cos **BOA**, hence,

To find the resolved part of a velocity in any direction, multiply the magnitude of the velocity by the cosine of the angle between it and the given direction.

95. Parallelogram of Accelerations.

If a body possesses simultaneously two accelerations which are represented in magnitude and direction by the two sides of a parallelogram drawn from a point, then the resultant acceleration is represented in magnitude and direction by the diagonal of the parallelogram drawn from the point.

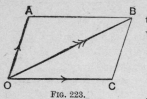

Fig. 223.

If **OC, OA** represent two accelerations given to a body, then **OC, OA** represent changes of velocity in unit time ;

∴ **OB** represents the resultant change of velocity in unit time,

i.e. **OB** represents the resultant acceleration.

It follows that we can resolve accelerations in the same way as we resolve velocities.

It may be deduced from Newton's Second Law that if two or more forces act on a body, each produces its own effect, in its own direction, independently of the other. Now we have already seen in Art. 60 that the acceleration produced in a body is proportional to the force acting on it, and is in the direction of the force, and consequently we may deduce the **Parallelogram of Forces** from the Parallelogram of Accelerations.

96. Ex. 1. *A man, facing W., walks at 3 ml./hr. across the deck of a steamer which is sailing due N., at 9 ml./hr. Find the resultant velocity of the man in magnitude and direction.*

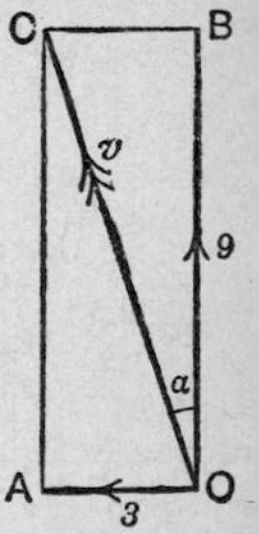

Draw **OA** due W. to represent a velocity of 3 ml./hr.,

     OB ,, N.   ,,   ,,   9 ml./hr.

Complete the parallelogram **OACB** (Fig. 224) and draw the diagonal **OC**; then

    OC represents the resultant velocity in magnitude and direction.

$$OC^2 = OB^2 + OA^2 = 9^2 + 3^2 = 90,$$
$$\therefore \; OC = 9.49, \qquad\qquad i.e. \; v = 9.49 \text{ ml./hr.}$$
$$\tan \alpha = \frac{CB}{OB} = \tfrac{3}{9} = 0.3333, \qquad \therefore \; \alpha = 18° 26',$$
$$i.e. \text{ direction is N. } 18° 26' \text{ W.}$$

Fig. 225.

Instead of drawing a parallelogram, the two velocities can be represented (Fig. 225) by the two lines **OB, BC**, with the arrows running continuously, and the resultant velocity is represented by **OC**, the third side of the triangle, the arrow in **OC** having the same starting point as that for the constituent velocities.

Fig. 224.

Ex. 2. *A river is 110 yards wide and flows at the rate of 3 ml./hr. A man rows across it, with a speed through the water of 5 ml./hr., in such a manner that his actual course is at right angles to the stream. How long will he take to cross the river ?*

Let **OA, OB** represent the velocities of 3 and 5 ml./hr. respectively, then the diagonal **OC** represents the resultant velocity of the boat, this velocity being at right angles to the direction of the bank **OA**.

FIG. 226.

Since
$$OC^2 = OB^2 - BC^2 = 25 - 9 = 16,$$

∴ resultant velocity along **OC** is 4 ml./hr. ;

∴ time taken to cross the river 110 yd. broad

$$= \frac{110 \times 60}{1760 \times 4} \text{ min.} = \tfrac{15}{16} \text{ min.} = 56\tfrac{1}{4} \text{ sec.}$$

Ex. 3. *What is the actual course and velocity of a steamer which is heading due S. at 15 ml./hr. through a tide running N.E. at 3 ml./hr. ?*

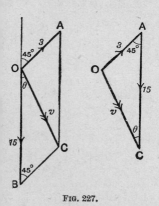

FIG. 227.

Let **OA, OB** represent the velocities of the tide and steamer respectively.

Complete the parallelogram **OACB**, then **OC** represents the resultant velocity in magnitude and direction.

$$v^2 = 3^2 + 15^2 + 2 . 3 . 15 \cos 135°$$
$$= 3^2 + 15^2 - 2 . 3 . 15 \cos 45°$$
$$= 170·4 ;$$
$$\therefore v = 13·1 \text{ ml./hr.}$$

From the △OAC, $\dfrac{\sin \theta}{3} = \dfrac{\sin 45°}{13·1}$,

i.e. $\sin \theta = \dfrac{3 \sin 45°}{13·1}$;

using logarithms, $\theta = 9° \ 19'$,

∴ true course is S. 9° 19′ E.

EXERCISE XXXII

1. A man faces E. and walks at 4 ml./hr. across the deck of a steamer which is steaming due S. at 10 ml./hr. Find the actual velocity of the man in magnitude and direction.

2. If a man is walking 4 ml./hr. in a N.E. direction, what is his velocity (i) due N., (ii) due E. ?

3. Find the magnitude of the resultant of velocities of 5 and 6 ml./hr. inclined at an angle of (i) 35°, (ii) 125°.

4. A raft is drifting due N. at 4 ml./hr. and a man walks across it in a direction N. 35° E. at $3\frac{1}{2}$ ml./hr. Find the magnitude and direction of his resultant velocity.

5. A stretch of river runs from W. to E., and a man who points his boat parallel to the banks rows at 5 ml./hr. due E. The wind carries him with a velocity of 2·3 ml./hr. in a direction S. 20° E. Find the magnitude and direction of his resultant velocity.

6. If a body is moving with a velocity of 5 ml./hr. due E., what new velocity must be given to it so that the resultant velocity is 8 ml./hr. due N. ?

7. If a body starts from rest with an acceleration of 5 ft./sec.² due N. and an acceleration of 7 ft./sec.² due W., what is its resultant acceleration and its position N. and W. of the starting point after 5 sec. ?

8. A boat is propelled through water at a speed of 8 ml./hr. How long will it take to go 8 miles up stream and back again to the starting point if the current is flowing at the rate of 2 ml./hr. ?

9. The deck of a steamer, which is moving at 20 ml./hr., is 66 ft. wide. A ball is rolled directly across the deck at 15 ml./hr. Find (to the nearest foot) the actual distance that the ball moves.

10. A cricket ball moving along AB is struck so that an equal additional velocity is communicated to the ball in the direction BC. In what direction will the ball actually move and with what speed ?

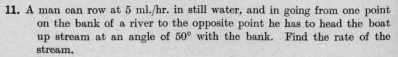

Fig. 228.

11. A man can row at 5 ml./hr. in still water, and in going from one point on the bank of a river to the opposite point he has to head the boat up stream at an angle of 50° with the bank. Find the rate of the stream.

12. A bird flies at the rate of 22 ml./hr. in still air. The wind is blowing from the S.W. at 9 ml./hr. In what direction must the bird try to fly in order that it may actually go N.W., and what will be its velocity in this direction ?

13. An aeroplane which travels through the air at 75 ml./hr. has to make a journey of 120 miles from N. to S. when the wind is blowing from W. to E. at 21 ml./hr. Find the time occupied on the journey.

14. A vessel is steaming at 15 ml./hr. in a current which is flowing towards the N.E. at 6 ml./hr. Find the direction in which the head of the steamer must point in order that her actual course may be due W. Find also the actual speed.

15. A motor boat with a speed of 15 knots is steered due S., but at the end of 10 minutes is 2 nautical miles S. 10° E. of its starting point. Find the strength and direction of the tide.

16. A tug steams at 6 ml./hr. in still water and crosses a channel, 40 miles broad, with a cross current of 2 ml./hr., reaching the port directly opposite. Show that the time of the journey is about 7 hr. 4 min.

17. A boat makes straight for a landing-stage that lies 600 yd. in a N.E. direction. The current of the river is flowing due W. at 1 ml./hr., and the boat is rowed at a uniform speed that would be 4 ml./hr. in still water. Find the angle E. of N. at which the boat must be steered, and find also the time taken for the journey.

18. A motor boat is steered, with a speed of 10 ml./hr., at an angle of 30° with the bank, up stream. If the current runs at 4 ml./hr., find how long the boat takes to reach the opposite bank, if the river is 200 yd. wide. Also find how far the boat travels up stream. (Solve graphically.)

19. A boat crosses an estuary ¾ ml. wide. If the boat can travel at 5 ml./hr. in still water and the current flows at 3 ml./hr., in what direction must the boat be steered so as to arrive at the opposite point from which it started ? How long will it take to cross the estuary ?

20. A ship heads S.E. at 12 knots, the wind blows N. at 3 knots, and a current flows due W. at 2 knots. What is the actual speed of the ship in magnitude and direction ?

21. A shell moving at 1200 ft./sec. explodes, and the fragments are given an additional velocity of 150 ft./sec. in all directions. Find the greatest angle which the direction of motion of any fragment can make with the direction before explosion.

22. A coin is dropped from a height of 4 ft. above the floor of a compartment of an electric train which is (i) just about to start with an acceleration of 2 ft./sec.², (ii) running with uniform speed of 30 ml./hr., (iii) just about to slow up with 2 ft./sec.² retardation. Where will the coin strike the floor in each case ?

23. If a car is running along a road at 15 ml./hr. and then travels along another road at right angles at 24 ml./hr., find the magnitude of the change of velocity.

24. A ball moving at the rate of 10 ft./sec. is struck in such a way that its velocity is increased to 12 ft./sec., and the direction of the new velocity makes an angle of 45° with that of the old velocity. Find graphically the velocity imparted by the blow and also its direction.

25. A particle moves along AB, a side of an equilateral triangle ABC, with a uniform velocity of 10 ft./sec. ; when it reaches B it proceeds along BC with a uniform velocity of 20 ft./sec. If AB is taken to represent its first velocity, find a straight line which represents the change of velocity in magnitude and direction.

97. Relative Velocity.

All motion may be considered as being relative. In most of our calculations we regard the earth as fixed, whereas, as a matter of fact, it is revolving round the sun, which again is moving relatively to the stars.

When investigating the motion of one body relatively to another which is itself moving, it is obvious that this relative motion is not altered if we give to both bodies some new common velocity. A simple case is when two bodies are moving in parallel directions ; suppose two trains are moving along parallel rails at rates of 30 and 40 ml./hr. respectively, there is no difficulty in seeing that the faster is overtaking the slower at the rate of 10 ml./hr. If we had given to each train a velocity of 30 ml./hr. in a direction opposite to that of the slower train, then the slower would have been reduced to rest and the faster would have had a velocity of (40−30), *i.e.* 10 ml./hr., and this would be the velocity of the faster relative to the slower, *i.e.* the velocity with which it seemed to be moving when viewed from the slower.

98. To find the Relative Velocity.

Let **A** and **B** be the positions of two bodies moving with velocities u and v in directions **AC**, **BD** respectively. If we wish to find the velocity of **B** relative to **A**, give to each body **A**'s velocity *reversed*, so that we may now regard **A** as fixed, and **B** as having two velocities, namely v in the original direction **BD** and u along **BE**, which is parallel to **CA**.

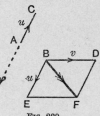

Completing the parallelogram **BDFE**, **B** *seems* to be moving with a velocity represented in magnitude and direction by the diagonal **BF**,

i.e. **BF** represents the velocity of **B** relative to **A**.

FIG. 229.

99. To find the Real Velocity.

Suppose a fly is walking along the hand of a clock which is itself turning round ; then the real velocity of the fly is compounded of its velocity relative to the hand and the actual velocity of the hand, *i.e.* we have to find the resultant of these two velocities.

So generally, to find the real velocity of a moving body **B**, we find the resultant of the velocity of **B** relative to **A** and the velocity of **A** ; this can be done by the method of Art. 91, so that if

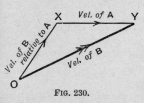

FIG. 230.

OX represents the velocity of **B** relative to **A**,
XY   ,,   real velocity of **A**,

the third side **OY** represents the real velocity of **B**.

Thus given the velocity of **B** relative to **A**, and the real velocity of **A**, we draw **OX**, **XY**, parallel to these velocities and with the arrows representing these velocities continuous, and complete the triangle **OXY** ; then **OY**, with the arrow also pointing from **O**, represents the real velocity of **B**.

It will be observed that this triangle might have been used for the determination of the relative velocity, given the two real velocities ; it will however be found less confusing if, in the first type of problem, the complete parallelogram is drawn.

100. Ex. 1. *A steamer* **A** *is sailing due W. at* 10 *ml./hr., while another* **B** *is proceeding due S. at* 15 *ml./hr. Find the velocity of* **B** *relative to* **A**, *and if, at a particular moment,* **B** *is 5 miles due S. of* **A**, *calculate what was the least distance between the ships.*

(i) Let **C** and **D** be the positions of the two steamers when **B** is 5 miles due S. of **A**. Give to both steamers a velocity of 10 ml./hr. due E., then we may regard the problem as if steamer **A** is at rest at the point **C**, and steamer **B** has velocities of 15 ml./hr. due S. and 10 ml./hr. due E., represented by the lines **DF** and **DE**;

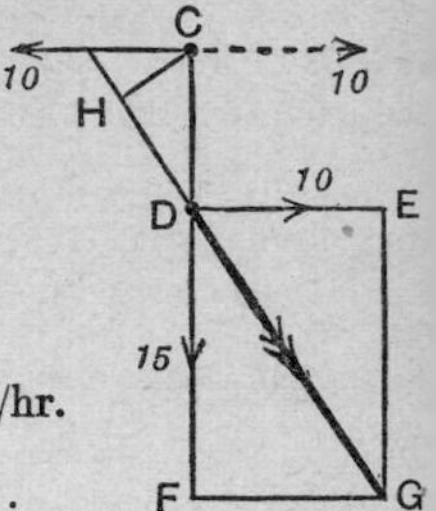

∴ **DG** represents the velocity of **B** relative to **A**.

$$DG^2 = DE^2 + DF^2 = 100 + 225 = 325,$$

∴   **DG** = 18·03,   *i.e.* relative velocity is 18·0 ml./hr.

$$\tan FDG = \frac{FG}{DF} = \frac{10}{15} = 0.6667, \qquad ∴ \ \widehat{FDG} = 33° \ 41';$$

∴ direction of relative velocity is S. 33° 41′ E.

Fig. 231.

(ii) To find the shortest distance apart, draw a perpendicular from **A**'s position at **C** to **GD** produced, then

$$\text{shortest distance} = CH = CD \sin CDH$$
$$= 5 \sin 33° \ 41' = 2.77 \text{ miles.}$$

Ex. 2. *To a ship sailing due N. at* 10 *ml./hr., the wind appears to come from the S.W. at* 15 *ml./hr. What is the true magnitude and direction of the wind?*

The true velocity of the wind is the resultant of the velocity of the wind relative to the ship, and the velocity of the ship.

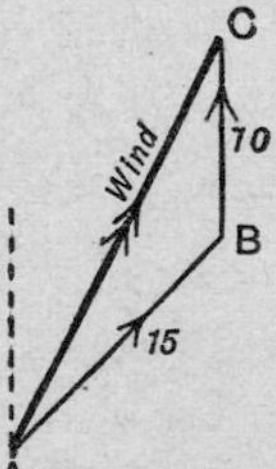

Draw **AB** in a N.E. direction to represent the velocity of the wind relative to the ship, and **BC** due N. to represent the real velocity of the ship.

Completing the △ **ABC**, it follows that

     AC represents the true velocity of the wind.

$$AC^2 = 15^2 + 10^2 - 2 \cdot 15 \cdot 10 \cos 135°$$
$$= 225 + 100 + 300 \cos 45°$$
$$= 537.1,$$

Fig. 232.   ∴ **AC** = 23·2,   *i.e.* velocity of wind is 23·2 ml./hr.

Also, $\dfrac{\sin ACB}{AB} = \dfrac{\sin ABC}{AC},$ ∴ $\sin ACB = \dfrac{15 \sin 135°}{23.2},$

i.e. $\widehat{ACB} = 27° \ 13',$

∴ true direction of wind is from S. 27° 13′ W.

Ex. 3. *Weights of* 1 *lb. and* 3 *lb. are connected by a light inextensible string passing over a movable pulley of negligible weight; the movable pulley is connected by a similar string, passing over a fixed pulley, to a weight of* 5 *lb. Find the tensions in the two strings and the accelerations of the weights.*

Let the tensions of the strings be T_1 and T_2 lb. wt. ;

$\quad a_1$ the acceleration of the 5 lb. wt. downwards,

$\therefore \ a_1 \quad$,, $\quad$,, $\quad$ movable pulley upwards,

$\quad a_2 \quad$,, $\quad$,, $\quad$ 3 lb. wt. downwards,

$\quad a_3 \quad$,, $\quad$,, $\quad$ 1 lb. wt. $\quad$,,

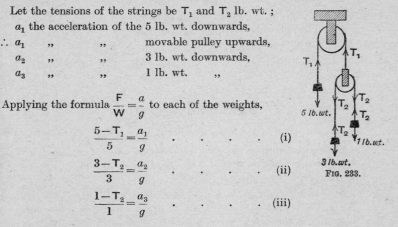

Applying the formula $\dfrac{F}{W} = \dfrac{a}{g}$ to each of the weights,

$$\frac{5-T_1}{5} = \frac{a_1}{g} \qquad \qquad \text{(i)}$$

$$\frac{3-T_2}{3} = \frac{a_2}{g} \qquad \qquad \text{(ii)}$$

$$\frac{1-T_2}{1} = \frac{a_3}{g} \qquad \qquad \text{(iii)}$$

Since the weight of the movable pulley is negligible,

$$T_1 = 2T_2 \qquad \qquad \text{(iv)}$$

$$\left[\text{Note that if its weight is } W, \text{ then} \qquad \frac{T_1 - 2T_2 - W}{W} = \frac{a_1}{g}. \right]$$

In addition to these 4 equations, we have the fact that since the string round the movable pulley is inextensible, the accelerations of the 1 and 3 lb. wt. relative to the pulley must be equal and opposite.

Now

the acceleration of the 1 lb. wt. relative to the pulley is $(a_3 + a_1)$ downwards,

$\quad$,, $\quad$,, $\quad$ 3 lb. wt $\quad$,, $\quad$,, $\quad$ $(a_2 + a_1)$ $\quad$,,

$$\therefore \ a_3 + a_1 = -(a_2 + a_1)$$

i.e. $\qquad 2a_1 = -a_2 - a_3 \qquad \qquad \qquad \text{(v)}$

Substituting from (iv) in (i), $\qquad \dfrac{5 - 2T_2}{5} = \dfrac{a_1}{g} \qquad \qquad \qquad \text{(vi)}$

Substituting from (vi), (ii), (iii), in (v),

$$2g(1-\tfrac{2}{5}\mathsf{T}_2)=-g(1-\tfrac{1}{3}\mathsf{T}_2)-g(1-\mathsf{T}_2)$$
$$\therefore \;\; \mathsf{T}_2=1\tfrac{7}{8}\text{ lb. wt.,}$$
and $\qquad \mathsf{T}_1=3\tfrac{3}{4}$ lb. wt.

Substituting in (i), $\quad a_1=g(1-\tfrac{1}{5}\mathsf{T}_1)=\tfrac{1}{4}g=8$ ft./sec.^{2} ;

,,   (ii), $\quad a_2=g(1-\tfrac{1}{3}\mathsf{T}_2)=\tfrac{3}{8}g=12$ ft./sec.^{2} ;

,,   (iii), $\quad a_3=g(1-\mathsf{T}_2) \;=-\tfrac{7}{8}g=-28$ ft./sec.^{2} ;

the last result indicating that the acceleration of the 1 lb. wt. is upwards and not downwards.

EXERCISE XXXIII

(*Relative Velocity.*)

1. A man in a car moving at 30 ml./hr. observes another car moving along a road at right angles at 40 ml./hr. Find the magnitude of the velocity of the second car relative to the first.

2. A hare runs across a road with a velocity of 10 ml./hr. in front of a motor car which is travelling at 21 ml./hr. Find the speed and direction of motion of the hare relative to the car.

3. One man is walking N.E. at a speed of 4 ml./hr., and a second man is walking N.W. at the same speed. Find the magnitude and direction of the velocity of the second man relative to the first.

4. A ship is sailing due E. at 15 knots in a wind which blows from N.W. at 10 knots. What is the magnitude and direction of the velocity of the wind relative to the ship ?

5. Explain why rain which is falling vertically appears to a person, who is travelling in a train, to fall in a direction inclined to the vertical. If the man is travelling at 30 ml./hr. through rain which is falling vertically at 22·5 ft./sec., find the magnitude and direction of the relative velocity of the rain.

6. A destroyer is travelling due W. at 30 knots and an enemy submarine is travelling N.E. at 18 knots. Find the velocity of the submarine relative to the destroyer, in magnitude and direction.

7. A cyclist is riding W. at 9 ml./hr., and the wind is blowing at 6 ml./hr. from 40° S. of W. Find the apparent direction of the wind as felt by the cyclist.

8. An engine driver standing in the cab of a locomotive, passing under a bridge at 40 ml./hr., is struck by a stone dropped from a point 30 ft. 3 in. above him. Find the magnitude and direction of the velocity with which the stone strikes him.

(True Velocity.)

9. A passenger, on the top of an omnibus, feels a breeze which to him appears to blow directly across the bus at 10 ml./hr. If the omnibus is travelling at 15 ml./hr., what is the magnitude and direction of the actual velocity of the wind ?

10. To an aeroplane flying N. at 100 ml./hr., a second aeroplane appears to be flying N.W. at 50 ml./hr. Find the actual course and speed of the second aeroplane.

11. A cyclist rides along a road at 9 ml./hr. A rabbit running straight across the road in front of the cyclist appears to the cyclist to be moving in a direction making an angle of 15° with the direction of the road. Find the velocity of the rabbit.

12. A cyclist is riding due E. at 10 ml./hr., and the wind, which really is blowing from the S.W., appears to him to blow from the S.E. Determine the true speed of the wind.

13. To a cyclist riding E. at 12 ml./hr., the wind seems to be coming from the S.E. at 20 ml./hr. Find the magnitude and direction of the true velocity of the wind.

14. Rain is falling vertically with uniform velocity. To an observer in a train running at 50 ml./hr., the rain appears to fall at an angle of 40° to the horizontal. Find the magnitude of the velocity of the rain in ft./sec.

15. To an observer in an aeroplane, travelling E. at 100 ml./hr., a train (directly underneath him) appears to be moving sideways (*i.e.* at right angles to itself) in a direction 35° S. of W. Find the actual speed and direction of motion of the train.

16. An aeroplane is gliding down to earth with a velocity of 40 ml./hr., at a gradient of 1 in 10 (*i.e.* an angle whose sine is 0·1) relative to the air current in which it finds itself. This is a horizontal following wind of 20 ml./hr. Prove, graphically or otherwise, that it is actually approaching the earth at a gradient of 1 in 15 approximately.

EXERCISE XXXIV

(*Harder Examples.*)

1. To a cyclist riding due E. at 10 ml./hr., the wind seems to be from the N.E. at 20 ml./hr. Find *graphically* what it will seem to be to him when he turns N.E. (First find the true velocity.)

2. To a man walking at 4 ml./hr. the rain appears to fall vertically ; when he runs at 8 ml./hr. it appears to meet him at an angle of 30° to the vertical. Find the real direction and speed of the rain.

3. A ship A, steaming 60° W. of S., crosses the path of another ship B, steaming N. at the same speed, at a point 2 miles ahead of B. Find the apparent course of A as observed from B, and the distance between the ships when nearest to each other.

4. A ship is steaming due S. at a speed of 20 ml./hr., and another ship is steaming due W. at a speed of 15 ml./hr. The second steamer passes the point of intersection of the two tracks one hour and a half before the first steamer reaches it. Find, relative to the point of intersection of the two tracks, the position of each ship in its course when the ships are nearest to each other. Find also this least distance.

5. Two roads cross at right angles. A car A moves along one road at 18 ml./hr., and a car B moves along the other road at 24 ml./hr. If A reaches the crossing 25 seconds before B reaches it, find when the cars are nearest to one another, and the distance between them at that time.

6. The smooth faces of a double inclined plane make angles 30°, 60°, with the horizontal ; two particles slide simultaneously from rest at the summit, one down each face. Determine the magnitude of their relative velocity at the end of 5 seconds.

7. A ship A is steaming E. at 14 ml./hr. and a ship B is steaming 40° E. of N. at 8 ml./hr. At noon, B is 5 miles N. of A. If the limit of visibility is 12 miles, for how long after noon is B visible from A ?

8. A ship A is steaming due N. at a steady speed of 16 knots. A look-out on A observes another ship B due E. of A, and subsequently notices that although the ships are getting nearer to each other, the ship B always appears to be due E. of A. Assuming that B is steering a fixed course at a steady speed of 20 knots, find the actual direction in which she is steaming. If the ships were originally 19 sea miles apart when B was first sighted, how long will it be before they are 1 sea mile from each other ?

9. A steamship is travelling N. at the rate of 10 ml./hr. and there is a N.E. wind blowing at the rate of 20 ml./hr. In what direction will the smoke from the funnel point? (Assume that each particle of smoke is immediately, on issuing from the funnel, carried off in a S.W. direction with the velocity of the wind.)

10. The smoke from a vessel steaming N. at 5 ml./hr. points 30° S. of E., the wind blowing from the W. Find the velocity of the wind.

11. A ship is steaming due N. at 16 ml./hr. in a wind whose speed is 28 ml./hr. The smoke from the funnel is observed from the ship to trail N.E. Find the direction of the wind.

12. The smoke track of a steamer travelling at 15 knots due N. appeared to an observer on the deck of the steamer to stretch out due W. Shortly afterwards, when the steamer had come to rest, the smoke appeared to travel N.W. What was the velocity of the wind?

13. A sheet of metal is placed on the floor of a truck open at the back, with its centre of gravity 3 ft. from the edge. If the coefficient of friction between the metal and truck is 0·35, find the greatest acceleration which can be given to the truck without causing the metal to slip out at the back.

If the truck has an acceleration of 12 ft./sec.², prove that the metal will fall out after the truck has moved 45 ft.

14. A cruiser is steaming due N. at 15 ml./hr. and a destroyer is $\frac{1}{2}$ mile away in a S.E. direction, the destroyer steaming S.W. at 30 ml./hr. A shot is fired from a gun on the cruiser with a speed of 2000 ft./sec., aim being taken at the bridge of the destroyer. How far aft will the destroyer be hit?

15. A ship steers at 12 ml./hr. due N. through an ocean current travelling at 4 ml./hr. N.W. A S.W. wind is blowing at 15 ml./hr. Find the apparent velocity of the wind to an observer on board.

16. A man rides a bicycle with a constant speed of 20 ml./hr. round a circular track. There is a N. wind blowing with a velocity of 10 ml./hr. Dividing the track into 8 equal parts, starting from the N., show in a geometrical construction, but do not work out numerically, the apparent direction and velocity of the wind to the rider as he passes each of the eight points of division.

17. A ship is steaming due N.E. at 10 ml./hr. ; a second ship proceeding
from W. to E. is sighted due N.W. of the first and 5 miles away. After
a certain time, the second ship is due N. of the first and 1½ miles
distant. If the velocities of the ships are constant,
find the relative velocity of the second from the first,
and their distance apart when the first crosses the
track of the second.

18. In the arrangement of pulleys shown in Fig. 234, A is
a weight of 4 lb., B 2 lb., C 1 lb., and the movable
pulley D is weightless. Find the tension in each
string.

19. If A (Fig. 234) is 100 grams, B 50 gm., C 40 gm., find
the acceleration of each weight and the tension of the
upper string. (Assume $g=981$ cm./sec.^{2})

20. In Fig. 234, if A is a weight of 4 lb., B 3 lb., C 5 lb.,
and the pulley D 2 lb., find the acceleration of each
weight and the tension in each string.
(Assume $g=32\cdot2$ ft./sec.^{2})

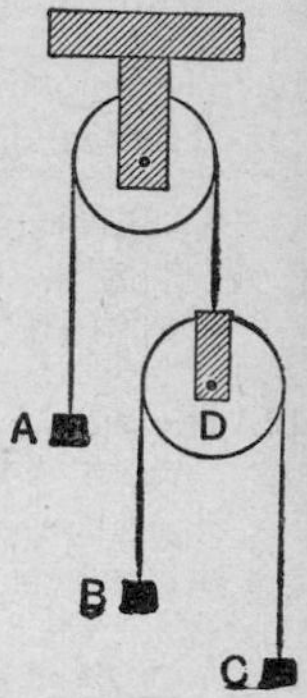

FIG. 234.

21. Two football players A and B are running straight down the field in
parallel lines 5 yd. apart. A who has the ball is 2 yd. ahead of B.
If both are moving 20 ft./sec., with what velocity (relative to himself)
must A pass the ball to B in order that the pass may just not be
'forward,' *i.e.* in order that the ball may travel in a direction at right
angles to the length of the field ? Find also the velocity of the ball
relative to the ground.

22. When a ship is steaming N. at 25 ml./hr., the direction in which a flag is
pointing is S. 25° W. When the speed is reduced to 10 ml./hr., the
direction in which the flag points is S. 40° W. Find graphically the
direction and velocity of the wind.

23. A steamer is travelling N. at 17 ml./hr., and the smoke from the funnel
appears to a person on board to be travelling S.E. When the velocity
of the steamer was 7 ml./hr. due N., the smoke appeared to be travelling
N.E. Prove that the wind is blowing at 13 ml./hr., and find its
direction.

24. A ship steams due W. at 20 ml./hr. relative to the current, which is
flowing at 8 ml./hr. due S. Find the magnitude and direction of the
velocity relative to the ship of a train going due N. at 40 ml./hr.

CHAPTER XIV

PROJECTILES

101. If a body is dropped in a railway carriage which is moving with constant velocity, it is a matter of experience that it appears to strike the floor at a spot vertically under the point from which it is let fall. The body really started with the same horizontal velocity as the carriage and actually moves in a curved path. It follows that the *horizontal* velocity of the body is not affected by the fact that the earth is attracting it *vertically*, for otherwise the body would seem to be moving backwards or forwards.

FIG. 235.

The further question arises whether the horizontal velocity in any way affects the vertical motion. This can be settled by allowing a ball **A** (Fig. 235) to roll down a groove **CD** and, at the moment it is about to leave the groove, allowing a second ball **B**, at the same level, to fall vertically. It will be found that the two balls reach the ground at the same moment, so that the *vertical* motion of **A** is unaffected by the fact that it also possessed a *horizontal* velocity.

We thus come to the same conclusion as that derived from Newton's Second Law, that if several forces act on a body each produces its own effect in its own direction independently of the others, and, in this particular case of projectiles, the vertical velocity is independent of the horizontal velocity.

102. *To show that the path of a body projected horizontally is a parabola.*

Exp. 21. Taking the groove shown in Fig. 236, fix it at the side of a squared blackboard; let the ball roll down the groove from any marked point on it, and note where its path cuts the lower edge of the board at **B**. Repeat

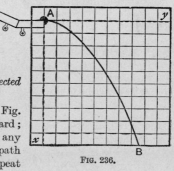

FIG. 236.

this several times, always starting the ball at the same point, and thus obtain **B** as accurately as possible.

Take the horizontal line through **A** as the axis of y, and the downward vertical through **A** as the axis of x, and note the co-ordinates of **B**.

Assuming that the equation of a parabola is $y^2 = ax$, substitute for x and y the co-ordinates of **B**, and thus find a.

In an experiment tried, **B** was (5, 3·8), thus

$$(3\cdot8)^2 = 5a, \qquad\qquad i.e. \ a = 2\cdot89,$$
$$i.e. \qquad\quad y^2 = 2\cdot89x.$$

Make out a table for values of x and y and plot the points on the board, drawing a curve through them.

Now let the ball roll from the marked point on the groove, and it will be found that its path traces out the chalked parabola on the board.

103. Ex. *A body is projected horizontally with a velocity of 45,000 cm./sec. Find the horizontal and vertical distances it has traversed in 5 seconds, and the magnitude and direction of the resultant velocity.*

Neglecting air resistance, the horizontal velocity is constant since it is not affected by the earth's vertical attraction,

$$\therefore \text{ horizontal distance} = 45,000 \times 5 = 225,000 \text{ cm.}$$
$$= 2,250 \text{ metres.}$$

The vertical displacement is the same as that of a body falling freely,

$$\therefore \text{ vertical distance} = \tfrac{1}{2} \times 981 \times 25 = 12262\cdot5 \text{ cm.} \qquad (s = \tfrac{1}{2}gt^2)$$
$$= 122\cdot6 \text{ metres.}$$
$$\text{Horizontal velocity} = 45,000 \text{ cm./sec.,}$$
$$\text{vertical velocity} = 981 \times 5 = 4905 \text{ cm./sec.} \qquad (v = gt)$$

$$\therefore \text{ resultant velocity} = \sqrt{45000^2 + 4905^2} \text{ cm./sec.}$$
$$= 45,270 \text{ cm./sec.}$$

If θ is the angle the resultant velocity makes with the horizontal,

$$\therefore \tan\theta = \tfrac{4905}{45000}, \qquad \therefore \theta = 6° \ 13'.$$

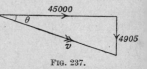

Fig. 237.

EXERCISE XXXV

(Neglect resistance of air.)

1. A body is projected horizontally with a velocity of 100 ft./sec. Find the distances it passes over (*a*) horizontally, (*b*) vertically, in 1, 2, 3 seconds respectively.

2. A gun mounted on the edge of a cliff 225 ft. high fires a shell horizontally with a velocity of 1000 ft./sec. How many seconds elapse before the shot strikes the water ? What horizontal distance has the shot traversed in this time ?

3. A shot is fired horizontally from the top of a cliff at a speed of 2000 ft./sec. Find the magnitude and direction of the velocity after 3 seconds.

4. A bomb is dropped from an aeroplane, 10,000 ft. high, which is travelling horizontally at 100 ml./hr. Prove that the bomb will reach the ground in 25 seconds, and find the horizontal distance travelled by the bomb during this time.

5. An aeroplane travelling parallel to the ground at a height of 1000 ft. at a speed of 100 ml./hr. releases a projectile when vertically over a certain spot. In what time, and how far from the spot, will the projectile reach the ground ?

6. A stone is thrown horizontally from the top of a cliff 64 ft. high, with a velocity of 48 ft./sec. How far from the foot of the cliff, and with what velocity, does it strike the water ?

7. A bullet is projected with a velocity of 1200 ft./sec. horizontally from a gun which is 25 ft. above the ground. Find the horizontal distance from the gun at which the bullet strikes the ground, and also the angle its direction of motion then makes with the horizontal.

8. A revolver bullet, fired horizontally at a mark on a wall 60 ft. away, hits the wall 3 in. below the mark. Find the velocity of the bullet.

9. A tennis ball is projected horizontally from a height of $7\frac{1}{4}$ ft. and just passes over the net, which is 3 ft. 3 in. high, at a horizontal distance of 39 ft. Find the velocity of projection and the point where the ball strikes the ground.

10. A jet of water is discharged in a horizontal direction from a small orifice in a vertical plate, and is found to strike a point which is at a horizontal distance of 92 cm. from the centre of the orifice and at a vertical distance of 36 cm. below this centre. Calculate the velocity of a particle in the jet whilst passing through the orifice, and also the magnitude and direction of the velocity with which the jet strikes the point.

11. An aeroplane, flying horizontally at a certain speed, at a height of 121 ft. above sea-level, releases a bomb which hits a submarine on the surface. When the bomb is released, the horizontal distance of the submarine from the aeroplane is 242 ft. Find the time of flight of the bomb, its velocity just before impact, and the speed of the aeroplane.

12. A bomber in an aeroplane flying horizontally at a height of 10,000 ft. starts his stop-watch when he notices the spire of a church vertically beneath him. Twelve seconds later he observes that his line of sight on the spire subtends an angle of 10° with the vertical; calculate the speed of the aeroplane in ml./hr. The bomber is flying towards a railway station which he intends to hit; find the angle his line of sight on the station must make with the vertical at the moment he releases the bomb.

13. An aeroplane drops a bomb from a height of 2000 ft. on to a ship below. How long does the bomb take to fall ?

The ship is steaming at 22 knots, and the aeroplane is travelling at 50 knots on the same course, and so as to pass directly over the ship. Take 1 knot as 6000 ft./hr. The length of the ship is 500 ft. What must be the position of the aeroplane when the bomb is let go if the bomb is just to hit the ship at the stern ?

What is the time-limit within which the bomb must be dropped in order to make sure of hitting the ship somewhere ?

14. A stone is whirled round in a vertical circle at the end of a string 21 in. long with a speed that may be regarded as uniform, and makes a revolution every second. The centre of the circle is 4 ft. above the ground. Find how long the stone takes to reach the ground and at what point, if the string breaks (i) at the instant the stone is at the lowest point of the path, (ii) a quarter of a revolution later.
(Assume $\pi = \frac{2 \cdot 2}{7}$.)

[*Arts. 104-106 may be deferred.*]

104. Oblique projection. In the examples hitherto considered we have taken the case of a body projected horizontally, and must now extend this to problems in which the body is projected at any angle to the horizontal. We shall be concerned with such questions as finding the horizontal and vertical distances passed over by the projectile in any given time, the greatest height reached, the range on a horizontal plane, the time of flight, the velocity at any moment, etc., and all of these details can be determined, by resolving the original velocity into its horizontal and vertical components and considering the horizontal and vertical motions independently. Each problem should be worked out on its own merits and the method will be illustrated by numerical examples.

Ex. 1. *A body is projected with a velocity of* 120 *ft./sec. at an elevation of* 40° ; *find the time of flight, the greatest height, and the range on a horizontal plane through the point of projection.*

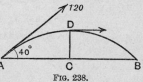

Original hor. velocity $= 120 \cos 40°$ ft./sec.,
,, vert. ,, $= 120 \sin 40°$ ft./sec.

The horizontal velocity remains constant, while the original vertical velocity *upwards* is subject to an acceleration g *downwards*.

FIG. 238.

(i) If t sec. is the time of flight, then since the vertical distance passed over is zero,

$$0 = 120 \sin 40° \cdot t - 16t^2, \qquad (s = ut + \tfrac{1}{2}at^2)$$
$$\therefore \ t = \tfrac{15}{2} \sin 40° = 4.82 \text{ sec.}$$

(ii) If **D** is the highest point of the path, then at this point the vertical velocity is zero,

$$\therefore \ 0 = (120 \sin 40°)^2 - 64 \mathbf{CD}, \qquad (v^2 = u^2 + 2as)$$
$$\therefore \ \mathbf{CD} = \frac{(120 \sin 40°)^2}{64} = 93.0 \text{ ft.}$$

Note also that the time to the highest point is also obtained from the fact that at this point the vertical velocity is zero. If t_1 sec. be this time,

$$0 = 120 \sin 40° - 32t_1 \qquad (v = u + at)$$
$$\therefore \ t_1 = \tfrac{15}{4} \sin 40° = \tfrac{1}{2}t.$$

(iii) The range **AB** is obtained by finding the horizontal distance passed over in time 4.82 sec.,

$$\therefore \ \mathbf{AB} = 120 \cos 40° \times 4.82 \qquad (s = ut)$$
$$= 443 \text{ ft.}$$

Ex. 2. *A body is projected at an angle of 35° with a velocity of 100 ft./sec. from the top of a tower 80 ft. high. Find at what horizontal distance from the foot of the tower it will strike the ground. Also find the magnitude and direction of the velocity after 3 seconds.*

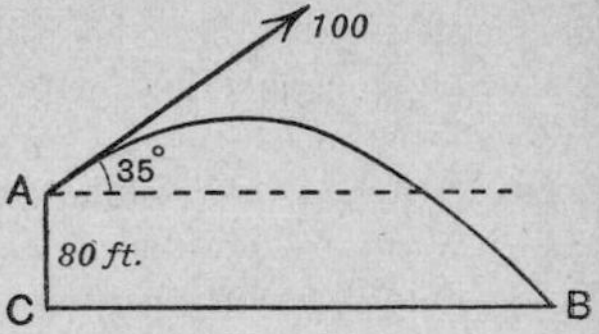

Original hor. velocity = 100 cos 35°   ft./sec.

  ,,   vert.   ,,   = 100 sin 35°   ft./sec.

The horizontal velocity is constant and the vertical velocity subject to an acceleration g downwards.

Fig. 239.

(i) Considering *upward* displacements and velocities to be *positive*, the body has to describe a resultant vertical distance of -80 ft. If t sec. is the time of flight from A to B,

$$-80 = 100 \sin 35° \,.\, t - 16t^2 \qquad (s = ut + \tfrac{1}{2}at^2)$$
$$= 57 \cdot 36t - 16t^2,$$
$$\therefore \quad t^2 - 3\cdot 585t - 5 = 0,$$
$$(t - 1\cdot 793)^2 = 5 + (1\cdot 793)^2 = 8\cdot 214,$$
$$\therefore \quad t = 1\cdot 793 \pm 2\cdot 866$$
$$= 4\cdot 659 \text{ sec.,}$$

the negative result corresponding to the instant when the body was at the level of B if the curve is supposed continued backwards.

CB = hor. displacement = 100 cos 35° × 4·659 = 382 ft.

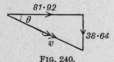

Fig. 240.

(ii) At the end of 3 sec.,

         hor. velocity = 100 cos 35° = 81·92 ft./sec. ;

         vert. velocity = 100 sin 35° − (32 × 3)

                       = −38·64 ft./sec.,

the *negative* result showing that the velocity is *downwards*.

If v is the resultant velocity,

$$v^2 = (81\cdot 92)^2 + (38\cdot 64)^2 = 6711 + 1493 = 8204,$$
$$\therefore \quad v = 90\cdot 6 \text{ ft./sec.}$$
$$\tan \theta = \frac{38\cdot 64}{81\cdot 92} = 0\cdot 4718, \qquad\qquad \therefore \quad \theta = 25° \, 15',$$

i.e. the body is moving downwards at an angle 25° 15′ to the horizontal.

105. Maximum Range on Horizontal Plane. The maximum range may be considered from a general point of view by taking a body projected with velocity u at an angle of elevation a. If t is the time of flight, the vertical distance passed over is zero,

$$\therefore \quad 0 = u \sin a \, . \, t - \tfrac{1}{2}gt^2,$$

i.e. $$t = \frac{2u \sin a}{g};$$

$$\therefore \text{ hor. range} = u \cos a \, . \, t = u \cos a \, . \, \frac{2u \sin a}{g} = \frac{u^2 \sin 2a}{g};$$

this expression will be a maximum with a given value for u when $\sin 2a$ is greatest,

i.e. when $2a = 90°$, or $a = 45°$.

With given values for the range and velocity of projection, if it is required to find a, it will be necessary to solve an equation of the type

$$\sin 2a = 0.5 \text{ (say)},$$
$$\therefore \quad 2a = 30° \text{ or } 150°,$$
i.e. $$a = 15° \text{ or } 75°,$$

i.e. there are two angles of projection giving the same range.

106. It can be shown that when the projection is oblique, the curve described is also a parabola, assuming we leave the resistance of the air out of consideration. In actual practice, the resistance of the air is very considerable and the result is that the angle of descent of a projectile is very much greater than the angle of elevation at the moment of projection. With long-distance naval guns, the shells descend nearly vertically and consequently penetrate armour plating much more easily than if they descend obliquely.

EXERCISE XXXVI

(Neglect resistance of air.)

1. From a point A on a horizontal plane a stone is projected so that the vertical and horizontal components of its velocity are 40 ft./sec. and 76 ft./sec. respectively. Find the distance from this point of the point B where the stone strikes the plane again.

2. A shot is fired with an initial velocity of 100 ft./sec. at an angle of 30° above the horizontal. Find the height reached after 2 seconds.

3. A body is projected with a velocity of 100 ft./sec. in a direction making an angle of 30° with the horizontal. Draw its path, during the first 4 seconds, on squared paper, (i) by calculating the horizontal and vertical distances, (ii) by assuming it traverses distances of 100 ft. during each second in the direction of projection and is dragged down vertically distances $16t^2$ at the end of each second.

4. If a cricket ball is thrown with an initial velocity, the horizontal component of which is 80 ft./sec. and vertical component 60 ft./sec., find how high it will rise, and how far away it will strike the ground.

5. A body is projected with a velocity of 80 ft./sec. at an elevation of 35°. Find its direction of motion after 4 seconds.

6. If the time of flight is 5 sec., and the range 100 yd., prove that the velocity of projection is 100 ft./sec.

7. Find the greatest range of a projectile with a muzzle velocity of 3000 ft./sec., and its time of flight.

8. A man throws a ball with a velocity of 60 ft./sec. in a direction making 30° with the horizontal. At what height will it strike a wall 40 ft. away ?

9. A ball is projected so as to pass horizontally just over the top of a wall 80 ft. distant and 40 ft. high. Find the direction and velocity of projection.

10. A ball is thrown with velocity 40 ft./sec. and elevation 30° from the top of a cliff 50 ft. high. Find at what distance from the foot of the cliff it will fall.

11. A stone is thrown to strike a vertical wall perpendicularly at a height of 36 ft. above the point of projection. If the horizontal distance of the wall from the point of projection is 32 yards, find the time of flight and the velocity of projection.

12. From the top of a tower 175 ft. high, a projectile is fired at an angle of 30° with the horizontal with a velocity of 240 ft./sec. Find (i) the time required for the projectile to reach the ground, (ii) the distance from the foot of the tower to the point of impact, (iii) the angle at which the projectile strikes the ground.

13. A golf ball has to be struck so as to pitch on a green distant 250 ft. horizontally and to clear a sandhill 36 ft. high, midway between the player and the green. Show that an initial velocity of 96 ft./sec. and an angle of elevation of 30° will approximately satisfy the conditions.

14. A boy stands 55 ft. away from the vertical wall of a house.   He throws a ball with a velocity of 60 ft./sec. from a height of 6 ft. from the ground.   If the ball is projected at an angle of 60° with the horizontal, find the height at which it strikes the house.

15. The bar of a goal is 10 ft. above the ground.   A ball is kicked from a distance of 30 yd. so as to leave the ground at an angle of 30° to the horizontal.   Find the least initial velocity which must be given to the ball in order that it may just clear the bar.

16. With what vertical velocity must a ball be thrown so as just to reach a window 25 ft. vertically above the thrower ?   How long will the ball take to reach the window ?   If the thrower is 12½ yd. away from the house, what must the velocity then be ?

17. A small object slides down a smooth roof inclined to the horizontal at an angle of 30° through a distance of 8 ft. and strikes the ground 24 ft. below the point at which it leaves the roof.   Find the horizontal distance that it has described between leaving the roof and striking the ground.

18. A batsman skies a ball and is caught by a fieldsman, standing 20 yd. from him, who has to wait 5 seconds for the ball to reach him. Assuming that the bat and the fieldsman's hands are in the same vertical plane, find the initial velocity of the ball and the maximum height reached.

19. A batsman skies a ball in the direction of a fieldsman 60 yd. off, who, by running in 20 yd. at an average speed of 5 yd./sec., catches the ball near the ground.   Find the initial speed of the ball when hit and its inclination to the horizontal.

20. A stone, projected from O, at an elevation of 60°, with velocity 48 ft./sec., strikes a vertical wall, so that the direction of motion at impact makes an angle of 60° with the upward drawn vertical.   Show that the wall is $12\sqrt{3}$ ft. from O.

21. A body is projected with a velocity of 120 ft./sec. and just clears a vertical wall 25 ft. higher than the point of projection and at a distance of 300 ft. from that point.   Find the two possible angles of projection and the corresponding distances, beyond the wall, where the body hits the ground.

22. A bullet is projected at an elevation of 60° with a velocity of 640 ft./sec. After a certain interval of time its direction of motion makes an angle of 45° with the horizontal. What is the length of this interval ?

23. A weight of 10 lb. slides a distance 5 ft. down the line of steepest slope of a rough plane inclined at 30° to the horizontal, and then falls freely to the ground through a vertical distance of 5 ft. If the coefficient of friction between the weight and the plane is 0·1, find the horizontal distance the weight will travel between leaving the plane and striking the ground.

24. Find what lengths of a straight horizontal trench are commanded by a trench mortar which can fire only at elevations between 45° and 65°, and whose muzzle velocity is 200 ft./sec., if the mortar is on the same level as the trench and at a perpendicular distance of 800 ft. from it.

25. If a bomb is released from an aeroplane flying at 120 ml./hr. in a downward direction inclined at 45° to the horizontal, and if at this moment the aeroplane is 2208 ft. above the ground, prove that the angle between the two straight lines drawn from the aeroplane respectively vertical and through the point of the ground that will be struck by the bomb is $\tan^{-1} \frac{11}{23}$.

26. A body is projected with a velocity of 120 ft./sec. at an angle of 30° to a plane inclined at 25° to the horizontal. Find the time taken to reach the plane again and the range along the plane. (Resolve velocity and acceleration perpendicular to the plane to find the time.)

27. If a body is projected with velocity u at an angle α to the horizontal, prove that

    (i) the resultant velocity at time t is $\sqrt{u^2 - 2ugt \sin \alpha + g^2t^2}$,

    (ii) the time of flight is $2u \sin \alpha/g$,

    (iii) the greatest height is $u^2 \sin^2 \alpha/2g$,

    (iv) the range is $u^2 \sin 2\alpha/g$.

28. If a body is projected with velocity u at an angle α to the horizontal, prove that the range on an inclined plane of angle β through the point of projection is $\dfrac{2u^2}{g} \cdot \dfrac{\cos \alpha \sin (\alpha - \beta)}{\cos^2 \beta}$.

(Resolve perp. to plane and find the time.)

CHAPTER XV

WORK AND ENERGY

107. Graphical Representation of Work.

i. If the *force* **F** doing work is *constant* and acts through a distance *s* in its own direction, then the work done by it, as we have seen, is measured by the product **F***s*; consequently, if we take two rectangular axes **OX** and **OY**, and mark off **OA** to represent **F** and **OC** to represent any particular value of *s*, then

$$\text{work} = \mathbf{F}s = \mathbf{OA} \times \mathbf{OC},$$

and consequently the *area of the rectangle* **OABC** represents the *work* done.

FIG. 241.

ii. If the *force* is *variable*, let the curve **A***fk***B** represent the connection between force and distance. If **OA** is the initial and **CB** the final value of the force after the distance **OC** has been described, suppose the distance **OC** divided into a number of small equal parts of which *de* is a type; draw *dfh*, *egk* parallel to **OY** to meet the curve in *f*, *k*, and through *f*, *k*, draw lines *fg*, *kh* parallel to **OX**.

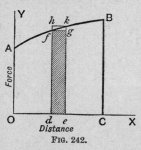

FIG. 242.

If the force represented by *df* remained constant, while the distance increased by *de*, the work done would be represented by the area of the rectangle *fe*; while if the force during this distance had been *ek*, the work would have been represented by the area of the rectangle *he*.

Since, however, the force increases from the value represented by *df* to that represented by *ek*, the work done is intermediate in value between the areas of the rectangles *fe* and *he*.

If all the rectangles of this type are drawn, the total work done will be intermediate between the sum of all the internal rectangles of the type *fe*, and all the external rectangles of the type *he*.

Now suppose the number of parts into which the distance **OC** is divided to increase indefinitely, and consequently the distances of the type *de* to decrease indefinitely, then the sum of the internal rectangles and the sum of the external rectangles will approach the value of the area of the figure **OA**f*kB***C**, which is bounded by the curve, the distance axis, and the two ordinates representing the initial and final values of the force, and in the limit the *work* done will be represented by the *area* **OABC**.

The value of this area can be obtained graphically by dividing **OC** into a convenient number of equal parts, drawing the ordinate at the middle point of each division, and thence obtaining the average ordinate, *i.e.* the average force, and multiplying by the distance **OC**.

iii. If the *force varies as the distance* moved through by its point of applica-

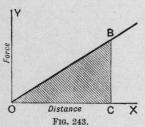

FIG. 243.

tion in the direction of the force, then since **F** ∝ *s*, it follows that the curve becomes a straight line passing through the origin, and consequently

work done is represented by area of triangle **OBC**, if the initial value of the force is zero.

We have already seen in Hooke's Law that

tension ∝ extension,

and in examples on this law shall obtain a straight line graph.

If the original force is not zero, then the work done will be represented by the area of a trapezium.

Ex. *A body is being acted on by a variable lifting force. When the body is lifted x ft. the force **F** lb. wt. is observed. From the given table plot the values of x and **F**, and find the work done when the body has been lifted 210 ft.*

x ft.	0	15	25	50	70	100	125	150	180	210
F lb. wt.	530	525	416	490	425	300	210	160	110	90

The values of x and **F** are measured along **OX** and **OY** and the curve plotted.

The work done is represented by the area **OABC**.

OC is divided into 10 equal parts and ordinates erected at the middle points of these parts. The average value of **F** is found by adding the lengths of these ordinates and dividing by 10 :

$$\text{average value of } \mathbf{F} = \tfrac{1}{10}(525+510+482+415+320+236+180+140+112+93)$$
$$= 301\cdot3 \text{ lb. wt. ;}$$

$$\therefore \text{ work done} = 301\cdot3 \times 210 = 63,300 \text{ ft.-lb. (approx.).}$$

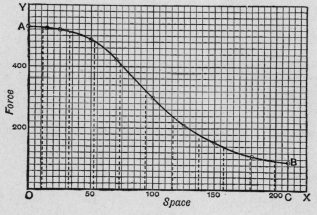

FIG. 244.

EXERCISE XXXVII

1. If a force of 5 lb. wt. stretches a string 1 inch, find the number of ft.-lb. of work done in slowly stretching it 4 in.

2. A force of 30 lb. wt. is necessary to compress a spring 1 inch. Find the number of ft.-lb. of work done in compressing it 3 in.

3. If the natural length of a spring is 5 inches and a force of 2 lb. wt. stretches it $\frac{1}{2}$ inch, find the work done in stretching it from 6 to 7 inches.

4. A body is being acted on by a variable lifting force. When the body is lifted x ft., the force F lb. wt. is observed.

x	0	15	25	50	70	100
F	530	525	516	490	425	300

Find graphically the work done by F in lifting the body 100 ft.

5. A weight is drawn up an inclined plane by a force parallel to the plane. If the values of the force and distance are shown in the given table, find graphically the work done by the force.

Distance (ft.)	0	50	100	150	200	250	300	350	400
Force (lb. wt.)	115	145	150	130	100	65	35	25	10

6. The following results were obtained during a tensile test on a steel bar :—

Load (tons wt.)	1	2	3	4	5	6	7	8	9	10	12
Elongations $\left(\dfrac{1}{10,000} \text{ in.}\right)$	12	24	35	47	61	75	88	102	160	260	510

Plot a curve and find the work done in in.-tons.

7. The pull on a cart at a distance x ft. along a road is F lb. wt. Find graphically the average pull on the cart and the work done in pulling it through 80 ft.

x	0	10	20	. 30	40	50	60	70	80
F	130	112	108	110	120	128	130	126	116

8. The following table gives the total powder pressure, P tons wt., on the base of a projectile, when it has travelled x ft. along the bore :—

x	0	0·5	0·75	1·0	1·25	1·5	2·0	2·5	3·0	3·5	4·0	4·5	5·0
P	3	93	118	125	119	102	78	60	48	38	29	24	23

Draw the force-distance curve, and hence find the total work done on the projectile.

108. Belts. If a belt passes round two wheels **A** and **B**, of which **A** is driven by machinery in a clockwise direction, then if the belt does not slip, **B** must also rotate in a clockwise direction. The tension **P** in the driving side of the belt tends to stretch that part of the belt, while the tension **Q** in the slack side gradually diminishes until a steady stage is reached, and **B** rotates uniformly under the action of a force **P** assisting its rotation and a force **Q** retarding it. If the slack side of the belt runs from the top side of the driving-wheel there is a minimum chance of the belt slipping,

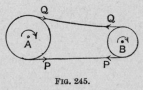

FIG. 245.

since in this arrangement a larger amount of the perimeters of the wheels is covered by the belt.

If the belt is moving at the rate of v ft./min., and the forces on the wheel are in lb. wt., then in 1 minute

the work done by the tension **P** lb. wt. is   **P**v ft.-lb.,

,,   ,,   against the resistance **Q** lb. wt. is   **Q**v ft.-lb. ;

∴ total work done on **B** per minute is   **(P−Q)**v ft.-lb.,

and this work is transmitted to the shaft attached to **B**.

It follows that

$$\text{the H.P. given to the wheel } \mathbf{B}=\frac{(\mathbf{P}-\mathbf{Q})v}{33,000}.$$

If the belt does not slip, it has been found that a rough working rule is that **P** must not be greater than 2·5 **Q**.

109. Problems on H.P. have already been given in Ex. XXVI; examples are now given in which the forces act in various directions.

Ex. 1. *An engine draws a train of* 100 *tons with uniform velocity up an incline of* 1 *in* 250, *the resistance being* 8 *lb. wt./ton ; find the distance moved over in* 12 *min. if the* **H.P.** *is* 110.

Let **P** lb. wt. be the pull of the engine up the plane, and v ft./sec. the uniform velocity.

The resultant force up the plane must be zero, since there is no acceleration;

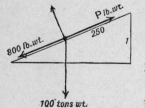

100 tons wt.

Fig. 246.

$$\therefore \quad P-800-\frac{100\times 2240}{250}=0,$$

i.e.   **P** = 1696 lb. wt.

Since this force acts over a distance v ft. in 1 second,

∴ work done per sec. = 1696 v ft.-lb. ;

but since the H.P. is 110, it follows that the work done by the engine in 1 sec. is 110×550,

$$\therefore \quad 1696\,v=110\times 550,$$

i.e. $v=\dfrac{110\times 550}{1696}$ ft./sec. ;

$$\therefore \text{ distance in 12 min.}=\frac{110\times 550\times 60\times 12}{1696}$$

$$=25{,}700 \text{ ft. (approx.).}$$

Ex. 2. *A train of 350 tons is ascending an incline of 1 in 200, and the resistance to motion is 12 lb. wt./ton. If at a particular moment the velocity is 15 ml./hr. and the* **H.P.** *developed then 500, what is the acceleration ?*

$$15 \text{ ml./hr.} = 22 \text{ ft./sec.}$$

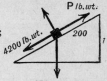

Let **P** lb. wt. be the pull of the engine up the incline; then the work done per sec. is (**P** × 22) ft.-lb.; but since the H.P. is 500, the work is also 500 × 550;

$$\therefore \ 22\mathbf{P} = 500 \times 550, \qquad i.e. \ \mathbf{P} = 12{,}500 \text{ lb. wt.}$$

350 tons wt.
Fig. 247.

Since the resistance down the plane is 4200 lb. wt.,

the resultant force up the plane $= (\mathbf{P} - 4200 - \frac{350}{200} \times 2240)$ lb. wt.
$$= 12500 - 4200 - 3920 = 4380 \text{ lb. wt.}$$

If a ft./sec.^{2} is the acceleration,

$$\frac{4380}{350 \times 2240} = \frac{a}{g}, \qquad \left(\frac{\mathbf{F}}{\mathbf{W}} = \frac{a}{g}\right)$$

$$\therefore \ a = 0 \cdot 18 \text{ ft./sec.}^2$$

EXERCISE XXXVIII

1. At what H.P. is an engine working which is dragging a load of 5 tons wt. up an incline of 1 in 10 at 12 ml./hr., if friction is neglected ?

2. What is the maximum speed (in ml./hr.) at which the North Wales express could climb a gradient of 1 in 70, supposing the weight of the whole train to be 560 tons and the engine capable of developing 1100 H.P., and neglecting all resistances ?

3. Determine the H.P. required to drive a car weighing 1600 lb. at a speed of 30 ml./hr. against a resistance equal to one-tenth of the weight of the car.

    If the car is driven up an incline of 1 in 20, against the same resistance, calculate the new speed, the H.P. remaining the same.

4. If an 8 H.P. motor car weighing 1 ton can maintain a speed of 25 ml./hr. on a level road, find in lb. wt. the resistance to motion. Find also the speed that the same car could maintain up a hill of 1 in 8, assuming that the resistance and the H.P. remain unaltered.

5. A tractor weighs 3 tons and hauls a load of 4 tons at 12 ml./hr. along a level road. The resistances amount to 52 lb. wt./ton. Find the H.P. developed. If the H.P. and resistance remain unaltered, find the speed on an ascending gradient of 1 in 100.

6. A train weighs 200 tons and the H.P. of the engine is just sufficient to maintain a speed of 60 ml./hr. on a level railroad against a constant resistance of 2000 lb. wt. If the total resistance is increased by a head-wind to 2200 lb. wt., and if the railroad becomes an ascending gradient of 1 in 240, prove that with the same H.P. the maximum speed of the train is approximately $29\frac{1}{2}$ ml./hr.

7. A motor car, weighing 2 tons, is driven at 20 ml./hr. along a level road, by an engine developing $2\frac{1}{2}$ H.P. What power would be required to drive it at the same speed up an incline of 1 in 50 ?

8. A rough plane (coefficient of friction $\frac{1}{2}$) is 1 mile long, and has a slope of 1 in 100. Find the H.P. required to drag a load of 1 ton wt., with uniform velocity, up it in 1 hour.

9. A motor van weighing 5 tons runs freely down a hill of 1 in 24 with a constant velocity of 15 ml./hr. What H.P. is required to drive it at the same speed up the hill, the frictional resistance being the same in each case ?

10. Assuming that the resistance to motion of a train travelling V ml./hr. is $9 + 0.007V^2$ lb. wt./ton, find the resistance for a train of 200 tons wt. travelling at 45 ml./hr., and the H.P. necessary to maintain this speed.

11. Assuming that the resistance to motion of a train on the level is $0.009V^2$ lb. wt./ton, where V is the speed in ml./hr., find the H.P. required to draw a train of 300 tons up an incline of 1 in 150 at a uniform speed of 20 ml./hr.

12. A fast cruiser is propelled at a speed of 40 ml./hr. by means of engines whose effective H.P. is 40,000. Calculate the resistance to the motion of the ship and, assuming that the resistance varies as the square of the speed, what H.P. (to the nearest 100) would be required for a speed of 45 ml./hr. ?

13. If power is transmitted by means of a belt running at 800 ft./min., and the tension in the tight part is 450 lb. wt., calculate that H.P. transmitted if the tension in the other part is 180 lb. wt.

14. A belt which runs at 1500 ft./min. has a difference of 220 lb. wt. between the tensions on the tight and slack sides. What H.P. is transmitted ?

15. A belt transmits 60 H.P. to a pulley 16 in. in diameter running at 263 rev./min. What is the difference of the tensions on the tight and slack sides ?

16. Find the speed (in ft./min.) at which the belt is running, if the difference between the tensions on the slack and tight sides is 280 lb. wt., and the H.P. transmitted is 8.

17. A train weighing 300 tons is driven from rest up an incline of 1 in 300, the frictional resistance being 16 lb. wt./ton. For the first mile, the tractive force is 9000 lb. wt., for the second mile 6000 lb. wt., and for the third mile 8000 lb. wt. Determine the velocity at the end of each mile.

18. A locomotive is hauling a train whose total weight is 100 tons up a slope of 1 in 100, the friction being 20 lb. wt./ton. If at a particular moment the speed is 30 ml./hr. and the H.P. 500, find the acceleration.

19. A motor car weighing 1½ tons is running at 30 ml./hr. on a straight horizontal road. It comes to a hill where the descent is 1 in 30. If, with the engine running free, the car on this slope just maintains a uniform speed of 30 ml./hr., find the total resistance.

On the return journey, the car starts from rest on this hill, and with uniform acceleration attains a speed of 30 ml./hr. in 15 minutes, thereafter maintaining this speed. Assuming the total resistance to be the same for all speeds, determine the maximum H.P. developed by the engine, and the H.P. developed immediately after the uniform speed has been attained.

Energy

110. We have already defined the energy of a body to be its *capacity for doing work*.

A body may possess energy owing to the fact that it is in *motion*; a familiar case is that of a bullet or shell which, on striking an object, is able to penetrate it and overcome the resistance offered, the destructive effect depending partly on the weight of the shell and partly on its velocity.

Other bodies are capable of doing work because of their *position* or *configuration*; a spring, when stretched, is capable of doing work in returning to its natural length ; a stone placed at 100 ft. above the earth's surface will, on falling, be able to do more work on reaching the surface than one placed only 1 ft. above the surface.

Besides such forms of energy as these, we have those due to Chemical, Electrical, and other physical actions.

111. The **Kinetic Energy** of a body is *the energy which it possesses in virtue of its motion.*

This form of energy is measured by *the amount of work which the body can do in being brought to rest.*

Suppose a body of weight **W** lb., moving with a velocity u ft./sec., is brought to rest by a force of **F** lb. wt. in a distance s ft., then the work done against the force is **F**s lb. wt.

If the retardation of the body is a ft./sec.^{2}, then

$$\frac{\mathbf{F}}{\mathbf{W}} = \frac{a}{g},$$

and

$$u^2 = 2as ;$$

$\therefore$ **kinetic energy** of body $= \mathbf{F}s = \dfrac{\mathbf{W}a}{g} \cdot s = \dfrac{\mathbf{W}a}{g} \cdot \dfrac{u^2}{2a}$

$$= \frac{\mathbf{W}u^2}{2g} \text{ ft.-lb.}$$

In the metric system, if **W** is measured in grams wt., and u in cm./sec., then the kinetic energy is $\dfrac{\mathbf{W}u^2}{2g}$ cm.-gm., where $g = 981$.

112. *The* **Potential Energy** *of a system is the amount of work it can do in moving from any particular position to some standard position.*

We have already referred to the energy possessed by a spring which is extended or compressed ; in either case it is capable of doing work in returning to its normal length or some other length, work in the first case having been done on the spring by changing its length.

In a similar manner, when we raise a body so that its distance from the earth's surface is altered, we are doing work on the system composed of the body and the earth, in fact we have to overcome the gravitational attraction between them. If then we raise a weight of **W** lb. through h ft., we have done **W**h ft.-lb. of work, and the body-earth system has its energy increased by **W**h ft.-lb., and the system is capable of performing this amount of work in returning to its original configuration.

The standard position of the body is usually taken to be the surface of the earth, and if a body of weight **W** lb. is raised h ft. above the earth's surface,

the potential energy of the body-earth system is **Wh ft.-lb.**

113. Many familiar instances of the change in the nature of energy may be noted.

A shooting star possesses a large amount of energy due to its high velocity ; this particular kind of energy is gradually destroyed as the star is caught in the earth's atmosphere, and in its place heat and light energy are produced.

Work is done in winding up the heavy weight of a clock and overcoming the friction of the various parts, but this is partly recovered as the weight falls and the machinery is kept in motion.

The pressure of steam, produced by heat on water, causes a dynamo to revolve, generates an electric current, which is afterwards used for giving out light and heat energy. These facts lead to an important principle, the truth of which rests on experimental evidence, and which is ' always acquiring additional credibility from the constantly increasing number of deductions which have been drawn from it, and which are found in all cases to be verified by experiment.'

Principle of Conservation of Energy. *The total energy of any material system is a quantity which can neither be increased nor diminished by any action between the parts of the system, though it may be transformed into any of the forms of which energy is susceptible.*

114. A body may have several forces acting on it, some increasing and others diminishing its velocity, and in all cases its changes of kinetic energy will be accounted for by the work done by or against the various forces acting.

In fact,

the **gain** *of kinetic energy of a body*

=the algebraic sum of the work done **by** *all the forces on the body,*

or, the **loss** *of kinetic energy of a body*

=the algebraic sum of the work done **against** *all the forces on the body.*

As a corollary we may state that if there is no change of kinetic energy, then the algebraic sum of the work done by all the forces is zero.

These results are most important, and the solution of problems by means of the principle of energy depends entirely on their truth.

Ex. *A heavy body of weight 10 tons falls vertically through 5 ft. Find the steady force which will bring it to rest in the next 4 inches.*

Method i. During the first part of the motion **AB**, the accelerating force is 10 tons wt.; the velocity at **A** is zero, and at **B** the velocity is v ft./sec.

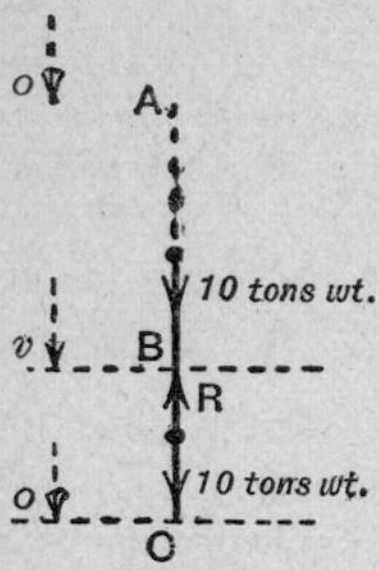

Gain of K.E. $= \dfrac{10v^2}{2g}$ ft.-tons ;

work done by external force $= 10 \times 5$ ft.-tons ;

$$\therefore \frac{5v^2}{g} = 50. \qquad . \qquad . \qquad . \quad \text{(i)}$$

During the second part **BC**, there is a force of 10 tons wt. *downwards* and **R** tons wt. *upwards*, so that the opposing force is $(R-10)$ tons wt. and this acts through 4 in., while the velocity of the body is reduced from v ft./sec. to zero ;

$$\therefore \text{ loss of K.E.} = \frac{10v^2}{2g} \text{ ft.-tons,}$$

and work done against forces $= \tfrac{1}{3}(R-10)$ ft.-tons ;

$$\therefore \frac{5v^2}{g} = \tfrac{1}{3}(R-10). \qquad . \qquad . \qquad . \quad \text{(ii)}$$

From (i) and (ii), $\tfrac{1}{3}(R-10) = 50,$

$$\therefore R = 160 \text{ tons wt.}$$

Method ii. This problem can be solved more shortly by considering the initial and final K.E. of the body, each of which is zero, so that

the algebraic sum of the work done by the external forces must be zero.

Now the force of 10 tons wt. acts *downwards* through $5\tfrac{1}{3}$ ft.,

„   **R** tons wt.   „   *upwards*   „ $\tfrac{1}{3}$ ft.,

$$\therefore (10 \times 5\tfrac{1}{3}) - (R \times \tfrac{1}{3}) = 0,$$

i.e.   **R** $= 160$ tons wt.

FIG. 248.

EXERCISE XXXIX

(Assume $g=32$ ft./sec.^{2} or 981 cm./sec.^{2})

1. Find the kinetic energy of

    (i) a body of 10 lb. wt. moving with a speed of 5 ft./sec.,

    (ii)   ,,   5 gm. wt.   ,,   ,,   100 cm./sec.,

    (iii)   ,,   8 tons wt.   ,,   ,,   10 ft./sec.

2. If a body at rest is acted on by a force of 5 lb. wt. moving through a distance of 10 ft., what kinetic energy does the body acquire ?

3. A body of weight 10 lb. is at rest 15 ft. above the ground ; if it is allowed to fall freely, what kinetic will it have on reaching the ground ?

4. A body of 5 lb. wt. lies on a smooth surface and is pushed by a force of 10 lb. wt. through a distance of 8 ft. ; what velocity does it acquire ?

5. Find the work done in increasing the velocity of a body of weight 8 lb. from 10 ft./sec. to 20 ft./sec.

6. If a resisting force reduces the velocity of a body of weight 5 lb. from 30 ft./sec. to 20 ft./sec., how much work has been done against the force ?

7. A train weighing 100 tons is reduced to rest from a speed of 30 ml./hr. in 400 yd. by a steady force. Find the magnitude of the force in tons wt.

8. A body weighing 800 kilograms is projected vertically upwards with a velocity of 1500 cm./sec. Find its initial kinetic energy in cm.-gm. and the height to which it will rise.

9. Calculate in ft.-tons the kinetic energy of a motor car of weight 5000 lb. moving with a velocity of 35 ml./hr.

10. Find the work in ft.-tons which must be done on a train of 200 tons wt. to increase its speed from 25 ml./hr. to 60 ml./hr.

11. A man in catching a cricket ball of weight $5\frac{1}{4}$ oz., travelling with a speed of 64 ft./sec., draws his hand back through 1 ft. Find the average force (in lb. wt.) that the ball exerts on his hand while coming to rest.

12. A truck of 3 tons wt. is moving with a velocity of 8 ml./hr. Calculate its kinetic energy in ft.-tons and the constant force (in tons wt.) which acting on it through a distance of 22 ft. produced this velocity.

13. A projectile weighs 18 lb. and its velocity of projection is 1500 ft./sec. Find its kinetic energy in ft.-tons as it leaves the muzzle.

　　　What is the average pressure of the powder gases on the projectile if the length of the bore of the gun is 4 ft. ?

14. Find the number of ft.-lb. of work done by a man who picks up a stone weighing $\frac{1}{2}$ lb. and throws it through a window 20 ft. above the ground with a velocity of 8 ft./sec.

15. In 3 seconds a machine has lifted a weight of a ton 2 ft. from the ground and has given it a velocity of 2 ft./sec. At what average rate, measured in horse-power, has the machine been working ?

16. A weight of 12 gm. is raised to a height of 200 cm. above the floor. Find its increase of potential energy in cm.-gm. If it is allowed to fall, with what velocity will it strike the floor ?

17. A bullet of 1 oz. wt. is moving horizontally at 1000 ft./sec. The bullet passes through a wooden wall 2 in. thick and emerges with a velocity of 500 ft./sec. Find the resistance (in lb. wt.) of the wood.

18. Calculate the number of ft.-tons of energy which are required to raise a 200 lb. shell to a height of 8 ft. and then project it with an initial speed of 960 ft./sec. What will be its height above its original level when its speed is 800 ft./sec. ?

19. A bullet moving with a velocity of 2000 ft./sec. strikes a fixed block of wood and penetrates it to a depth of 18 inches. Assuming that the resistance of the wood is constant, find with what velocity the bullet would emerge had the block been 6 inches thick.

20. A motor car, whose weight is 2500 lb., increases its speed in 10 seconds from 6 ml./hr. to 30 ml./hr. Find the horse-power exerted by the engine, assuming it to be constant, and neglecting all resistances.

21. A pump is employed to raise water from a depth of 150 ft. and to deliver it with a velocity of 20 ft./sec. Show that 96 per cent. of the work done by the pump is employed in raising the water and 4 per cent. in imparting to it its velocity of efflux.

22. A weight of 40 lb. falls a vertical distance of 30 ft. and is subject to a resistance of 12 lb. wt.   Find its final velocity.

23. A train weighing 300 tons is drawn by an engine which can exert a pull of 45 tons wt.   If the resistance due to friction is 14 lb. wt./ton, find how long it will take the engine to get up a speed of 20 ml./hr. on the level.

24. Find the H.P. of an engine which projects 8000 lb. of water in 1 minute with a velocity of 70 ft./sec.

25. A train starting from rest attains a speed of 30 ml./hr. in 2 minutes. Find the acceleration, assuming it to be constant.   How far does the train travel before reaching a speed of 45 ml./hr. ?

　　If the various resistances to motion amount to a backward force of $\frac{1}{2}$ ton wt., find the pull exerted by the engine, given that the weight of the train is 120 tons.

115. We shall now consider various types of problems in which the forces are not all acting in the same direction.

Ex. 1. *An engine weighing 25 tons pulls a train of 50 tons at a speed of 30 ml./hr. up an incline of 1 in 200 ; if the couplings break, how far will the train run before coming to rest, if the resistance to motion is 15 lb. wt./ton ?*

The train loses K.E. as the velocity is reduced from 44 ft./sec. to zero.   The forces opposing motion are 750 lb. wt. down the plane, and 50 tons wt. vertically downwards ;

∴ the *loss* of K.E. equals the work done *against* these two forces.

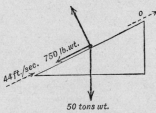

50 tons wt.
FIG. 249.

If the train travels x ft. before stopping,

the work done against the force of 750 lb. wt. $=750x$ ft.-lb. ;

the work done against the force of gravity $=50 \times 2240 \times \dfrac{x}{200}$ ft.-lb. ;

$$\text{loss of K.E.} = \frac{50 \times 2240 \times 44^2}{2g} \text{ ft.-lb. ;}$$

$$\therefore\ 750x + \left(50 \times 2240 \times \frac{x}{200}\right) = \frac{50 \times 2240 \times 44^2}{2g}$$

$$1310gx = 25 \times 2240 \times 44^2 ;$$

$$\therefore\ x = 2586 \text{ ft.}$$

Ex. 2. *A simple pendulum has a weight of 20 gm. at the end of a string 75 cm. long ; if the string is displaced from the vertical through an angle of 25° and then let go, what is the velocity of the weight in its lowest position ?*

Let v cm./sec. be the velocity at the lowest point.

The forces acting are 20 gm. wt. vertically downwards and the tension of the string along BA ; since the motion is always at right angles to the string, the tension does no work, it follows that

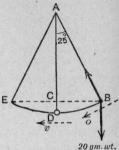

20 gm. wt.

Fig. 250.

the gain of K.E. equals the work done by the force of 20 gm. wt., and this vertical force acts through a vertical distance CD, where BC is the horizontal through B.

$$\therefore \quad \frac{20v^2}{2g} = 20\text{CD}.$$

Now $\text{CD} = \text{AD} - \text{AC} = 75(1 - \cos 25°) = 75 \times 0\cdot0937$ cm.,

$$\therefore \quad v^2 = 150g \times 0\cdot0937,$$

i.e. $v = \sqrt{150 \times 981 \times 0\cdot0937} = 117$ cm./sec.

EXERCISE XL

1. A body whose weight is 4 lb. slides from rest down a perfectly smooth plane, inclined at 20° to the horizontal, for a distance of 100 yd. Find its velocity at the bottom of the plane.

2. An eight-ton tramcar, running at 12 ml./hr. on the level, can be stopped by the brakes in 16 yards. At what speed could it be stopped in the same distance when running uphill on a road rising 1 ft. vertical to 50 ft. along the road ?

3. An inclined plane 40 ft. long is set up at an inclination of 1 in 3. Find the speed with which a body, let go from the top of the plane, would reach the bottom if the plane were smooth.

     If the body loses 10 per cent. of its energy owing to friction, with what velocity will it reach the bottom ?

4. If a train is running down an incline of 1 in 250 with steam shut off at 40 ml./hr., find the speed after it has run another mile, if the resistance is 14 lb. wt. per ton.

5. A heavy body weighing 5 cwt. starts from rest and slides down an incline of 1 in 20. It attains a speed of 25 ft./sec. after rolling 100 yd. Find (i) the work done in overcoming friction, (ii) the average value of the resisting force.

6. A cyclist weighing, with his machine, 160 lb., free-wheels down a hill 20 ft. high (measured vertically), starting with a speed of 6 ft./sec. and arriving at the bottom with a speed of 30 ft./sec. How many ft.-lb. of energy has he lost on the way ?

7. A chute, for conveying parcels from one floor of a warehouse to the floor below, consists of a spiral track of uniform gradient winding round a vertical pillar 25 ft. high. A parcel of weight 10 lb. is placed in the chute and arrives at the bottom with a velocity of 22 ft./sec. Show that there must be a loss of energy due to friction and calculate its amount.

8. A train moving on the level can be brought to rest by its brakes exerting a constant force in 440 yards, when its initial velocity is 45 ml./hr. Prove that if the train were moving down a slope of 1 in 100, the same brakes would stop the train in about 546 yards.

9. The top of a hill is 420 ft. above sea-level, and the bottom, which is $\frac{1}{4}$ mile further on, is 360 ft. above sea-level, after which the road is level. A cyclist who, with his machine, weighs 150 lb., starts from the top and coasts down. How far from the bottom will he come to rest if he experiences a resistance of 3 lb. wt. during the whole period ?

10. A 5 H.P. engine is used to drive a pump which delivers 50 gallons of water a minute in a jet. Assuming that no energy is wasted, find the speed of the water in the jet.

11. At a certain railway station there is a gradient of 1 in 200. A train going down comes to rest in 500 ft., and a train going up comes to rest in 400 ft., the initial velocities being the same. Find the frictional resistance per ton.

12. A truck runs 2 miles from rest down an inclined plane of 1 in 200 and, without change of velocity, runs up an equal incline until it comes to rest. If the resistance to motion is 10 lb. wt./ton, find how far it travels up the second incline.

13. A 10-ton railway truck carrying a load of 5 tons runs from rest down an incline of 1 in 100, the incline being ¼ mile long, and the track then becomes level. The truck reaches the bottom with a velocity of 25 ft./sec. Show that air resistance, friction, etc., supposed uniform, are equivalent to a retarding force of approximately 6 lb. wt./ton. How far does the truck travel along the level from the bottom of the slope before coming to rest, if the resistance is taken as this approximate amount ?

14. An engine projects 1200 gallons of water a minute with a speed of 75 ft./sec. If the efficiency is 0·6, find the H.P., given that 1 gallon of water weighs 10 lb.

15. A steam pump delivers 500 cu. ft. of water per minute to a height of 60 ft. Determine the H.P. of the engine, if the efficiency of engine and pump is 33 per cent., and 1 cu. ft. of water weighs 62·3 lb.

16. A weight hangs by a thread 8 ft. long from a fixed point and swings like a pendulum. If it swings 30° on either side of the vertical, find the maximum velocity.

17. If 30 per cent. of the power developed is wasted in frictional resistances, what H.P. is required to pump water from a depth of 18 ft. and to deliver it through a pipe of 1 sq. in. section with a velocity of 120 ft./sec. ? Assume 1 cu. ft. of water weighs 62·3 lb.

18. A steam hammer, of weight 25 tons, falls vertically a distance of 3 ft., being pressed down by steam pressure equal to the weight of 50 tons. What velocity will it acquire, and how many foot-tons of work will it do before coming to rest ?

19. A string 8 ft. long has its extremities attached to two fixed points on the same horizontal, distance 4 ft. apart. A heavy ring, which slides on the string, is held vertically below one of the fixed points, so that the string is taut, and released. Find its velocity on passing the lowest position.

20. A ball weighing 5½ oz. is thrown horizontally, with a velocity of 90 ft./sec., from the top of a cliff 100 ft. high. Find how far from the foot of the cliff it strikes the sea.

    Find also, in ft.-lb., the kinetic energy of the ball when it strikes the sea.

116. Ex. 1. *Two bodies of weight 6 and 8 lb. respectively are suspended by a string over a smooth pulley. Find the velocity of either body after it has moved through 2 ft., and also the tension of the string.*

Let **T** lb. wt. be the tension of the string; the external forces on the system, composed of the two moving bodies, are 8 lb. wt. and 6 lb. wt. vertically downwards, the tension being an internal force and doing no work. As the heavier body descends and the lighter rises,

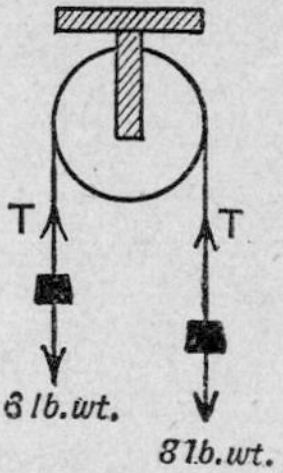

the total work done on the system $= (8-6) \times 2$ ft.-lb.

$$= 4 \text{ ft.-lb.};$$

$\therefore$ gain of K.E. of both bodies $= 4$ ft.-lb.,

i.e. $\qquad \dfrac{14v^2}{2g} = 4, \qquad\qquad \therefore v^2 = \tfrac{4}{7}g \quad . \quad . \quad . \quad$ (i)

i.e. $v = 4 \cdot 28$ ft./sec.

6 lb. wt.

8 lb. wt.

FIG. 251.

Considering the 8 lb. only,

the work done on it $= (8-\mathbf{T}) \times 2$ ft.-lb.,

$\therefore$ gain of K.E. of the heavier body $= 2(8-\mathbf{T})$ ft.-lb.;

$$\therefore \frac{8v^2}{2g} = 2(8-\mathbf{T}),$$

$$\therefore 8-\mathbf{T} = \tfrac{8}{7}, \qquad\qquad \text{from (i),}$$

i.e. $\mathbf{T} = 6\tfrac{6}{7}$ lb. wt.

Ex. 2. *A flywheel of diameter 1 ft., mounted on a frictionless horizontal axle of diameter 2 in., is set in motion by a 20 lb. wt. attached to a string wound round the axle. When the weight has descended 4 ft., the speed of the rim of the wheel is 8 ft./sec. What is the kinetic energy of the flywheel at this stage and the tension of the string?*

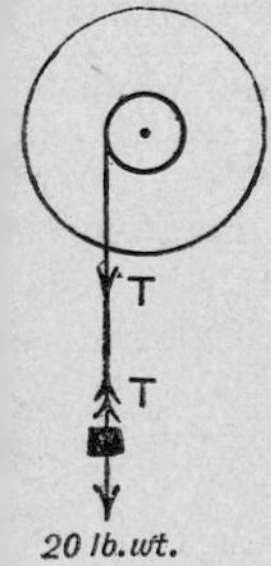

Since the velocity of a point on the rim of the wheel is 8 ft./sec., and the ratio of the diameters of the axle and wheel is $\tfrac{1}{6}$,

$\therefore$ velocity of 20 lb. wt. $=$ vel. of point on circumference of axle

$$= \tfrac{1}{6} \times 8 = \tfrac{4}{3} \text{ ft./sec.},$$

20 lb. wt.

FIG. 252.

and gain of K.E. of 20 lb. wt.

$$= \frac{20 \times 16}{2g \times 9} \text{ ft.-lb.}$$

(i) The only external force acting on the system *wheel, axle* and *weight,* is 20 lb. wt. vertical downwards,

$$\therefore \text{ work done on system} = 20 \times 4 = 80 \text{ ft.-lb. ;}$$

$$\therefore \text{ gain of kinetic energy of wheel and axle}$$
$$+ \text{gain of kinetic energy of 20 lb. wt.} = 80 \text{ ft.-lb. ;}$$

i.e. gain of kinetic energy of wheel and axle $+ \dfrac{20 \times 16}{2g \times 9} = 80,$

$$\therefore \text{ K.E. of wheel and axle} = 80 - \tfrac{5}{9} = 79\tfrac{4}{9} \text{ ft.-lb.}$$

(ii) Considering the *weight* by itself, the forces acting on it are 20 lb. wt. downwards and the tension, **T** lb. wt., upwards,

$$\therefore \text{ gain of K.E. of weight} = (20 - \mathbf{T}) \times 4 \text{ ft.-lb.,}$$

$$i.e. \quad \frac{20 \times 16}{2g \times 9} = (20 - \mathbf{T})4,$$

$$\therefore \mathbf{T} = 19\tfrac{31}{36} \text{ lb. wt.}$$

Ex. 3. *A flywheel weighing 2000 lb. is rotating at the rate of 5 rev./sec., and is such that all its weight may be supposed concentrated uniformly on the circumference of a circle of radius 2 ft. The coefficient of friction between its axle and supports is 0·24, and the radius of the axle is 5 in. If the steam is shut off, find how many times the wheel will rotate before it comes to rest.*

It should be noted that the various particles of the wheel, at different distances from the centre, have different velocities, so that in using the formula $\dfrac{\mathbf{W}v^2}{2g}$ we have to take a kind of mean value of v, and in this problem it is the velocity of a particle at a distance of 2 ft. from the centre ; later, the student will learn that this distance is called the radius of gyration of the wheel.

The velocity of any particle on the circumference of the circle of radius 2 ft. is 20π ft./sec.,

$$\therefore \text{ loss of K.E. of flywheel} = \frac{2000 \times 400\pi^2}{2g} \text{ ft.-lb.} \qquad . \qquad . \qquad . \text{ (i)}$$

The normal pressure on the axle $= 2000$ lb. wt.,

$$\therefore \text{ frictional force} = 2000 \times 0\cdot24 \text{ lb. wt.}$$

The normal pressure does no work, and the only force which stops the flywheel is the frictional force which acts along a tangent to the circle of radius 5 in. ;

in 1 revolution the frictional force acts over a distance $\dfrac{5\pi}{6}$ ft.,

$\therefore$ work done against friction in n rev. $= 2000 \times 0.24 \times \dfrac{5\pi}{6} \times n$ ft.-lb.

$$= 400\pi n \text{ ft.-lb.}$$

$\therefore$ from (i), $\qquad\qquad 400g\pi n = 400{,}000\pi^2,$

$$\therefore\ n = \frac{1000\pi}{32} = 98.2.$$

EXERCISE XLI

(*Harder Problems.*)

1. Two bodies of weight 5 lb. and 6 lb. respectively are suspended by a string passing over a smooth pulley. Find the velocity of either body after it has moved through 2 ft.

2. A weight of 5 lb. rests on a smooth table and is attached by means of a string, passing over a smooth pulley, to a weight of 6 lb. hanging freely. After each body has moved through 3 ft., find their common velocity.

3. A weight of 10 lb. rests on a smooth plane of angle 30° and is attached by a string, passing over a smooth pulley at the top of the plane, to a body of weight 8 lb. hanging freely. After each body has moved through 5 ft., find their common velocity and the tension of the string.

4. A heavy wheel is mounted so that it can turn freely on a horizontal axle. It is set in motion by a weight of 3 lb. hanging by a string wound on the axle. This weight after descending 4 ft. has a velocity of 2 ft./sec. What is the kinetic energy of the wheel ?

5. A flywheel and spindle, rotating in smooth bearings, are set in motion by a weight of 8 lb. hanging at the end of a rope coiled round the spindle. The weight falls 12 ft. in 5 seconds from rest ; find at this instant the kinetic energy of the wheel.

6. An aeroplane is flying horizontally at 120 ml./hr. The engine is shut off and the aeroplane glides down 2000 yd. in a straight line inclined at 10° to the horizontal. The steering is then altered in such a way that the aeroplane ascends at the same inclination. As soon as the speed again reaches 120 ml./hr., the engine is started once more and the horizontal flight is resumed.

Assuming that the resistance during the descent and ascent is 10 lb. wt./ton, and that no speed is lost when the aeroplane is turned upwards at the bottom of the descent, show that the ascent will continue for about 1900 yd.

7. Two smooth inclined planes of the same height, and angles 30° and 40°, are placed back to back. Weights of 4 lb. and 5 lb. are placed respectively on the planes and connected by a string passing over a smooth pulley at the tops of the planes. After each body has moved through 10 ft., find their common velocity and the tension of the string.

8. A flywheel of 8 in. diameter is set in motion by a weight of 1 lb. attached to a string wound round the axle which is supposed frictionless and is 1 in. in diameter. When the weight has descended 2 ft., the speed of the rim of the wheel is 3 ft./sec. What is the kinetic energy of the flywheel at this stage, and what will be the velocity of the rim when the weight has descended 4 ft. ?

9. A shaft, of diameter 5 in., makes 70 revolutions per minute. If the weight of the shaft and load is 3 tons and the coefficient of friction 0·4, find the H.P. absorbed in the bearings of the shaft. (Assume $\pi = \frac{2\,2}{7}$.)

10. Two bodies of weights 7·5 lb. and 8·5 lb. respectively are connected by a light inextensible string that passes over a smooth pulley. The smaller weight begins to move when 8 ft. from the ground beneath it, but after 2 sec. the string suddenly snaps. After what further interval will the smaller weight reach the ground and with what kinetic energy ?

11. Prove that if a train travelling along a level track at V ml./hr. is stopped in d yards by brakes applying a constant resistance, then, provided all other resistances are neglected, d/V^2 is constant. Assuming that when travelling at 30 ml./hr. it can be brought to rest in 100 yards, find the distance covered when the speed is being reduced from 54 to 36 ml./hr.

12. A truck detaches itself from the rear end of a train running at 30 ml./hr. on an upward gradient of 1 in 80. The resistance offered by the rails to the truck is 10 lb. wt./ton. Assuming the speed of the train to remain unchanged, find how many yards the truck will fall behind in 1 minute, and how far it will go before coming to rest.

13. A truck of weight 3 cwt., containing 5 cwt. of lead ore, is lowered down a mountain side on a rail 500 yd. long by means of a cable. The gradient is 1 in 3. Over the first 1200 ft. the tension in the cable is 2 cwt. The tension is then increased and is kept constant the rest of the way. Find the tension in the last 300 ft. if the truck just comes to rest at the bottom, and find the whole time taken to do the journey. Neglect all resistances.

14. A car weighing 1 ton starts from rest on a level road. The tractive force acting on it is initially 80 lb. wt., and this falls, the decrease being proportional to the distance travelled, until its value is 30 lb. wt. at the end of 200 yd., after which it remains constant. There is a constant frictional resistance of 30 lb. wt. Find the speed of the car at the end of 200 yd.

15. A weight of 100 lb. hangs freely from the end of a rope. The weight is hauled up from rest by means of a windlass. The pull in the rope starts at 150 lb. wt. and then diminishes uniformly at the rate of 1 lb. wt. for every foot of rope wound in. Find the velocity of the weight after 50 ft. of rope have been wound. The weight of the rope may be neglected.

16. A trolley of weight 7 lb. is placed on an inclined plane which is tilted so that the trolley will run down with uniform velocity. The trolley is then connected with a weight of 2 lb. by means of a string passing over a smooth pulley at the bottom of the plane, the 2 lb. hanging vertically. Find the speed of the trolley and the tension of the string, when the 2 lb. weight has fallen through 2 ft.

17. A rectangular channel, 4 ft. wide and 2 ft. deep, is full of water flowing at the rate of 6 ft./sec. The water subsequently passes over a fall 7 ft. high and is used to drive a water-wheel at the foot of the fall. Calculate (i) the weight of water flowing per second, (ii) the kinetic energy of the water which passes over the top of the fall in one second, (iii) the energy per second which is available to drive the water-wheel at the foot of the fall, neglecting any losses due to impact, etc., (iv) the effective H.P. of the wheel, assuming that the efficiency of the whole arrangement is 40 per cent. (Assume 1 cu. ft. of water weighs 62·5 lb.)

18. A flywheel, 3 ft. in diameter, is rotating at 2000 rev. per min.　Its weight is 1000 lb. and its material may be supposed concentrated on the circumference of a circle of radius 15 in.　A brake-shoe is applied to the rim with constant normal pressure P lb. wt. resulting in a tangential drag due to friction.　Find P if the wheel is brought to rest in 5 min.　The coefficient of friction between brake-shoe and rim of the flywheel is 0·20.

19. A shell of 650 lb. wt. is fired from a gun at an elevation of 30° and the range is found to be 8500 yd.　Find the kinetic energy of the shell when it is at its greatest height.

20. A truck starting from rest and weighing 15 tons is drawn along the level against a constant resistance of 30 lb. wt./ton.　The draw-bar pull is found to vary with the distance travelled according to the following table :—

Distance travelled (ft.)	0	10	20	30	40	50
Draw-bar pull (lb. wt.)	900	890	868	822	763	679

Draw a graph and find (i) the work done by the pull, (ii) the kinetic energy of the truck, (iii) the velocity of the truck, when the truck has travelled the first 50 ft.

21. A certain machine exerts a lifting force of P lb. wt. upon a load of 400 lb. wt.　The mechanism is such that P decreases while the height (x ft.), through which the body is raised, increases, according to the following table :—

x	0	20	40	60	80	100	120
P	600	580	550	500	440	340	280

Draw a graph and use it to find (i) at what height the acceleration of the weight is zero, (ii) the maximum kinetic energy acquired, (iii) the kinetic energy which the body possesses at the height of 120 ft.

22. The distances of a train from a station at successive seconds are :—

Time (sec.)	0	1	2	3	4	5	6
Distances (ft.)	250	187·5	125	62·5	31·25	15	5

Plot a graph and describe the motion of the train.

What is the velocity of the train during the first 3 seconds, and what is the velocity at the end of 5 seconds ?

What fraction of the original kinetic energy of the train has been lost at the end of 5 seconds ?

REVISION PAPERS

[Including Relative Velocity, Projectiles, Energy]

PAPER 34

1. A train starts from rest with a constant acceleration 1·4 ft./sec.², which it retains for 15 seconds ; the acceleration is then changed and remains constant for a further 20 seconds, the final velocity being 30 ml./hr. What distance is travelled (i) in the first 15 sec., (ii) in the 35 sec. ?

2. A man drags a body weighing 100 lb. along a smooth horizontal plane, working at the rate of $\frac{1}{8}$ H.P. What is the acceleration of the body when it is moving at the rate of 5 ft./sec. ?

3. A cyclist A rides E. at 8 ml./hr., and a cyclist B rides N. at 14 ml./hr. Find the speed and direction of motion of B as viewed from A.

4. A golf ball is struck from the ground at an angle of 30°, and pitches 60 ft. further on. Find to the nearest foot the greatest height that it attains, and show that it is in the air a little less than $1\frac{1}{2}$ seconds.

5. A train, including the engine, weighs 300 tons and is ascending a gradient of 1 in 150. The resistance of track and wind amounts to 1 ton wt. If under these conditions the engine is just able to pull the train up the slope at a uniform speed of 30 ml./hr., calculate the H.P. at which it is working. If the steam is shut off, show that the train comes to rest in 3025 ft.

PAPER 35

1. A body starts from rest and moves for 10 seconds in a straight line with a constant acceleration of 2 ft./sec.² It then moves uniformly for another period of 10 sec. with the velocity which it has attained. Calculate (i) the average velocity for the first 10 sec., (ii) the average velocity for the whole period of 20 sec.

2. If a motor cycle can travel on a level road at 50 ml./hr. when the engine is working at 5 H.P., find the total resistance to the motion. What additional H.P. would be needed to take a load weighing 5 cwt. up a slope of 1 in 30 at the same speed ?

3. A boy stands 15 ft. away from a house and throws a ball so that it just reaches the height of a window-sill 25 ft. above him and falls into the room. With what velocity and at what angle of elevation must he throw the ball ?

4. A ferryman can row his boat through still water at 4 ml./hr. The river is running at 3 ml./hr. Find the direction in which he must point the nose of his boat so that the boat may move straight across the river to a point exactly opposite the point from which he started.

5. (a) If the weight on the driving wheels of a locomotive is w tons, and the coefficient of friction between the driving wheels and the rails is μ, what is the greatest pull that the locomotive can exert ?

(b) If a train of W tons is running on the level at uniform speed, and the passive resistance (wind, friction, etc.) is r lb. wt./ton, what is the tractive force of the driving wheels at the rails ?

(c) A train of 200 tons is running at a uniform speed of 42 ml./hr. on the level. Find the H.P. the locomotive is exerting, if the passive resistance is taken at 20 lb. wt./ton.

PAPER 36

1. A and B are two points on a straight road 1 mile apart. A motor car, whose speed is being uniformly accelerated, passes A with a speed of 30 ml./hr. and B with a speed of 33 ml./hr. Calculate the speed with which it passes a point on the road 1 mile beyond B.

2. A truck, of weight 9 tons, is sent into a level siding at 4 ml./hr. and comes to rest in 40 yards. Find the uniform resisting force which has brought it to rest. Also find how long it takes to move those 40 yards.

3. A ship A observes another B at a distance of 8 miles in a direction due N. ; B is steaming S. at 12 ml./hr., and A is steaming N.E. at 15 ml./hr. Find the velocity of B relative to A, and prove that the ships are nearest together about 17 minutes after B is first observed.

4. A golf ball projected with a velocity of 160 ft./sec. at an angle of elevation whose tangent is $\frac{3}{8}$, just clears a bunker whose horizontal distance from the point of projection is 480 ft. Find the height of the bunker above the point of projection.

5. A weight of 5 tons is pulled horizontally by means of a horizontal cable which is wound up on a drum by a stationary engine working at 5 H.P. If the weight is moving uniformly at 40 yd./min., find the resistance to its motion in tons wt. If the cable breaks, find the distance the weight moves afterwards before it come to rest, assuming the resistance to remain the same.

PAPER 37

1. A train starting from rest moves with acceleration f until its velocity is 30 ft./sec., and then with acceleration $\frac{1}{2}f$ until its velocity is 60 ft./sec., after which the velocity remains uniform. The train takes 118 seconds to travel the first mile ; find the value of f.

2. The side elevation of a packing-case measures 6 ft. by 8 ft., and the case with contents weighs 3 cwt., the centre of gravity being at the centre of the case. Find the amount of work done in rolling the packing-case from position A to position B.

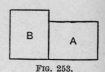

FIG. 253.

3. A cyclist is riding due N. at the rate of 12 ml./hr., and the wind, which is actually blowing at the rate of 16 ml./hr., appears to him to be coming from a direction 25° W. of N. Find *graphically* the true direction of the wind.

4. Find the direction in which a body must be projected with a velocity of 480 ft./sec. so as to strike perpendicularly a vertical plane 120 yd. distant from the point of projection.

5. Find the extra H.P. that must be exerted by a locomotive to keep up the speed of 45 ml./hr. during the time that it is picking up 2400 gallons of water at a uniform rate from a trough $\frac{1}{4}$ mile long between the rails. (1 gallon of water weighs 10 lb.)

PAPER 38

1. The driver of an express train, travelling at 60 ml./hr. on the level, suddenly notices a stationary train on the line only 310 yd. ahead. He instantly shuts off steam and applies the emergency brakes. Three seconds elapse before the brakes take effect, and then speed is reduced 4 ml./hr. every second. Find what happens.

2. A 280 lb. shell is discharged from a gun whose barrel is 15 ft. long with a velocity of 2400 ft./sec. Find in tons wt. the pressure on the base of the shell during its passage along the barrel, assuming that the pressure is constant.

3. A train is moving at 20 ml./hr. towards a station, and another is moving at 10 ml./hr. away from the station. The station is due E. of the first train, and 60° N. of E. from the second train. Find the magnitude of the velocity of one train relative to the other.

4. A cricket ball is thrown at an angle of 45° with the ground and pitches 100 yd. from the thrower, whose height above the ground may be disregarded. With what velocity must the ball be thrown and how high will it rise in the air ? Would a different elevation give a better result ?

5. A train, moving on the level, can be brought to rest by its brakes exerting a constant retarding force, in a distance of 440 yd., when its initial velocity is 45 ml./hr. Prove that if the train were moving down a slope of 1 in 100, the same brakes would stop the train in 546 yd. approximately.

PAPER 39

1. Two bodies of weight $3\frac{3}{4}$ lb. and $\frac{1}{4}$ lb. are connected by a light string. The former is placed on a smooth horizontal table at a distance of 4 ft. from the edge, and the latter hangs over this edge ; the bodies are then allowed to move under the action of gravity. Find how long the first body remains on the table.

2. A machine is driven by a pulley round which passes a belt, the tensions in the tight and slack sides of which are 50 lb. wt. and 20 lb. wt. respectively. The diameter of the pulley is 2 ft. and it is turning at a speed of 200 rev./min. Calculate the H.P.

3. A bowler delivers a ball horizontally at 96 ft./sec., his hand being 6 ft. 3 in. above the ground. How far from him does the ball pitch and what is its time of flight ? If another ball takes twice as long to pitch in the same spot, how high must it rise in its flight ?

4. A branch road running N.E. joins a main road running due N. At a particular instant, two motor cars, A and B, each travelling at 12 ml./hr., are approaching the junction, A being on the branch road and distant $1\frac{1}{2}$ miles from the junction, and B being on the main road and 1 mile S. of the junction. If the speeds of the cars remain constant, find (i) how close to one another they get, (ii) the distance of A from the junction when this occurs.

5. A flywheel of weight 4 tons is carried on a shaft 8 in. in diameter and its weight may be supposed concentrated on the circumference of a circle of radius 4 ft. If it is running at 75 rev./min. and the coefficient of friction of the shaft on its bearings is 0·06, find how many revolutions the flywheel will make before it comes to rest. (Assume $\pi = \frac{2.2}{7}$.)

PAPER 40

1. A man standing in an electric tramcar drops a penny from a height of 4 ft. above the floor, (a) when the car is running at a uniform speed of 15 ml./hr., (b) when it begins to slow up with a uniform retardation $5\frac{1}{2}$ ft./sec.[2] Indicate with diagrams the path of the falling penny relative to the floor of the car in each case, and also relative to the road.

2. An 11-ton tramcar arrives at the foot of an incline of 1 in 14 at a speed of 15 ml./hr., and commences to climb with a constant tractive effort of 1 ton wt. The road resistance is 16 lb. wt./ton. Find the speed of the car and the effective H.P. 30 seconds later.

3. A weight of 7 lb., placed on a rough horizontal table (coefficient of friction 0·3), is pulled along the table by a weight of 5 lb. hanging over the edge and attached to the former weight by an inelastic string. Find the kinetic energy of the system and the tension of the string when the system has been in motion 5 seconds from rest.

4. A string hanging over a pulley has at one end a weight of 9 lb., and at the other end weights of 4 and 8 lb. The system starts from rest, and after the weights have moved through a distance of 15 in., the weight of 8 lb. is detached. How far will the weight of 4 lb. descend ?

5. A launch is distant 10 miles, 30° S. of E., from a ship that is steaming due N. at 20 ml./hr. The launch travelling at 30 ml./hr. in a straight course just catches the ship. Find the angle W. of N. at which the launch travels and the time taken by it to reach the ship.

PAPER 41

1. A shell weighing 1960 lb. can just penetrate 18 in. of armour-plate when the velocity of impact is 2430 ft./sec. Calculate the velocity with which it would emerge from 16 in. of similar armour-plate, resistance being assumed uniform, and find its kinetic energy in ft.-tons just after piercing the 16 in. armour-plate.

2. A batsman hits a ball in the direction of a fielder standing 100 yd. away from him, and the ball leaves the bat with a velocity whose horizontal and vertical components are each 60 ft./sec. Prove that the fielder can just reach the ball in time to catch it, if he starts when the ball is hit and runs at 20 ft./sec.

3. A wind is blowing at 20 ml./hr. from S. to N., and an aeroplane, which can fly at 100 ml./hr. in still air, wishes to reach a point whose bearing from the starting point of the aeroplane is N. 60° E. In what direction should the aeroplane steer so as to reach the point in a straight line, and with what speed will it approach it ?

4. A weight of 102 grams descending vertically draws up a weight of 100 grams by means of a light string passing over a pulley. If the string breaks 5 sec. after starting from rest, find how much higher the 100 gram weight will go. Answer in cm.

5. A gas is compressed in a cylinder by the movement of the piston. The relation between the force on the piston (F lb. wt.) and D inches, the distance from the inside face of the piston to the inside end of the cylinder, is given by the table :—

D	18	15	12	9	6	3
F	110	142·5	196	294	523	1401

Plot a graph showing the relation between F and D, as D decreases from 18 in. to 3 in. ; thence find the work done during the compression.

PAPER 42

1. If a motor car is travelling with velocity v ft./sec., prove that the force exerted by the engine, which is working at n horse-power, is equal to $550n/v$ lb. wt.

   A car is travelling along a straight level road at 30 ml./hr., the engine working at 20 H.P. Find the magnitude of the total resistance to the car's motion, due to friction, etc.

2. A body is dropped from a balloon at a height of 2500 feet when it is moving upwards at 10 ml./hr. at an angle of 50° with the horizontal. Find after what time the body will reach the ground.

3. An aeroplane travels in still air at the rate of 100 ml./hr. It starts from A to reach a point B due N. 150 miles away. There is a wind blowing due W. at 20 ml./hr., but when half the distance has been covered the velocity of the wind increases to 30 ml./hr. Find the time taken over the flight to the nearest minute.

4. Two railway stations A and B are half a mile apart. A train starts from A, and travels with acceleration f up to a certain point, when the steam is shut off and the brakes applied. The retardation of the train is then $4f$, and the train is just brought to rest at B. If the journey occupies 2 minutes, find the value of f (in ft./sec.^{2}), and also the greatest speed attained during the journey.

5. A railway has an upward gradient of 1 in 150 from A to B, a distance of 3 miles, and a downward gradient of 1 in 250 from B to C, a distance of 5 miles. When the engine exerts a constant pull against a constant frictional resistance, the speed falls from 50 ml./hr. to 30 ml./hr. between A and B. Beyond B the same constant pull is maintained against the same frictional resistance, until the speed is again 50 ml./hr. At what distance from B is this speed reached ?

PAPER 43

1. A pumping engine is required to pump 11,000 gallons of water to a height of 30 ft. in 1 hour. Owing to frictional and other losses, only 60 per cent. of the power delivered by the engine is usefully employed. Find the actual H.P. the engine must develop.
   (1 gallon of water weighs 10 lb.)

2. A body is projected with a velocity of 75 ft./sec. at an elevation of 40°. Find its velocity in magnitude and direction after 5 seconds.

3. A train travelling at 30 ml./hr. is pulled up in a distance of 220 yd., and after a momentary stop proceeds. It regains its original speed after describing a certain distance D. The loss of time occasioned by the stop is 1 minute. If the retardation and acceleration are uniform, find the distance D.

4. A man walks along a compartment of a railway carriage at right angles to the direction of motion of the train, when the train is travelling at 10 ml./hr. ; he then walks back, with the same velocity relative to the train, when the train is travelling at 21 ml./hr. His resultant velocity in the latter case is twice that in the former case. Prove that his velocity relative to the train is nearly 3·7 ml./hr.

5. A body moves in a straight line so that the force P lb. wt. acting on it when it is at a distance x ft. from a fixed point on the line is given by the following table :—

x	0	5	10	15	20	25	30	35	40
P	18	23·5	28	32	34·5	36	37	36	32

   Plot P against x and thence find the work done on the body in this motion. If the weight of the body is 156 lb., and it starts from rest when x is 0, find the velocity when x is 40 ft.

PAPER 44

1. If 200 lb. of water are discharged by a pipe 5 in. in diameter in a second, find the velocity of the water, and if 80 per cent. of its kinetic energy can be used to drive a machine, find the H.P. of the machine.
   (Assume 1 cu. ft. of water weighs 62·5 lb. and $\pi = 3·14$.)

2. A rocket is to be fired from the top of a cliff 80 ft. high with velocity 200 ml./hr. to a ship in distress, half a mile from the base of the cliff.

   Find the proper elevation at which the rocket should be fired. Why are there two solutions?

3. In the system of smooth pulleys shown in Fig. 254, prove that the upward acceleration of the weight m is

   $$4g \cdot \frac{M - 4m}{M + 16m}.$$

   Find the values of this acceleration and the tensions in the ropes if the weights, M and m, are respectively 200 lb. and 40 lb.

FIG. 254.

4. A motor-cyclist is riding clockwise in a circular track at a speed of 30 ml./hr. while a N.W. wind of 10 ml./hr. is blowing. Show by means of a diagram the apparent directions of the wind to the cyclist when he is at the N. and W. points of the track.

   A liner proceeding on a course 24° N. of W. appears to be moving N.W. from a tug moving at 9 knots in a westerly direction. Find, by construction, the speed of the liner.

5. A box of weight 50 lb. is made to slide forward along the horizontal platform of a trolley of weight 1 cwt. by a horizontal force of 40 lb. wt. steadily applied. If the coefficient of friction between the box and the platform is 0·3, and the resistance to the motion of the trolley is 10 lb. wt., find the acceleration of the trolley and the acceleration of the box relative to the trolley.

PAPER 45

1. A wooden wedge whose faces are inclined at an angle of 45° rests with one of these faces on a smooth horizontal plane and a small object of weight 4 oz. slides down the other face. If there is no friction between the object and the wedge, find the horizontal force that must be applied to the wedge to keep it from moving.

2. If the back wheel of a bicycle is 28 in. in diameter and revolves 2·5 times as fast as the pedals, how many times must the pedals revolve in 1 second when the bicycle is travelling at 20 ml./hr. ?

   If the bicycle is being driven at this speed by a force of 100 lb. wt. at the end of a crank 7 in. long, at what rate is the rider doing work ? (Assume $\pi = \frac{2\,2}{7}$.)

3. A man who swims at 3 ml./hr. in still water wishes to cross a river 176 yd. wide flowing at 5 ml./hr. Indicate graphically the direction in which he should swim in order to reach the opposite bank, (a) as soon as possible, (b) as little down stream as possible. How long will he take to cross and how far will he be carried down the stream in each case ?

4. The speed of a train of weight 100 tons varies with the time as shown :—

Speed (ml./hr.)	0	17	27	33	37	39	39·5
Time (sec.)	0	10	20	30	40	50	60

   Illustrate graphically. If the train is running down an incline of 1 in 448, find the H.P. being exerted by the engine at the end of the first ½ min., if the frictional resistance at that instant is 10 lb. wt./ton.

5. A train of 140 tons wt., travelling along a level track, slips the last coach which weighs 20 tons. The coach comes to rest without application of the brakes after 3 min., and the rest of the train is then $\frac{2}{3}$ mile ahead of it. At the instant of slipping, the speed of the train is 40 ml./hr. The resistance to motion, R lb. wt./ton, may be taken as uniform for both portions of the train, and P lb. wt., the pull of the engine, is unaltered throughout. Find R and P.

Determine also the H.P. at which the engine was working at the instant of slipping, and in ft.-sec. units the rate at which the train was gaining or losing speed at that instant.

A FIRST COURSE IN MECHANICS

ANSWERS

Page 5 **Exercise I**

3. 2 in. **4.** $5\frac{1}{3}$ lb. wt. **5.** 5 lb. wt.

7. (i) 3 lb., 3 lb. ; (ii) 3 lb., $3\frac{1}{4}$ lb. **8.** 83 lb. wt.

9. 6, 5, 3 lb. wt **10.** 2 lb. wt., 6 lb. wt. **11.** $3\frac{1}{2}$ lb. wt., $3\frac{1}{2}$.

12. $1\frac{1}{2}$ lb. wt. **13.** 4 lb. wt., $4\frac{1}{4}$ lb. wt. **14.** 4 lb. wt.

15. 3 lb. wt. **16.** 4 lb. wt. **17.** 148, 158 lb. wt.

Page 11 **Exercise II**

1. (i) 0, 15, 32, 0 lb. ft. ; (ii) 16, 0, 0, 25 lb. ft. ; (iii) 24, 0, —16, 25 lb. ft.

2. (1) 4·34 kg. m. ; (ii) 20·48 kg. m. **3.** 154 lb. in., 25·7 lb. wt.

4. 17·5 lb. **5.** 12 in. from middle. **6.** $3\frac{4}{7}$ ft.

7. 10·4 lb. wt., 20·8 lb. wt. **8.** $\frac{9}{11}$ in. from 10 lb. wt.

9. 84 lb. wt. **10.** 10 lb. wt. **11.** 10 ft.

12. 2 ft. 8 in. **13.** 70·4 lb. wt. **14.** 8 in.

15. 8 oz. **16.** $7\frac{8}{19}$ ft. **17.** 5 cm.

18. $7\frac{3}{4}$ lb. wt. **19.** $27\frac{1}{2}$ lb. wt. **20.** $186\frac{2}{3}$ lb. wt.

21. 140 lb. in. ; $93\frac{1}{3}$ lb. wt. **22.** $\sqrt{P} : \sqrt{Q}$; $\sqrt{PQ}$.

23. $91\frac{7}{23}=91\cdot3$ lb. wt. **24.** 2 ft. from A. **25.** 9 lb. wt. ; $3\frac{1}{3}$ ft.

Page 15 **Exercise III**

1. 10·0 lb. wt. **2.** 33° 40′. **3.** 51 lb. wt.

4. 15 lb. wt. **5.** $1230\frac{10}{13}=1230\cdot8$ lb. wt. **6.** 93·3 lb. wt.

7. 25 lb. wt. **8.** 15 lb. wt./sq. ft. **9.** $2\frac{1}{2}$ lb. wt.

10. 26·6 gm. wt. **11.** 45·0 lb. wt. **12.** 6 in.

13. 412 lb. wt. **14.** (i) 25 lb. wt. ; (ii) 24·7 lb. wt.

15. Middle point. **16.** (a) 30 lb. wt. ; (b) $37\frac{1}{2}$ lb. wt.

17. 0·259 lb. wt. **18.** $\dfrac{W\sqrt{3}}{6}$.

Page 20   **Exercise IV**

1. $4\frac{1}{4}$, $\frac{3}{4}$ tons wt.   2. $33\frac{3}{5}$, $22\frac{2}{5}$ lb. wt.   3. 9, 15 lb. wt.

4. $3\frac{1}{3}$ ft. from greater weight.   5. 21, 33 lb. wt.

6. 5 in. from nearer balance.   7. 4 ft. from one end.

8. 1 ft. 4 in.   9. 7 in.   10. $173\frac{1}{3}$, $186\frac{2}{3}$ lb. wt.

11. Front 104, back wheel 69 lb. wt.   12. 11, 4 lb. wt.

13. $\frac{1}{4}$ lb. wt. ; $13\frac{1}{2}$, $4\frac{1}{2}$ lb. wt.   14. $1\frac{8}{17}$ ft.

15. 12 lb. wt. ; $CE = 1.5$ ft.   16. 15 cwt.

17. 2 in.   18. A, $61\frac{2}{3}$ lb. wt. up ; other, $191\frac{2}{3}$ lb. wt. down.

19. 20, 5 lb. wt.   20. O and 250 lb. wt. ; B, 240 lb. wt. ; D, 130 lb. wt.

21. 90 lb. wt. ; 1 ft. 8 in.   22. 50 lb. wt., 330 lb. wt. ; yes.

23. $78\frac{1}{3}$ lb. wt.   24. 10 in.

Page 26   **Exercise V**

1. 10 lb. wt.   2. 5·48 lb. wt.   3. 15 : 16.   4. $56\frac{1}{2}$ lb. wt.

5. 28 in.   6. $3\frac{5}{8}$ lb. wt.   7. 1 in. from scale-pan.

8. $20\frac{1}{2}$, 15 lb. wt. ; $1\frac{1}{2}$.   9. 10 lb. wt.   11. 10 lb. wt.

12. $11\frac{1}{4}$ lb. wt.   13. $93\frac{1}{3}$ lb. wt.   14. 880 lb. wt.

15. 3072 lb. wt.   16. 1116 lb. wt.   17. $\frac{5}{5}\frac{5}{7} = 0.96$ lb. wt.

18. Radii to small weights make angles 60° with horizontal ; $\dfrac{R}{r} w$.

19. Loses $\frac{1}{4}$d.

Page 33   **Exercise VI**

1. 4·1, 4·6 lb. wt.   2. 8·2, 9·5 kg. wt.   3. 5·4, 7·3 gm. wt.

4. 24·2 lb. wt.   5. 22·3 lb. wt.   6. 301 gm. wt.

7. 102°, 136°.   8. 138°, 122°.   9. 130°, 104°.

10. $P = 7$ lb. wt., $R = 10.7$ lb. wt.   11. $Q = 9.4$ gm. wt., $R = 4.2$ gm. wt.

12. $A\hat{O}B = 99°$, $B\hat{O}C = 137°$.   13. 29·2 lb. wt.   14. 28, 26 lb. wt.

15. 15·1 kg. wt.   16. 64·8 lb. wt. ; 19° S. of W.

17. 6·5 lb. wt.   18. 256 lb. wt.   19. 40, 96 lb. wt.

20. $2\frac{1}{2}$ oz. wt.   21. 8·40 lb. wt.   22. 13·8 lb. wt.

23. (i) 4·6 lb. wt. ; (ii) 4 lb. wt.   24. 115 lb. wt., 115 lb. wt.

25. 3·9, 6·0 cwt.   26. 83, 141 lb. wt.   27. 3·8, 4·2 cwt.

28. 112 lb. wt.   29. 15·2 lb. wt.   30. 1·2, 2·2 lb. wt.

Answers

Page 39 **Exercise VII**

1. 32 lb. wt. ; $7\frac{1}{2}$ ft. **2.** 122 lb. wt. ; $8\frac{16}{61} = 8\cdot26$ ft. **3.** 5 lb. wt. ; 60 ft.
4. 2 lb. wt. ; $40\frac{1}{2}$ in. **5.** $AO = 4\frac{1}{2}$ ft. ; 28 ft. **6.** 5 lb. wt. ; 5 ft.
7. 4 lb. wt. ; $10\frac{3}{4}$ ft. **8.** 2 lb. wt. at A. **9.** 3 lb. wt. ; 6 ft.
10. 6 lb. wt. down, 10 in. from D in AD produced.

Page 41 **Exercise VIII**

1. $28\cdot7$ lb. wt. ; $21°$. **2.** 297 lb. wt. ; $28\frac{1}{2}°$. **3.** $9\cdot06$ lb. wt. ; $25°$.
4. $16\cdot5$ lb. wt. ; $63\frac{1}{2}°$. **5.** $9\cdot20$ lb. wt. ; $88°$. **6.** $8\cdot31$ lb. wt. ; $62\frac{1}{2}°$.
7. $18\cdot8$, $11\cdot2$ lb. wt. **8.** $28\cdot7$, $19\cdot0$ lb. wt. **9.** $58\cdot3$, $42\cdot2$ lb. wt.
10. (i) $102°$; (ii) $122°$; (iii) $82°$. **11.** $46°$, $52°$.
12. $9\cdot5$ kg. wt. **13.** $9\cdot0$ lb. wt. **14.** 366 lb. wt.
15. 173 lb. wt. **16.** 13 lb. wt. **17.** $26\cdot8$ lb. wt.

Page 44 **Exercise IX**

1. $4\cdot8$ lb. wt. **2.** 35 miles ; $40°$ E. of N.
3. 57 lb. wt. ; $39°$. **4.** 77 kg. wt. ; N. $18°$ E.
5. $10\cdot5$ lb. wt. ; N. $68°$ E. **6.** 30 lb. wt. ; E. $33°$ S.
7. 10 lb. wt. ; $37°$. **8.** Runs $74°$ W. of N. ; 81 lb. wt.
9. $9\cdot8$ lb. wt., $23°$ W. of N. **10.** $10\cdot8$, $9\cdot0$ lb. wt.
11. $0\cdot71$, $3\cdot54$ lb. wt. **12.** $1\cdot09$, $18\cdot5$ tons wt.
13. AD, $4\cdot3$ tension ; AE, $0\cdot89$ tension.
14. Upper 5 lb. wt., $37°$; lower $2\cdot2$ lb. wt., $26\frac{1}{2}°$.

Page 48 **Exercise X**

1. $35\cdot8$ lb. wt. ; $35°$. **2.** $58\cdot5$ lb. wt. ; $46°$. **3.** $24\cdot2$ lb. wt. ; $111°$.
4. $54\cdot7$ lb. wt. ; $77°$. **5.** 249 lb. wt. **6.** $8\cdot45$ lb. wt.
7. $74°$. **8.** $108°$ **9.** $85°$. **10.** $6\cdot46$ lb. wt.
11. $9\cdot67$ lb. wt. **12.** $4\cdot26$ lb. wt. **13.** $51\cdot7$ lb. wt.
14. $3\cdot38$ oz. wt. **15.** $4\cdot8$ tons wt. **16.** 12, 16 lb. wt.

Page 53　　　　　　**Exercise XI**

1. 7·66, 6·428 lb. wt.　　　　2. 7·5, 12·99 lb. wt.

3. 11·47, −16·38 lb. wt.　　　4. −20·48, −14·34 lb. wt.

5. −14·14, 14·14 lb. wt.　　　6. −1·736, 9·848 lb. wt.

7. 8·604, 12·29 lb. wt.　　　　8. −15·32, −12·86 lb. wt.

9. 18·79, 6·84 lb. wt.　　　　10. −5, −8·66 lb. wt.

11. 7·5, 12·99 lb. wt.　　　　12. −19·15, 16·07 lb. wt.

13. −12, 0, 0 lb. wt.

14.　(i) 2 cos 25°, 2 cos 60°, 0, −2 ;

　　(ii) 3 cos 65°, 3 cos 35°, 3 cos 25°, −3 cos 25° ;

　　(iii) 4 cos 30°, −4 cos 60°, 4 cos 35°, 4 cos 60° ;

　　(iv) 0, 5 cos 30°, 5 cos 65°, 0.

15. 65·3 lb. wt.　　　　　　16. 57°.

17. (i) 773 lb. wt. ; (ii) 207 lb. wt.　　18. 6·72 lb. wt./ton.

Page 54　　　　　　**Exercise XII**

1. 10·6 lb. wt.　　　2. 4·20, 6·53 lb. wt.　　3. 31·1, 23·8 lb. wt.

4. 34·2 lb. wt.　　　5. 36° 32′.　　　　　6. 17 lb. wt.

7. 0·79 lb. wt.　　　8. 5·77, 5·77 lb. wt.　　9. 58·0 lb. wt.

10. 8·40, 7·32 lb. wt.　　11. 0·577 lb. wt.　　12. 5 oz. wt.

13. 46·2 lb. wt.　　　14. 2, 3·46 lb. wt.　　15. 24·1 lb. wt.

16. 4⅚ cwt.　　　　17. 28° 31′.　　　　18. 82·8 lb. wt. ; 24° 39′.

19. 153, 98·5 lb. wt.　　20. 30° 38′.　　　21. 9·06, 2·16 lb. wt.

22. (i) **6·43, 7·66** lb. wt. ; (ii) 11·9 lb. wt.

Page 58　　　　　　**Exercise XIII**

1. 13·2 lb. wt. ; 46°.　　2. 4·62 lb. wt.　　3. 8·73 lb. wt. ; E. 28° N.

4. 16° N. of W. ; 77·1 lb. wt.

6. 16·8 lb. wt. ; S. 46° E.　　5. 13·4 lb. wt. ; S. 77° W.

8. 4·44 lb. wt. ; S. 83° W.　　7. 8·78 lb. wt. ; S. 36° W.

9. 10·8, 8·98 lb. wt.

Page 60   **Exercise XIV**

1. 6·44, 12·5 lb. wt.   **2.** 15·2, 21·5 cwt.   **3.** 19·2, 16·1 gm. wt.

4. 49·0 lb. wt.   **5.** 11·5, 23·1 kg. wt.   **6.** 8·40, 14·6 lb. wt.

7. 2·48 tons wt., tension ; 3·73 tons wt., compression.

8. *AB*, 33·0 ; *BC*, 26·9 ; *CD*, 39·3 ; *W*, 39·3 lb. wt.

9. At *B*, 10 ; *D*, 3·66 ; *AB*, 17·3 ; *BC*, 10 ; *CD*, 10 ; *DE*, 12·3 lb. wt.

10. *P*, 6·4 ; *Q*, 4·8 ; *AB*, 14·5 ; *BC*, 12·7 ; *CD*, 12·1 ; *DE*, 13·7 lb. wt.

Page 62   **Exercise XV**

1. 8·7, 13 lb. wt.   **2.** 2·5 lb. wt.   **3.** 3·8 lb. wt.

4. *A*, 15 ; *B*, 9·4 lb. wt. ; 63°.   **5.** 9·2, 3·8 lb. wt.

6. 5·6, 7·7 lb. wt.   **7.** 7·1 ft.   **8.** 4·2, 10·9 lb. wt.

9. 8·3 lb. wt.   **10.** 280, 240 lb. wt.   **11.** 1·1 lb. wt.

12. 28° ; 1·8, 1·1 lb. wt.   **13.** Upper 110 ; lower 170 lb. wt.

14. 12·5 in.   **15.** 1·7 in. ; 12·2 lb. wt.

16. 5·5 lb. wt.   **17.** 30° ; 2·3, 2·3 lb. wt.   **18.** 9·2 lb. wt.

REVISION PAPERS

Page 66   **Paper 1**

1. 4 ft.   **2.** $2\frac{1}{2}$, $3\frac{1}{2}$ lb. wt.   **3.** 9600 lb. wt.

4. 61·2 lb. wt.   **5.** 10·25 lb. wt.

Page 66   **Paper 2**

1. 15, 25 lb. wt.   **2.** 6 in.   **3.** $562\frac{1}{2}$ lb. wt.

4. $34\frac{5}{6}$ in. from fulcrum.   **5.** 7·4 lb. wt.

Page 67   **Paper 3**

1. 20, 3 lb. wt.   **2.** $6\frac{9}{11}$ in.   **3.** $103\frac{3}{19} = 103·2$ lb. wt.

4. 10 lb. wt. ; at *C*.   **5.** 31 in. from fulcrum.

Page 68   **Paper 4**

1. 1 ft.   **2.** 4 lb. wt.   **3.** 15 lb. wt. ; 1 ft. from C.
4. 17·3 gm. wt.   **5.** $2\frac{13}{16}=2\cdot81$ lb. wt.

Page 68   **Paper 5**

1. 2 lb. wt.   **2.** 85° 36′.   **3.** $12\frac{1}{2}$, $13\frac{1}{2}$ lb. wt.
4. 78°, 146°, 136°.   **5.** $5\frac{1}{7}$, $13\frac{1}{7}$, $29\frac{1}{7}$, $61\frac{1}{7}$ in.

Page 69   **Paper 6**

1. 7·07 lb. wt.   **2.** 24 ft.   **3.** 5 ft. from bank.
4. 7·3, 9·0 lb. wt.   **5.** 80 lb. wt.

Page 70   **Paper 7**

1. 36·6 lb. wt.   **2.** $3\frac{11}{15}=3\cdot7$. $10\frac{4}{15}=10\cdot3$ in.
3. 143 in.   **4.** 5·5 tons wt.   **5.** 1800, 2600 lb. wt.

Page 70   **Paper 8**

1. 8, 10 lb. wt.   **2.** 25, 10 lb. wt.   **3.** 42 lb. wt. ; 22°.
4. 6 lb. wt. ; 120° with first force.   **5.** A, 4 ; C, 16 ; 12 ; 12 lb. wt.

Page 71   **Paper 9**

1. 4 lb. wt. ; $\frac{1}{2}$ ft.   **2.** 224, 2228 lb. wt.   **3.** 36·9 lb. wt.
4. 36° 52′.   **5.** 97, 148 lb. wt.

Page 72   **Paper 10**

1. 15·7 lb. wt. ; 67° 6′ with smaller force.   **2.** 64·7 lb. wt. ; N. 38° W.
4. 0·403.   **5.** 930, 540 gm. wt. ; 38° with horizontal.

Page 72   **Paper 11**

1. 10·4, 6 lb. wt.   **2.** 10·39, 6 lb. wt.   **3.** 3·46 lb. wt.
4. 300 lb. wt. ; 9·6 ft.   **5.** 0·7 ft.

Page 73

1. 4·74 lb. wt. ; 53° 59′.
3. 35½° ; 8·6 lb. wt.
5. 11·5, 5·8 lb. wt.

Paper 12

2. 6·68 lb. wt. ; S. 54° 18′ E.
4. 100 lb. wt. ; 5·4 ft. .

Page 75 — **Exercise XVI**

1. 44, 66, 36⅔ ft./sec.
2. 15, $20\frac{5}{11}$, $34\frac{1}{11}$ ml./hr.
3. 10 ml./hr.
4. 2½ m.
5. 200 metres/min.
6. $4\frac{2}{5}$ ml./hr.
7. $3\frac{23}{32}=3\cdot72$ ml./hr.
8. $34\frac{2}{7}=34\cdot3$ ml./hr. ; 2 hr. 20 min.
9. $22\frac{46}{47}=23\cdot0$ ml./hr.
10. 14·6 ml./hr.
11. 6, 4·2 ml./hr.
12. $\dfrac{a+b}{x+y}$ ft./sec.
13. $\dfrac{au+bv}{a+b}$ ml./hr.
14. $3\frac{3}{4}$ ml./hr. ; $3\frac{7}{11}$ ml./hr.
15. (i) 1800° per sec. ; (ii) $10\pi=31\cdot4$ radians/sec. ; (iii) $50\pi=157$ ft./sec.
16. 20 ft./sec.
17. (i) 377½, (ii) $150\frac{6}{7}$ ft./sec.
18. 8⅓ radians/sec.
19. (i) and (ii) 0·000073 rad./sec. ; (iii) 1037, 849 ml./hr.
20. 2750 ft./sec.

Page 78 — **Exercise XVII**

1. 14 ft./sec.
2. 4, 2 ft./sec. ; body at rest.
3. 17, 29 ft./sec.
4. 77 ft. ; 1st sec. ; −18 ft./sec.
5. (i) 6·1 ft. ; (ii) 16 ft./sec.
6. 6, 12, 18, 18, 18, 18 ft./sec. ; velocity constant between 3rd and 6th sec.
7. 19·8 ft./sec.
8. (i) 9·82, 0·9676, 0·0966 ft. ; (ii) 98·2, 96·8, 96·6 ft./sec. ; (iii) 96·6 ft./sec.
9. Doncaster and Selby ; 47·6 ml./hr.

Page 83 — **Exercise XVIII**

1. 37½ ft.
2. 940 ft.
3. 35·5 ml.
4. 1·3, 7·8 ft.
5. 310 ft.
6. 1600 ft.
7. 1300 ft.
8. 86 ft.

Page 88   **Exercise XIX**

1. $1\frac{1}{3}$ ft./séc.^{2} 2. 300 ml./hr.^{2}

3. (i) 58,080 ft./hr.^{2}; (ii) $16\frac{2}{15}=16\cdot1$ ft. per sec. per hr.; (iii) $0\cdot00448$ ft./sec.^{2}

4. $\frac{11}{6750}=0\cdot00163$ ft./sec.^{2} 5. 38,400 yd./min.^{2}

6. 480 ft./sec.   7. $0\cdot91$ cm./sec.^{2} 8. $2\cdot75$ sec.

9. $5\cdot2$ ft./sec.   10. $14\cdot6$ cm./sec.   11. $\frac{1}{20}=0\cdot05$ ft./sec.^{2}

12. $7\cdot2$, $2\cdot4$ ft./sec.^{2} 13. $10\cdot3$ ft./sec.^{2} 14. 4, $10\cdot6$ ft./sec.^{2}

15. $(8+2x)$ cm./sec.^{2}; 8 cm./sec.^{2} 16. 4, 4, 4, $3\frac{2}{3}$, $3\frac{1}{4}$, $2\frac{1}{2}$ ft./sec.^{2}

17. $2\cdot2$ rev. per min. per sec.

18. 2 ft./sec.^{2}; 44 ft./sec.; 22 sec.

19. $2\cdot75$, $7\cdot75$, $13\cdot5$, $18\cdot5$, $23\cdot5$, $26\cdot5$, 26, $26\cdot5$ cm./sec.

20. $17\cdot0$, $15\cdot0$ ft./sec.   21. 30 ml./hr.

Page 93   **Exercise XX**

1. 120 ft.   2. $2\frac{52}{55}=2\cdot95$ sec.   3. $1\frac{1}{2}$ miles.

4. $10\cdot18$ cm./sec.; $2\cdot036$ cm./sec.^{2} 5. $\frac{1}{40}$ sec.

6. 27 cm./sec.; 81 cm.   7. 90 yd.; 18 sec.

8. $\frac{1}{5}$ ft./sec.^{2}; 40 ft./sec.

9. (i) $\frac{44}{45}=0\cdot98$ ft./sec.^{2}; (ii) $\frac{44}{135}=0\cdot33$ ft./sec.^{2}

10. 2200 ft. further, after 1 min.   11. $1\frac{1}{20}$ ft./sec.^{2}

12. $204\frac{1}{4}$ ft.   13. 25 miles.   14. 22 ft./sec.^{2}

15. 180 ft.   16. 2100 ft.   17. $10\frac{5}{12}$ yd.

18. $-2\cdot2$ ft./sec.^{2}; $\frac{1}{1\frac{1}{2}}$ mile.   19. $1\frac{1}{2}$ min.; $22\cdot4$ ml./hr.

20. 66 ft./sec.; $544\cdot5$ ft.   21. $1\cdot76$, $3\cdot52$ ft./sec.^{2}; 396 yd.

23. 20 ft./sec.; $82\frac{1}{2}$ sec.   24. 105 ft./sec.

Page 99   **Exercise XXI**

1. 100 ft.   2. 3 sec; 96 ft./sec.   3. 120 ft./sec.; $2\frac{1}{2}$ sec.

4. 64 ft./sec. up; 64 ft./sec. down.   5. $76\cdot7$ m./sec.

6. 8 ft./sec.   7. $20\cdot4$ metres; $4\cdot08$ sec.

8. $125\frac{11}{25}$ ft.; $89\frac{3}{5}$ ft./sec.; $0\cdot36$ sec.; $78\cdot2$ ft./sec.

10. 80 ft./sec.; 800 ft.; 900 ft.   11. $42\frac{2}{3}=42\cdot7$ ft./sec.

12. 0·81 sec., 2·32 sec.

13. 45 ft. ; 53·7 ft./sec.

14. $5\frac{5}{6}$ sec. ; $202\frac{2}{9}$ ft.

15. 10 sec. after second is dropped.

16. 80 ft./sec. ; 100 ft.

17. $31\frac{5}{9}$ ft.

18. $\sqrt{\frac{2}{3}} = 0·817$.

19. $\frac{1}{4}h - \left(\dfrac{h}{v}\right)^2$ ft.

20. 88 ft./sec. ; 2·86 sec.

21. 168, 232 ft./sec.

22. 196 ft. ; 112 ft./sec. ; 4 ft.

23. 168 ft./sec.

24. 100 ft. ; 32 ft./sec.

25. 121 ft. ; 104 ft./sec. ; 144 ft.

Page 106   Exercise XXII

1. 64, 32, $25\frac{3}{5}$ ft./sec.²

2. $3\frac{3}{4}$ lb. wt.

3. 80 ft./sec.²

4. 16 lb. wt.

5. 15·3 gm. wt.

6. $10\frac{2}{3}$ ft./sec.² ; $7\frac{1}{2}$ sec. ; 80 ft./sec.

7. $2\frac{1}{2}$ sec.

8. $\frac{32}{111} = 0·29$ ft./sec.²

9. 307·2 ft./sec.

10. 45 ft.

11. $7\frac{47}{54} = 7·73$ tons wt.

12. 2075 lb. wt.

13. $\frac{121}{120} = 1·01$.

14. $468\frac{3}{4}$ lb. wt.

15. (i) $\frac{3}{25} = 0·12$ tons wt. ; (ii) $\frac{18}{25} = 0·72$ tons wt.

16. 29·5 ml./hr.

17. 0·91 sec.

18. $19\frac{11}{20}$ tons wt.

19. $1\frac{7}{45} = 1·16$ ft./sec.²

20. 9·30 ft./sec.²

21. $168\frac{3}{4}$, 150, $140\frac{5}{8}$ lb. wt.

22. 10, $13\frac{1}{8}$ tons wt.

23. 22·6 ft./sec. ; 28·7 ft.

24. 11·2 lb. wt./ton ; $756\frac{1}{4}$ ft.

25. 0·26 sec.

27. 1° 18′.

28. $814\frac{22}{27} = 814·8$ lb. wt.

29. $\frac{96}{119} = 0·807$ ft./sec.² ; $15\frac{95}{192} = 15·4$ ft.

30. 11·1 tons wt./sq. in.

Page 111   Exercise XXIII

1. 34 lb. wt.

2. 51 lb. 9 oz. each.

3. 63 lb. wt.

4. 188 lb. wt.

5. $6\frac{1}{8}$, 7, $7\frac{7}{16}$ lb. wt.

6. 540, $157\frac{1}{2}$ lb. wt.

7. 306, 170 lb. wt.

8. $122\frac{1}{2}$, 112, 105 lb. wt.

9. $22\frac{2}{9}$, 20 lb. wt.

10. 240 ft./sec.²

11. 31,800 lb. wt. (approx.).

12. 7° 6′.

13. $6\frac{26}{33}$ ft./sec.²

Page 114   **Exercise XXIV**

1. $7\frac{7}{8}$ lb. wt.   **2.** $5\frac{1}{19} = 5\cdot05$ ft./sec.^{2} ; $9\frac{5}{19}$ lb. wt. ; $18\frac{10}{19} = 18\cdot5$ lb. wt.

3. 3 oz. wt. ; 2 ft.   **4.** $3\frac{3}{4}$ lb. wt. ; $1\frac{1}{2}$ lb. wt.

5. $7\frac{1}{17}$ lb. wt. ; $5\frac{15}{17}$ lb. wt.   **6.** $11\frac{3}{7}$ ft./sec.^{2} ; $3\frac{3}{14}$ lb. wt.

7. $3\frac{1}{3}$ lb. wt. ; $2\frac{1}{2}$ lb. wt.   **8.** 12 ft./sec.   **9.** $1\cdot888$ lb. wt. ; $3\cdot57$ ft.

10. 2, $1\frac{1}{3}$ lb. wt. ; $10\frac{2}{3}$ ft./sec.^{2} **11.** $1\cdot12$ sec.

12. 2 sec.   **13.** $\frac{3}{5}$ sec.   **14.** $1\cdot82$ sec.   **15.** 4 ft.

16. $\frac{32}{33} = 0\cdot97$ ft./sec.^{2} ; $0\cdot087$ sec.   **17.** $3\frac{13}{16}$ sec.

18. (i) 2 ft. ; (ii) 60 gm. wt. ; $6\cdot4$ ft./sec.^{2} ; $12\cdot8$ ft./sec.^{2}

19. $10\frac{2}{3}$ ft./sec.^{2} ; $2\frac{2}{3}$ lb. wt.

REVISION PAPERS

Page 117   **Paper 13**

1. $2\frac{7}{9} = 2\cdot78$ m./sec.   **2.** $5\cdot66$ ml./hr.   **3.** 2750 ft.

4. 47 ft./sec.   **5.** $96735\cdot5$ ft./sec.^{2}

Page 117   **Paper 14**

1. $16\frac{5}{73} = 16\cdot8$ ml./hr.   **2.** 36 ft./sec.   **3.** 13, 24 ft./sec.

4. $5\cdot28$ ft./sec.^{2}

5. (i) $\frac{25}{32} = 0\cdot78$, $\frac{75}{32} = 2\cdot34$ sec. ;   (ii) $\frac{5}{8}$, $2\frac{1}{2}$ sec.

Page 118   **Paper 15**

1. 7 rad./sec.   **2.** $70\cdot8$ ft.   **3.** $\frac{11}{60}$ ft./sec.^{2}

4. 2 sec.   **5.** 144 ft.

Page 119   **Paper 16**

1. (i) $1080°$ per sec. ; (ii) $6\pi = 18\cdot84$ rad./sec. ; (iii) $75\cdot36$ ft./sec.

2. 4, 8 ft./sec.^{2} **3.** $\frac{1}{25}$ ft./sec.^{2} ; 11,250 ft. ; $12\frac{1}{2}$ min.

4. $122{,}727\frac{3}{11}$ ml./hr.   **5.** $172\cdot98$ metres.

Page 119   **Paper 17**

1. 2 sec.   **2.** $\frac{3}{8}$ sec. ; 28 ft./sec.
4. $\frac{2}{3}$ sec. ; $21\frac{1}{3}$ ft./sec. ; $7\frac{1}{9}$ ft.   **5.** (i) 0·6 ft./sec.^{2} ; (ii) 12·8, 28·7 ft.

Page 120   **Paper 18**

1. 3075 ft.   **2.** 36 ft.   **3.** 100 ft.
4. 2 min. 56 sec. ; $10,325\frac{1}{3}$ ft.$=1$·96 miles.   **5.** 30 sec. ; 220 yd.

Page 121   **Paper 19**

1. $1\frac{41}{128}=1$·32 lb. wt.   **2.** $128\frac{4}{7}$ ft.   **3.** 6·4 ft./sec.^{2} ; 9·6 lb. wt.
4. 30 ml./hr.   **5.** $34\frac{1}{11}$ ml./hr. ; $1\frac{1}{19}$ ft./sec.^{2}

Page 121   **Paper 20**

1. $2\frac{1}{2}$ ft./sec.^{2} ; $5\frac{7}{32}$ lb. wt.   **2.** 119 lb. wt.   **3.** 9·6 ft./sec.^{2}
4. $1\frac{15}{16}$ or 3 sec. ; 81 ft./sec.   **5.** 20 cm./sec.^{2}

Page 122   **Paper 21**

1. 1 lb. wt.   **2.** $16\frac{2}{3}$ sec.   **3.** $774\frac{2}{5}$ ft.
4. 24 ft./sec. ; $3\frac{2}{3}$ miles.   **5.** 4 sec. from start ; 16 ft. from O.

Page 123   **Paper 22**

1. $16\frac{4}{11}$ ml./hr.   **2.** $9\frac{1}{7}$ ft./sec.^{2} ; $1\frac{3}{7}$ lb. wt. ; 0·66 sec.
3. (i) $1013\frac{1}{4}$, $131\frac{1}{4}$ lb. wt. ; (ii) $1302\frac{3}{4}$, $168\frac{3}{4}$ lb. wt.
4. 144 ft.   **5.** 55 ft./sec. ; 11 ft./sec.^{2}

Page 123   **Paper 23**

1. $6\frac{7}{8}$ tons wt.   **2.** $5\frac{5}{6}$, $11\frac{2}{3}$ Kg. wt.   **3.** 3·16 lb. wt. ; 30·2 ft.
4. $1\frac{1}{3}=1$·33 ft./sec.^{2} ; $\frac{22}{51}=0$·43 ft./sec.^{2} ; 40 ml./hr.
5. 23 cm./sec.^{2} ; 11·7 Kg. wt.

Page 124   **Paper 24**

1. $2\frac{1}{60}$ cwt.   2. $2\frac{1}{8}$ tons wt.   3. 3 in.

4. $2\frac{6}{7}$, $2\frac{4}{7}$ lb. wt. ; $9\frac{1}{7}$ ft./sec.²   5. 1355 yd. ; 52 and 98 sec. (approx.).

Page 128   **Exercise XXV**

1. 5 lb. wt. ; $\frac{5}{12}=0.42$.   2. 4 lb. wt.   3. $7\frac{7}{20}$ tons wt.

4. $7\frac{11}{27}$ lb. wt.   5. 2·59 lb. wt.   6. 18·1 lb. wt.

7. 100, 89·6 lb. wt.   8. $5\frac{1}{2}$ stone.   9. 5·625 lb. wt.

11. 0·27 ; 2·68 lb. wt.   12. 10, 17·3 lb. wt.   13. 14·9 lb. wt.

14. 3·25 lb. wt.   15. 1·93, 0·24 tons wt.   16. 24° 14′.

17. $\frac{2}{3}$; $5W$.   18. 0·268.   19. 23·4 lb. wt.

20. $\frac{6}{13}$ lb. wt. ; $\frac{3}{8}$.

Page 133   **Exercise XXVI**

1. 498,960 ft.-lb.   2. 1,344,000 ft.-lb.   3. 255,000 ft.-lb.

4. 2,700,000 ft.-lb.   5. 599,000 ft.-lb.   6. 122,343,750 ft.-lb.

7. 15,000,000 ft.-lb.   8. 320.   9. 4200 ft.-lb.

10. 375 lb. wt.   11. 180.   12. $4\frac{11}{16}$ lb. wt.

13. $29\frac{73}{88}=29.8$ ml./hr.   14. 39·1.   15. 72·5 min.

16. 152,600 cu. ft.   17. $7\frac{59}{99}=7.60$.   18. 152·9.

19. 4·58 ft. tons ; 9·33.   20. 3·41.   21. 272·7.

Page 137   **Exercise XXVII**

1. 22,160 ft.-lb.   2. 357 ft.-lb.   3. 10 ft.-lb.

4. 0·112.   5. 40 ft.-lb. ; 4 lb. wt.   6. 90·6 ft.-lb.

7. 71,380, 15,380 ft.-lb.   8. 61 lb. wt.   9. $13\frac{3}{4}$; $\frac{11}{12}=0.92$.

10. 120 lb. wt.   11. $34\frac{2}{7}$ lb. wt.   12. $6\frac{4}{75}=6.61$.

13. $\frac{5}{8}=0.625$.   14. 0·55.   15. 0·63 Kg. wt.

16. 2600 ft.-lb. ; 0·675.   17. $43\frac{1}{13}=43.1$ lb. wt.   18. 2250 lb. wt.

19. 0·91.   20. $\frac{25}{96}=0.260$; $a=2.2$, $b=0.085$.

21. 0·078, 0·137, 0·222, 0·253, 0·351 ; 0·29.

22. 480 lb. wt. ; 0·4.

Page 143   **Exercise XXVIII**

1. 6 lb. wt.   **2.** 3 ; 45 lb. wt. ; 47 lb. wt.

3. 45 lb. wt.   **4.** 5 ; 71 lb. wt.   **5.** $43\frac{1}{3}$ lb. wt. $183\frac{1}{3}$ lb. wt.

6. 30 lb. wt. ; 80 per cent.   **7.** 700, 400, 300 ft.-lb.

8. $127\frac{3}{11}$ lb. wt.   **9.** 50 lb. wt.   **10.** $\frac{23}{100}$.

11. 40 lb. wt.   **12.** 0·5904.

13. Better to have grapnel at A ; 2520 lb. wt.

14. 46.   **15.** $P = 10 + 20W$; 63·6, 65·3.

16. 21 lb. wt. ; 154 lb. wt.   **17.** 42 lb. wt.

Page 149   **Exercise XXIX**

1. (i) 10 ; (ii) 12 ; (iii) $\frac{48}{5} = 9·6$; (iv) $\frac{28}{3} = 9·33$.

2. 640 lb. wt.   **3.** $119\frac{1}{21}$ lb. wt.   **4.** $89\frac{3}{5}$ lb. wt.

5. (i) 10·8 lb. wt. ; (ii) $125\frac{5}{7}$ ft.-lb.   **6.** $P = 6·75 + 0·25W$; 47·7.

7. (i) 40 ; (ii) 48.   **8.** 46·7.   **9.** $10\frac{30}{77} = 10·4$ lb. wt.

10. 567 lb. wt.   **11.** 14.   **12.** 56 ft./min.

13. 30.   **14.** 3·75 ; 37·5.   **15.** $39\frac{43}{63} = 39·7$ lb. wt.

16. $21\frac{6}{7}$ lb. wt. ; 0·34 ; 1104 ft.-lb.

Page 154   **Exercise XXX**

2. 24.   **3.** 1·39 lb. wt.   **4.** $124\frac{4}{9}$ lb. wt. ; $217\frac{7}{9}$ ft.-lb.

5. $1600\pi = 5029$ lb. wt.   **6.** $66\frac{2}{3}$ lb. wt.

7. 26,400 lb. wt. ; $412\frac{1}{2}$ ft.-lb.   **8.** 396 lb. wt.

9. $1206\frac{6}{7}$ lb. wt.   **10.** 88 ; 25·5 ; 77·1 lb. wt.

11. (i) $1\frac{1}{2}$; (ii) $1\frac{4}{9}$.   **12.** 48 lb. wt.   **13.** $502\frac{6}{7}$ lb. wt.

14. 15·3 ; 0·78.   **15.** 81 lb. wt.   **16.** $1312\frac{1}{2}$ lb. wt.

17. 7·8 ; 0·48.   **18.** $8\frac{40}{49} = 8·82$ lb. wt.

19. $P = 5·4W + 18·6$; 0·59 ; 0·80.

20. $181\frac{1}{35} = 181·0$; $P = 0·015W + 5$; 47 lb. wt. ; 0·33.

Page 157 **Exercise XXXI**

1. 70 lb. wt.   2. 240 lb. wt.   3. 12·4.

4. 30·3 ml./hr.   5. $134\frac{8}{13}=134\cdot6$ lb. wt.   6. 6 ; 0·6.

7. 4·75 ; 0·296.   8. 0·198, 0·400, 0·496.   9. 0·423.

10. $1\frac{9}{11}$ lb. wt.   11. 2 ; $8\frac{1}{2}$ lb. wt. ; $10\frac{5}{7}$ lb. wt.

12. 4 ; 10 lb. wt.   13. 2, 4, 8 ft. ; 233 lb. wt.   14. 0·59.

15. 1, 3, 7 ft. ; $5\frac{65}{147}=5\cdot44$ lb. wt.   16. 30·1 lb. wt.   17. 0·15.

18. $P=3+0\cdot00268W$; 21 lb. wt. ; 0·42.   19. $198\frac{3}{5}$ lb. wt. ; $245\frac{8}{9}$ lb. wt.

REVISION PAPERS

Page 161 **Paper 25**

1. 40, 20 lb. wt. ; $33\frac{1}{3}$, $26\frac{2}{3}$ lb. wt.   2. 1, 1·73 tons wt.

3. 35 lb. wt. ; 30°.   4. 2·70 lb. wt.   5. $298\frac{2}{3}$.

Page 161 **Paper 26**

1. $\dfrac{Ql}{P+Q}$.   2. 27° 28′.   3. 20·6 lb. wt.

4. 0·62.   5. 7392 ft. lb.

Page 162 **Paper 27**

1. $22\frac{1}{2}$, $55\frac{1}{2}$ lb. wt.   2. 27° 58′.

3. 3·13 lb. wt., 23° N. of E.   4. 1·42 lb. wt.   5. $59\frac{11}{15}$.

Page 163 **Paper 28**

1. 44, 56 lb. wt. ; $3\frac{3}{4}$ lb. wt.   2. 5·66 lb. wt. ; 31° 59′.

3. 7·47, 14·7 lb. wt.   4. 0·13.   5. 85·0 ; 112·6.

Page 163 **Paper 29**

2. 29·8, 26·9 lb. wt.   3. 96, 28 lb. wt.   5. 0·747.

Page 164   **Paper 30**

1. 2 ft.   2. 59·6 lb. wt. ; 25° 36'.   3. 7·3 lb. wt.
4. 46·3 lb. wt.   5. 27·8.

Page 165   **Paper 31**

1. 35 lb. wt. ; 26 lb. wt. ; 41° with vertical.   2. 41·8 lb. wt.
3. 5·32, 6·84 lb. wt. ; between 7·53 and 6·22 lb. wt.
4. 17·8, 71·3 lb. wt.   5. 46·7.

Page 166   **Paper 32**

1. 1·2 ft. ; 18·4 lb. wt.
2. AB, 8·5 ; BC, 6·3 ; CD, 6 ; DE, 8·5 lb. wt. ; 72°, 90°.
3. 5 ; 0·64 ; 126 ft.-lb.   4. 10,560 lb. wt.   5. $16\frac{2}{17} = 16\cdot1$ lb. wt.

Page 167   **Paper 33**

1. 400 ft.-lb.   2. $4\frac{1}{6}$ ft.-lb.   3. $\frac{1}{4}W$; $\frac{1}{6}W$.
4. $5\frac{5}{8} = 5\cdot625$; 56.   5. $23\frac{1}{3}$; 0·51 ; $583\frac{1}{3}$ ft.-lb.

Page 174   **Exercise XXXII**

1. 10·8 ml./hr. ; S. 21° 48' E.   2. 2·83 ml./hr. ; 2·83 ml./hr.
3. 10·5 ml./hr. ; 5·16 ml./hr.   4. 7·15 ml./hr. ; N. 16° 18' E.
5. 6·18 ml./hr. ; S. 69° 31' E.   6. 9·43 ml./hr. ; N. 32° W.
7. 8·60 ft./sec.² ; 62·5 ft. N., 87·5 ft. W.   8. 2 hr. 8 min.
9. 110 ft.   10. 60° with AB ; with original velocity.
11. 3·21 ml./hr.   12. N. 69° 9' W. ; 20·1 ml./hr.   13. 1 hr. 40 min.
14. S. 73° 34' W. ; 10·1 ml./hr.   15. 3·81 knots ; N. 33° 11' E.
17. 55° 11' ; $6\frac{1}{3}$ min.   18. 82 sec. ; 560 ft.
19. 53° 8' with bank, up stream ; $11\frac{1}{4}$ min.
20. 8·49 knots ; S. 49° 46' E.   21. 7° 11'.
22. 3 in. behind, just under, 3 in. in front of original place.
23. 28·3 ml./hr.   24. 8·6 ft./sec. ; 100° with old velocity.
25. BD, where $AD = 2AB$ and is parallel to BC.

Page 180   **Exercise XXXIII**

1. 50 ml./hr.   2. 23·2 ml./hr. ; 154° 32′ with direction of car.
3. 5·66 ml./hr. ; W.   4. 10·6 knots, from N. 48° 15′ E.
5. 49·4 ft./sec. ; 27° 5′ with horizontal backwards.
6. 44·6 knots ; 16° 35′ N. of E.   7. S. 74° 10′ W.
8. 73$\frac{1}{3}$ ft./sec. ; 53° 8′ with vertical.   9. 18·0 ml./hr. ; 33° 41′ with bus.
10. N. 14° 38′ W. ; 140 ml./hr.   11. 2·4 ml./hr.
12. 7·07 ml./hr.   13. 14·3 ml./hr. ; S. 8° 36′ E.
14. 61·5 ft./sec.   15. 57·4 ml./hr. ; S. 35° E.

Page 182   **Exercise XXXIV**

1. 24·0 ml./hr. ; from N. 28° E.   2. 8 ml./hr. ; 30° to vertical, forwards.
3. S. 30° W. ; 1 ml.   4. 1st, 10$\frac{4}{5}$ ml. ; 2nd, 14$\frac{2}{5}$ ml. ; 18 ml.
5. 9 sec. before B reaches crossing ; $\frac{1}{10}$ ml.   6. 160 ft./sec.
7. 47 min.   8. N. 36° 52′ W. ; 1$\frac{1}{2}$ hr.   9. S. 30° 22′ W.
10. 8·66 ml./hr.   11. From S. 21° 10′ W.   12. 21·2 knots.
13. 11·2 ft./sec.^{2} 14. 79 ft.   15. 14·1 ml./hr. ; from N. 72$\frac{1}{2}$° W.
17. 14·2 ml./hr., S. 60° 4′ E. ; 2·61 mile.   18. 1$\frac{3}{5}$, 3$\frac{1}{5}$ lb. wt.
19. A, 57·7 cm./sec.^{2} down ; B, 57·7 cm./sec.^{2} down ; C, 173·1 cm./sec.^{2} up ;
    94·1 gm. wt.
20. A, 13·1 ft./sec.^{2} up ; B, 8·3 ft./sec.^{2} down ; C, 17·9 ft./sec.^{2} down ;
    top, 5·63 lb. wt. ; bottom, 2·22 lb. wt.
21. 53·85 ft./sec. at 111° 48′ with A's velocity ; 50 ft./sec.
22. From N. 61° E. ; 18 ml./hr.   23. Towards N. 22° 37′ E.
24. 52 ml./hr. ; N. 22° 37′ E.

Page 187   **Exercise XXXV**

1. (a) 100, 200, 300 ft. ; (b) 16, 64, 144 ft.   2. 3$\frac{3}{4}$ sec. ; 3750 ft.
3. 2002 ft./sec., 2° 45′ to horizontal.   4. 3666$\frac{2}{3}$ ft.=0·694 ml.
5. 7·9 sec. ; 1160 ft.   6. 96 ft. ; 80 ft./sec.
7. 1500 ft. ; 1° 54′.   8. 480 ft./sec.
9. 78 ft./sec. ; 52·5 ft. from start.

10. 340 cm./sec. ; 431 cm./sec. (approx.), 38° 3′ with horizontal.
11. 2¾ sec. ; 84·8 ml./hr. ; 60 ml./hr.   12. 100 ml./hr. ; 20° 10′.
13. 11·2 sec. ; 522 ft. behind stern ; 10⁵⁄₇ sec.
14. ⅜ sec., 4⅛ ft. away ; 0·95 sec., underneath.

Page 191   **Exercise XXXVI**

1. 190 ft.   2. 36 ft.   4. 56¼ ft. ; 300 ft.
5. 51° 24′ with horizontal, downwards.   7. 53·3 ml. ; 133 sec.
8. 13·6 ft.   9. 45° ; 71·6 ft./sec.   10. 86·6 ft.
11. 1½ sec. ; 80 ft./sec.   12. 8¾ sec. ; 1820 ft. ; 37° 36′.
14. 47·5 ft.   15. 64·1 ft./sec.
16. 40 ft./sec. ; 1¼ sec. ; 50 ft./sec.   17. 13·9 ft.
18. 80·9 ft./sec. ; 100 ft.   19. 70·7 ft./sec. ; 64° 53′.
21. 26° 34′, 68° 12′ ; 310 ft., 360 ft.   22. 7·32 or 27·3 sec.
23. 4·06 ft.   24. 434 ft.   26. 4·14 sec. ; 314 ft.

Page 197   **Exercise XXXVII**

1. 3⅓ ft.-lb.   2. 11¼ ft.-lb.   3. 6 in.-lb.
4. 45,800 ft.-lb.   5. 35,800 ft.-lb.   6. 0·44 in.-ton.
7. 119 lb. wt. ; 9550 ft.-lb.   8. 310 ft.-tons.

Page 201   **Exercise XXXVIII**

1. 35·8.   2. 23·0 ml./hr.   3. 12·8 ; 20 ml./hr.
4. 120 lb. wt. ; 7½ ml./hr.   5. 11·6 ; 8·39 ml./hr.=12·3 ft./sec.
7. 7·28.   8. 3·05.   9. 37⅕.
10. 4635 lb. wt. ; 556·2.   11. $296\frac{8}{15}=296\cdot5$.
12. 375,000 lb. wt. ; 57,000.   13. $6\frac{6}{11}=6\cdot55$.
14. 10.   15. 1796 lb. wt.   16. 943 ft./min.
17. 21·4, 14·7, 21·0 ml./hr.   18. $\frac{201}{700}=0\cdot287$ ft./sec.²
19. 112 lb. wt. ; 18·3, 17·9.

Page 207   **Exercise XXXIX**

1. (i) 3·91 ft.-lb. ; (ii) 25·5 cm.-gm. ; (iii) 12·5 ft.-tons.

2. 50 ft.-lb.   **3.** 150 ft.-lb.   **4.** 32 ft./sec.

5. 37·5 ft.-lb.   **6.** $39\frac{1}{16}=39\cdot1$ ft.-lb.   **7.** $2\frac{25}{48}=2\cdot52$ tons wt.

8. $9\cdot17\times10^8$ cm.-gm. ; 1147 cm.   **9.** 91·9 ft.-tons.

10. 20,000 ft.-tons.   **11.** 21 lb. wt.

12. $6\frac{34}{75}=6\cdot45$ ft.-tons , $\frac{22}{75}=0\cdot293$ tons wt.

13. 283 ft.-tons ; 70·6 tons wt.   **14.** 10·5 ft.-lb.

15. 2·8.   **16.** 2400 cm.-gm. ; 626 cm./sec.

17. 4395 lb. wt.   **18.** 1286 ft.-tons ; 4008 ft. **19.** 1633 ft./sec.

20. 13·2.   **22.** 36·7 ft./sec.   **23.** 6·38 sec.

24. 18·6.   **25.** $\frac{11}{30}$ ft./sec.² ; $1\frac{1}{3}$ miles ; $1\frac{7}{8}$ tons wt.

Page 210   **Exercise XL**

1. 81 ft./sec.   **2.** 13·1 ml./hr.   **3.** 29·2 ft./sec. ; 27·7 ft./sec.

4. 35·3 ml./hr.   **5.** (i) $2931\frac{1}{4}$ ft.-lb. ; 9·77 lb. wt.

6. 1040 ft.-lb.   **7.** $174\frac{3}{8}$ ft.-lb.   **9.** 560 yd.

10. 145 ft./sec.   **11.** 100·8 lb. wt./ton.   **12.** 598 ft.

13. 3646 ft.   **14.** 53·3.   **15.** 172.

16. 8·28 ft./sec.   **17.** 32·8.   **18.** 24 ft./sec. ; 225 ft.-tons.

19. 5·45 ft./sec.   **20.** 225 ft. ; 77·9 ft.-lb.

Page 215   **Exercise XLI**

1. 3·41 ft./sec.   **2.** 10·2 ft./sec.   **3.** 7·30 ft./sec. ; $6\frac{2}{3}$ lb. wt.

4. $11\frac{13}{16}=11\cdot8$ ft.-lb.   **5.** 93·12 ft.-lb.   **7.** 9·29 ft./sec. ; 2·54 lb. wt.

8. 1·998 ft.-lb. ; 4·24 ft./sec.   **9.** 7·47.

10. 1 sec. ; $91\frac{7}{8}$ ft.-lb.   **11.** 180 yd.   **12.** 326 yd. ; 594 yd.

13. $5\frac{1}{3}$ cwt. ; $37\frac{1}{2}$ sec.   **14.** 20·7 ft./sec.   **15.** 28·3 ft./sec.

16. $5\frac{1}{3}$ ft./sec. ; $1\frac{5}{9}$ lb. wt.

17. 3000 lb. wt. ; $1687\frac{1}{2}$ ft.-lb. ; $22,687\frac{1}{2}$ ft.-lb. ; 16·5.

18. 114 lb. wt.   **19.** $7\cdot18\times10^6$ ft.-lb.

20. (i) 41,400 ft.-lb. ; (ii) 18,900 ft.-lb. ; (iii) 6·00 ft./sec.

21. (i) 89 ft. ; (ii) 11,280 ft.-lb. ; (iii) 9000 ft.-lb.

22. 62·5 ft./sec. ; 12·5 ft./sec. ; 0·96.

Page 220   **Paper 34**

1. 157·5 ft. ; 807·5 ft.   2. 4·4 ft./sec.²
3. 16·1 ml./hr. ; N. 29° 45′ W.   4. 9 ft.   5. 537⅖.

Page 220   **Paper 35**

1. (i) 10 ft./sec. ; (ii) 15 ft./sec.   2. 37½ lb. wt. ; 2·49.
3. 41·8 ft./sec. ; 73° 18′.   4. 41° 24′ with bank.
5. (a) μw tons wt. ; (b) Wr lb. wt. ; (c) 448.

Page 221   **Paper 36**

1. 35·75 ml./hr.   2. $90\frac{26}{75}$ = 90·3 lb. wt. ; $40\frac{10}{11}$ sec.
3. 25·0 ml./hr. ; S. 25° 8′ W.   4. 15¾ ft.
5. $\frac{275}{448}$ = 0·614 tons wt. ; $\frac{28}{55}$ ft.

Page 222   **Paper 37**

1. 1¼ ft./sec.²   2. 672 ft.-lb.   3. N. 43° W.
4. 2° 52′ or 87° 8′.   5. 148·5.

Page 223   **Paper 38**

1. Express stops 2 yd. before reaching other train.   2. 750 tons wt.
3. 26·5 ml./hr.   4. 98·0 ft./sec. ; 75 ft. ; no.

Page 223   **Paper 39**

1. 2 sec.   2. 1·14.   3. 60 ft. ; ⅝ sec. ; $9\frac{49}{64}$ ft.
4. (i) 0·462 ml. ; (ii) ¼ ml.   5. $122\frac{43}{56}$ = 122·8.

Page 224   **Paper 40**

2. 23·1 ml./hr. ; 138.   3. 280⅓ ft.-lb. ; 3·79 lb. wt.
4. 5⁴⁄₇ in.   5. 24° 44′ ; 41·4 min.

Page 225   **Paper 41**

1. 810 ft./sec. ; $8970\frac{15}{128} = 8970 \cdot 1$ ft.-tons.
3. N. 69° 59′ E. ; 108 ml./hr.   4. 1·20 cm.   5. 430 ft.-lb.

Page 226   **Paper 42**

1. 250 lb. wt.   2. 12·9 sec.   3. 1 hr. 33 min.
4. $\frac{11}{24}$ ft./sec.^{2} ; 30 ml./hr.   5. 1·40 miles.

Page 227   **Paper 43**

1. $2\frac{7}{9}$.   2. 126 ft./sec. ; 62° 48′ with horizontal, downwards.
3. 660 yd.   5. 1270 ft.-lb. ; 22·8 ft./sec.

Page 228   **Paper 44**

1. 23·5 ft./sec. ; 2·5 (approx.).   2. 35° 8′, 53° 8′.
3. $6\frac{2}{21} = 6\cdot10$ ft./sec.^{2} ; upper, $47\frac{13}{21} = 47\cdot6$ lb. wt. ; lower, $95\frac{5}{21} = 95\cdot2$ lb. wt.
4. 18 knots.   5. $1\frac{3}{7}$ ft./sec.^{2} ; $14\frac{4}{7}$ ft./sec.^{2}

Page 229   **Paper 45**

1. 2 oz. wt.   2. 1·6 ; 587 ft.-lb./sec.
3. (a) 2 min. ; 880 ft. ; (b) $2\frac{1}{2}$ min. ; 704 ft.   4. 496.
5. $R = 22\cdot8$; $P = 1825$; 195 ; $-0\cdot14$ ft./sec.^{2}